INNOVATIVE
DOCTORING

SOLUTIONS LIE WITHIN US

INNOVATIVE
DOCTORING

SOLUTIONS LIE WITHIN US

Jeffrey S. Grossman, M.D

Kelly
think out of the
Box

Bob Senoskey

The author has made every effort to present material that is accurate and up-to-date in this book. He cannot guarantee that all information is correct or that it is applicable to your particular situation. This book is made available with the understanding that the publisher and the author are not engaged in providing legal and/or other professional services. All readers should exercise good judgment and seek the advice of competent professionals.

CONTENTS

ACKNOWLEDGEMENTS

The creation of a book such as Innovative Doctoring requires a great deal of hard work from interviewing experts to writing and endless rewriting. Most of all it demands perseverance in the face of competing demands for time, frustrations of every sort and, of course, the naysayers who contend that it can't or shouldn't be done.

During the course of writing Innovative Doctoring, I've learned many things and one of the most important is the power of collaboration. There's a saying that it takes a village to raise a child and certainly the birthing of this book has required the efforts of just as many people. Without their faith, support, advice and hard work it would not have been possible.

I also discovered the truth that every project is much like a living organism. While you can channel energy into developing it, you cannot control the path that it will take. Over the course of the last two years, it evolved into a work that is not only different, but also much better than the one that I had originally envisioned. As it grew and matured so did I. As its ideas and concepts became more sophisticated so did my own. Much of that process is a tribute to many creative individuals who agreed to tell their stories and share their ideas for the book.

I am also indebted to all the people who encouraged and worked with me.

From the very beginning, I received unstinting encouragement in this project from my family including my mother Sandi, my father Irwin and his wife Cathy, my brother Marc and his wife Ilene. I also want to thank my cousin Murray, his wife Georgia and Jenny Jo for their love and support on so many different levels.

I'm grateful to two individuals who have been both friends and mentors. Rabbi Philip Kranz taught me the power of saying no so that I could say yes to the best things in life. Alan Grodin has been a wise and steady guide as I have made my way in the world of business and life over these past few years.

I'm also grateful to the hard work and sound financial advice of my CPA and friend Barry Fruchter who helped me make wise choices during the months that I devoted to the book. My business advisor John Guzowski provided his expertise not only to help my practice, but also proved a valuable resource in the writing of the book as well. My patent attorney Ryan Schneider lent his expertise in explaining the complicated and often misunderstood patent process.

For helping me refine my thoughts and create a bigger and better vision for this book several individuals deserve special recognition: Piotr Jaroskaw Juszkiewicz, Mir Imran, Ramie Tritt, Kim McCormick and Neil Shulman.

I was encouraged and challenged to undertake Innovative Doctoring in the first place by my college roommate, fraternity brother and good friend Brad Meltzer, himself a New York Times best selling author and a true inspiration for any first time book writer.

Several people have done yeoman's work in the development, editing, graphic design and marketing of this book and I am very grateful to: Melanie James, Lisa Calloway, Dawn Palzewicz, Tara Levene, and Jill Becker. I'm also grateful to Randy Southerland for helping me take these ideas and experiences and refine them into words on a page.

As I began sharing my ideas on the role of innovation in medicine with colleagues, I found great support and a shared vision with the Medical Association of Atlanta and its 1,700 member physicians. In particular, let me acknowledge the support and cooperation of the MAA's staff including Sharon Rice, Joyceé Lever and Janet DelVescovo.

I wish to thank my partner Matt Richardson at Peachtree Spine and Pain Physicians and my staff including Kerry, Hester, Lisa, Bercita, Christine, Julieta and Kia for helping me fulfill the demands of a full time practice while writing this book.

I also want to acknowledge someone whose ideas and philosophy have been a guiding force in my life. The 12th century physician, philosopher and Talmudic scholar Moses Maimonides has inspired and challenged me to live a life dedicated to the principles of Tzedakah in all its many forms.

INTRODUCTION

This book is for physicians, residents, interns, and medical students alike. It is for everyone involved in the practice of medicine, and anyone who each day faces the satisfactions, challenges, and frustrations that are an integral part of the modern healthcare system.

While medicine has always been one of the most rewarding of professions, being a doctor today is in many ways far more difficult than at any time in history. We know more about the causes of disease, and we have a powerful and growing arsenal of drugs and other treatments that have improved the human condition to a degree that could scarcely have been imagined just a few decades ago. Yet, many of us are dissatisfied, and a growing number of healthcare professionals are giving up and quitting long before the traditional age of retirement. The reasons given are many. Rising malpractice rates and increasingly heavy-handed managed care companies are common examples. However, those are just the most obvious challenges to a successful practice.

I believe that the greatest threat to our well-being as physicians can be found within each of us. Malpractice rates and uncooperative patients are just external challenges that can be overcome – or at least mitigated. The hardest problem to solve is a negative mindset and attitude, and it is here that we must focus our attention if we want to change our situations and give our lives new meaning.

When you finished residency and made the jump to private practice physician, you were suddenly faced with challenges on a daily basis. No matter how good your training, in that first year you were faced with situations and conditions that you likely had never dealt with before. In those days, I talked to friends in the same position and everyone said the same thing: "This is so scary, I can't believe it."

As you make the transition into private practice, you're working as hard as you can to learn as much as possible, and there's no time or inclination to yearn for anything more. You're not thinking about taking a vacation or starting a family or any of the other human activities that most people devote at least a part of their waking hours to. You're just concentrating on surviving, taking care of your patients, not making a mistake, and doing the best job you can as you learn and grow as a physician.

After a year or two of practice, things begin to change. You've seen nearly everything and you've done just as much. And if you haven't seen it or done it, there's no anxiety because you've already been through the phase of not knowing what you should or shouldn't know.

Today, when I'm presented with a condition that I may have only seen once or that requires a procedure that I may not be familiar with, I can refer that patient to a colleague for a second opinion. I already have a busy practice and the referring physician isn't going to lose any respect for me because I admitted my own limitations.

Eventually, you settle into a routine. You still go to meetings and read journal articles and learn new things, but in terms of the patients who will present in your office, you've really reached a plateau of confidence. Of course, you'll continue to get better, but you now begin to feel that you've truly mastered the day-to-day challenges of private practice.

By now, nearly all situations have become familiar, and much of what you do each day becomes almost rote. It is here that the problem begins, and many of us harbor a secret that we hide from our patients and sometimes even from ourselves. While few will admit it, we become bored with the daily procession of patients and the seemingly unending repetition of complaints that sometimes have little to do with the diagnosis and treatment that we will ultimately render. Yet we must not interrupt this litany for fear of undermining the doctor/patient relationship.

Encouraging patients to speak their minds about their chief complaint in their own words is part of good doctoring. In my own practice, I spend more time listening than many doctors have either the time or the inclination to. I recognized long ago that time invested in this process created a more satisfied, cooperative, and compliant patient. But I also recognized that much of what I heard had little bearing on the treatment I would prescribe, and everything I needed to know could have been obtained in five minutes or less of asking the right questions.

One of the unavoidable truths about the practice of medicine is that unlike many other professionals, the physician can't leverage his knowledge and experience to change the way he works. Whereas an attorney, as he gains experience and seniority, can become choosey about the cases he takes on and delegate mundane research to junior partners, a practicing physician can't. Twenty years after beginning private practice, he is still seeing the same patients and performing the same duties. While you can select your medical specialty, you really can't choose which patients walk in your door or decide to see only the truly interesting cases – particularly if you're in a referral-based practice.

This situation has been complicated by the fact that in the eyes of many patients, medicine has become a commodity. The bond between provider and patient has been eroded by managed care plans and closed networks that dictate where and from whom patients may seek care. A patient may see a particular physician for many years, but the moment he or she is no longer part of the network, then the patient goes to someone who is on the approved list so that he can maintain coverage.

All of these factors have created an environment in which physicians can become complacent, and sometimes even bitter and stale. Years of practice filled with constant frustration squeeze the joy and life out of what is truly an exciting and privileged profession.

I had a taste of these feelings early in my own career and realized that unless I found a way to take back control of my life and practice, I would soon become one of those doctors who dreamed of getting out of medicine. For me, the answer lay in putting creativity and innovation at the heart of my work.

Within these pages you will find a blueprint for achievement that will expand your mind, increase your knowledge, enhance your productivity, and put you on the road to becoming a creative innovator in every aspect of your life and practice. By following the process outlined in these pages you will embark upon a path that will lead you to renewal in every aspect of your life.

When I set out to write this book, I wanted to give my medical colleagues a resource for enhancing life and practice that had never before existed. Drawing upon my own experiences as a physician in private practice and an inventor of medical devices, I developed a simple and easy-to-follow plan for enhancing creativity and putting innovation into action. In these pages you'll discover a process for looking at the way you work and finding better, more effective, more life affirming ways of doing things.

By following the Five Step Process of Creativity, you will learn to recognize problems and find innovative solutions for them. For many of you, this will mean transforming your practice and the way you serve your patients, and that will be enough. On the other hand, you may want to make one of the creative paths profiled in Section III your own. In that section you'll meet researchers and entrepreneurs, along with poets, filmmakers, and even clowns who have found new ways of advancing the cause of medicine and their own creative desires.

For some, nurturing the creative spark will lead you to turn your ideas into products and services that will benefit our profession and, ultimately, humanity as well. For you I've developed – based upon my own journey – a guide in Section IV to becoming a successful inventor of medical devices. These chapters will show you how others have turned their ideas into tangible products, sometimes even creating entire companies based on them.

To inspire you still further, in Section V you'll find profiles of some of the most prolific and groundbreaking inventors in the medical field. While each one has a unique story, they all share one very common and very essential trait – each one kept going and, despite obstacles, achieved their goals. By sharing the descriptions of some of the great innovators who have moved forward and realized their dreams, you can see the greater truth of possibility. Along with the insight you'll gain from their experiences, you'll also find the steps you need to spark your own creativity, as well as the business know-how you need to make your ideas a tangible reality. You can join them, and perhaps some day a book on inventors will feature your story as well.

If you're the type of person who has ever been just a bit different in your thinking, then this is the book you've been waiting for. It's intended for those who challenge the status quo regarding their life and profession. It provides a solution for those who might be frustrated by the way things are and have asked the question, "Why does it have to be that way?"

While this is an exploration of creativity in medicine, it is also much more. It is a start – not a finish. It will set you on a journey where each accomplishment will prompt you to keep going to find answers to questions you never thought to ask, as well as solutions to problems you may never have considered before.

While this book is based on scientific research into the creative process, it is nevertheless practical in its approach. As a fellow professional, I know that your time is valuable and that results are what count. Its success is not in whether you buy it, read it, and put it on the shelf, but in whether you use the tools within its pages to become a creative innovator filled with a new sense of passion and accomplishment.

In writing it, I wanted to offer you – the medical doctor – a guide to making creativity and innovation an integral part of your life and practice. It does that by offering you an understanding of what creativity really is and how it works.

The Meaning of Creativity

Perhaps the best place to begin is by defining this elusive and little understood process. Researchers Michael Mumford and Sigrid Gustafson have laid out several means of describing it. The first consists of the production of ideas. It also involves "the recognition of possibilities" as well as the development of "a form of problem solving ability."

The authors go on to point out that creativity is also reflected in the external recognition of professional achievement, publications and patent awards, along with the judgments of knowledgeable peers or supervisors.

All of this evidence of creativity's manifestations points to the real results that we and the rest of society cherish: "novel, socially-valued products." I believe this is the best way for us to look at creativity, because it allows us to see, measure, and judge its worth in very concrete terms.

This definition is also broad enough to encompass all the many variations of creativity and innovation that we will experience at different times and places in our lives as medical practitioners. Creativity is sometimes about developing a new medical device – as I will show you in the chapters on my own creative journey – and it is about changing the way you do things in your office, which I will also explain. It can be about finding new and more innovative forms of practice.

Patch Adams, the real life inspiration for the doctor played by Robin Williams in the movie of the same name, has spent the past several decades trying to create an environment in which the medical field treats not just the individual, but also the family and community as well. His vision is one in which no money changes hands and doctors don't carry malpractice insurance because they're given the right to make mistakes.

For most doctors, Adams' model may seem extreme and unworkable, but there are many other variations. A number of doctors have opened boutique practices that seek to get back to the older idea of a closer and more intimate relationship with patients. These doctors don't take insurance and they may charge more than most, but patients are guaranteed the ability to see the doctor in a timely manner during an appointment that isn't rushed. In all of these forms, creativity is the process you use to find solutions to the frustrations and problems you face.

I also believe that practicing creativity and innovation isn't about just making your own life better and more productive – although that is certainly a worthy and important goal. The true objective is to become the kind of person who is willing and able to change the profession in ways that benefit not only doctors, but also patients and everyone else who has a stake in our nation's healthcare system.

On a global level, tapping into our creativity in a dedicated and thoughtful manner gives us the opportunity to begin to solve some of society's most intractable problems. At the very least, it allows us to ask the right questions, and that is perhaps the most important step of all.

In the chapters to come, I'll show you what it means to be creative and I'll give you the tools to begin formulating new ideas that will address the problems you encounter. You will be able to take it from there.

In my years of education, I always found that the greatest teachers were those who didn't seek to simply fill my head with mere facts. Instead, their primary goal was to inspire each student to search for knowledge on their own and discover their own answers. I hope that this book will be the inspiration that puts you on the path to finding your own answers.

Section I

The Heart
Of Innovation

Chapter 1

THINK INSIDE YOUR BOX

Craig is a friend of mine who's spent the past several years trying to build a practice in internal medicine. Beset by sky-high malpractice rates, he often speaks of how frustrated he's become with the world of medicine and how he wants to get out.

During one conversation, he told me that he was buying up urban real estate properties and trying to rehab them for resale. So far, he's made no money on the deals, but he's convinced that real estate is the way to increase his income.

He's just one of a long list of physicians who have taken the idea of "thinking outside the box" to mean they should delve into an area in which they have no experience. Some, like my friend Craig, read the myriad books on buying distressed properties with no money down or getting rich in penny stocks and think, "Yes, this is what I need to do to make the money I deserve."

With distressing regularity, it seems that whenever a group of doctors gets together, talk will at some point turn to buying a restaurant or opening a bar. They may think nothing of investing $100,000 or more in a venture that statistics show will fail nine times out of ten. Eight or more years of college and medical school give them no better preparation for such a venture than someone else's high school diploma.

While it's true that some people do get rich by venturing into an unfamiliar area of expertise, most of the players in any endeavor already have considerable knowledge and experience to fall back on. Buying distressed properties isn't much of a stretch for a real estate broker, and many of them have done so successfully. We physicians usually have no such specific knowledge.

In my own research into the components of creativity, I found that the most important factor, when it comes to innovation, is what might be called domain-specific knowledge. True creativity arises from the deep and intimate understanding of your field. As healthcare providers, no one has more intimate knowledge of medicine than we do, and nobody has a better opportunity to understand the techniques and procedures we practice every day.

If you're a doctor, you've spent 12 or more years mastering your profession. Doesn't it make more sense to put all that knowledge to work in finding new ways to improve the place where you already find yourself?

In other words, don't think outside the box. Instead, think differently within your own box. Stick to what you do best. Don't strike out into unknown territories in which you possess no special knowledge or advantage. When you're working within an area that you know, even failures will present new opportunities for advancement and knowledge. On the other hand, if you're working in an area that you don't know, you are in essence a novice and a beginner. Your failures will come while in the process of acquiring elementary skills that many others already possess.

Denise Shekerjian, writing in *Uncommon Genius*, her study of the creative impulse as reflected in 40 winners of the MacArthur Foundation Fellowship, noted, "The trick to creativity, if there is a single useful thing to say about it, is to identify your own peculiar talent and then settle down to work with it for a good long time. Everyone has an aptitude for something. The trick is to recognize it, to honor it, to work with it. This is where creativity starts."[1]

If we, as physicians, are to know true success and be able to unleash our full measure of creativity, we must return to what we know and do best – the practice of medicine. There's no need to try to solve problems in other fields when we have so many problems and so many opportunities in medicine.

Everyday we confront the various crises that have plagued this profession for many years. These include rising malpractice rates, uninsured patients, mounting paperwork, and declining reimbursements. There is the continuing need to find new and better tools and techniques to treat our patients.

Perhaps the greatest challenge of all is the question of who really runs medicine these days. Nearly everyone realizes that healthcare providers no longer control their own profession. While doctors prescribe drugs and use medical devices every day, the burgeoning profits generated by these products belong to large, faceless corporations. It often seems that those who know the least about healthcare and patient needs – whether they are insurance companies, pharmacy benefit managers, drug companies, or managed care organizations – are those who have the greatest control over what physicians do and how they're able to treat their patients.

For the nearly 700,000 physicians in America, the days of private practice – in which doctors use their best judgment to make decisions for patients – are long gone. Most now work for large hospitals or HMOs that are bureaucratic and heavy-handed in their approach. Managers and administrators tell doctors where, when, how, and with whom they must practice, even down to the smallest details.

The frustration with this situation runs wide and deep. Studies show that more than 45 percent of doctors are dissatisfied and thinking of giving up their practice. In addition, 63 percent would not recommend clinical practice as a profession to their children. Those doctors who do continue their practice seem to always be thinking of how to move into some other field of endeavor.[2]

I know those feelings very well. I was once a young resident finding my way through the ins and outs of the medical system. Even then, I was disgruntled and unhappy with the system. I was profoundly dissatisfied with the large medical center where I was serving, with its rigid bureaucratic structure that neither demanded much from its staff nor offered much to its patients. At that time, I was already thinking about getting out of medicine and finding something that was more satisfying.

Fortunately, the exit strategy that came to me wasn't a means of escape at all. Rather it was a way to revitalize my life and work through the path of invention. As you will read in the coming chapters, I found inspiration in my own situation and invented a medical device that could serve both doctors and patients in new and better ways.

My story is just one small example of how unleashing the creativity inside you can lead to a sense of accomplishment, renewal, and freedom. Each of you can find your own path and can do so by asking some simple questions. The first of these questions is, who is better qualified to find solutions to medical problems than a medical professional? You are in a perfect position to deal with the many frustrations that beset your practice and your specialty.

The problems and the opportunities are legion. You can look around and see any number of situations that can only be termed ridiculous if they weren't so serious in their implications for doctors and patients alike.

"We have a host of high-tech diagnostic instruments and we can do heart transplants on an almost routine basis," says Dr. Dan Budnitz, a scientist with the federal Centers for Disease Control and Prevention. "Yet when one of these $100,000 operations is over, we write down what we did with a pen and paper and then stuff it in a filing cabinet."

In another example, Dr. Budnitz notes that when he takes the family car into the dealership for service, the technician has at his fingertips a computer link that gives detailed information on every service that has been performed on his car – even at dealerships on the other side of the country. Yet when he takes his child to the family pediatrician, the doctor doesn't know about the treatment his son received at the local hospital last night.

As physicians, we can wait until a government bureaucrat or an insurance company imposes a solution that primarily benefits them or we can take charge and begin to find our own solutions within our own profession.

While I'm not advocating that you run out and change the world right now, I want you to begin to realize that because of your domain-specific knowledge, you have within your grasp the power to begin finding solutions for the problems that plague you. Creativity and innovation are above all about recognizing frustrations, defining problems, and then developing solutions. Creativity is a process that works, whether it's about finding a better surgical technique or developing a system of universal medical records.

You can always endure your frustrations, sometimes even pretending they don't exist, or you can begin recognizing them, defining the shape and contours of the problem they represent, and then discovering innovative solutions. How much better and more exciting will our lives be when we take back control of what should, in all rights, be ours in the first place?

In these pages I offer a solution to this frustration and a challenge to take back control of your profession and your life. It is a process that you can apply to the way you run your office, manage your staff, treat your patients, and, even more importantly, the way you live your life. Innovation when applied to your practice can create a more exciting and satisfying experience for you, your staff, and your patients.

I will also show you how to be a creative source of new ideas that are not only useful, but potentially profitable. Too many people waste their time and never achieve their potential. For a doctor not to be an innovator within his profession seems much like an agile and athletic seven-footer who turns down a big-league basketball scholarship. He has the right to do so, but it certainly seems like a waste of talent and opportunity.

If you choose, you can stake your claim to at least a small share of the profits being reaped through the sale of medical devices by becoming an inventor of said devices, just like the individuals profiled in Section V. Innovations by physicians, when applied to this $1.4 trillion industry, can result in the creation of new medical inventions and procedures that may not only reward you, but also improve the lives of patients on a grand scale.

The U.S. medical device and supply market generated approximately $75 billion in sales in 2002. Creativity and the invention process represent one way out for the physicians who want to become a part of the industry and win their share of the profits. More importantly, they represent a way to win back autonomy and become empowered to serve both your patients and your profession.[3]

I use the medical device field as perhaps one of the best examples of utilizing the creative process in an extremely elegant, yet imminently practical way. For those of you who want to use your creative impulses in this field, these sections will serve as a road map to success. For the rest of you, it will serve as real-life examples of how the creative process can be put to practical ends.

Let's not pretend that getting involved in creating new medical devices is the answer to all of your problems, or that it is the right choice for everyone. But for some of you, it can provide a path and an opportunity to be autonomous once again. The medical-device industry is just one example of creativity at work, as you will see in the chapter on developing an office where creativity can flourish, and in the profiles of innovative physicians later in this book.

The Five Step Process is just as much at work in other fields of endeavor, such as writing novels or works of poetry or producing television dramas. Whatever path you choose for yourself, being in a position to come up with a viable idea becomes the ultimate in self-reliance and creative expression.

Doctors such as John Stone and Neil Shulman became poets and writers. Through the written word they were able to find a way of renewing and revitalizing the practice of medicine. Through their works they found insights and new avenues of communications that they in turn have shared with the rest of us.

You also find these qualities of creativity and innovation on display in the inventor profile section. The doctors cited there have found an escape from the healthcare rat race through the process of inventing medical devices. Richard Schatz, for example, is an eminent cardiologist practicing in California. He collaborated with Julio Palmaz and helped develop the heart stent – one of the most important advances in the treatment of heart disease in this century. After reaping a vast fortune from the sale of the device to Johnson & Johnson, he has been able to maintain what he calls a boutique practice, in which he sees only the most challenging cases. He no longer feels the pressure to take every case in order to pay the bills and maintain his lifestyle. If autonomy and independence appeals to you, then you might just have the passion to follow through with your ideas, like Dr. Schatz did, to achieve great success.

On the other hand, researchers like Dr. Joseph Sodroski of Harvard are exploring the most fundamental structure and function of the virus that causes AIDS, and in the process, have charted a course that is leading to not just better understanding, but better treatment as well. Better treatment for AIDS includes drugs, such as those developed by Emory University researcher Raymond Schinazi that are helping transform what was once a fatal disease into a chronic and manageable one. The drive to develop better treatments for injury and disease can be found in the work of Dr. Scott Boden in the area of the spine and Ron Crystal in the development of gene transfer. These and other brilliant minds are creatively pushing the boundaries and making life better for both patients and the medical profession that seeks to treat their conditions.

Creativity and innovation, of course, can take many forms. Some physicians, for example, have jumped ship, abandoning the big corporate employers and choosing instead to form small private practices. Clearly, these small business owners are not doing it for the money, since running a solo or small group practice can be extremely difficult. They are thinking inside their own box and going back to an earlier and purer form of work structure.

Obviously, self-employment is not for everyone. Many doctors don't want to deal with the challenges of personal entrepreneurship. Yet there is a path that can revitalize their commitment to medicine and allow them to reap new sources of income, as well as much greater personal satisfaction.

As you make innovation a part of your professional life, you will find, as I have, that it creates a new passion for your field as well. You'll begin thinking about the processes of medicine in new ways. You'll start reading journal articles to acquire new knowledge, and, best of all, you'll look at everything you do in light of the creative process. Idea generation and problem solving will become second nature.

Through the process of developing your creativity, many of you will find qualities that you had lost or perhaps never even knew you possessed. You will find new worlds and new ideas opening up for you, and in the process, medicine and its practice will become what you always hoped it would be – innovative, exciting, rewarding, and, most of all, revitalizing.

REFERENCES

1.   Denise Shekerjian, Uncommon Genius (New York Viking Penguin, 1990)
2.   Kaiser Family Foundation. National survey of physicians part III: doctors' opinions about their profession, March 2002. (Accessed April 19, 2006, at http://www.kff.org/kaiserpolls/upload/Highlights-and-Chart-Pack-2.pdf)
3.   Health Care Industry Market Update, December 5, 2003 (Centers for Medicare and Medicaid Services.)

Chapter 2

SEEDS OF INNOVATION

One of the biggest mysteries about inventing is simply discovering what it is that gives birth to creativity. Inspiration often arises from unexpected sources. Even frustration and dissatisfaction can spark the creative urge.

It sometimes seems these days that many doctors are dissatisfied with their professional life. They run their own offices, but they often feel like slaves to the insurance companies that attempt to control their treatment recommendations and at the same time consistently drive down the fees paid for their services. Against their better judgment, some doctors even feel compelled to practice defensive medicine. For many, medicine is a treadmill they hope to escape. It becomes easy to lose sight of the great privilege we have as healthcare providers to do good, and to practice a profession that is still respected and honored.

Early in my career, I got a taste of this dissatisfaction. As a resident, I was smart, cocky, and often outspoken. Among the group of residents I worked with, I was usually the one who spoke up to authorities about the issues that concerned us. I was on top of the world, my head full of dreams of fame and fortune, when I experienced a humbling situation that reminded me that life was not always easy — and that no matter how good you might be, not everyone is willing to reward you.

I was doing a rotation in the physical medicine and rehabilitation department of a big-city medical center. I had done well in every other aspect of my residency, garnering glowing evaluations from attending physicians I admired and respected.

That was all about to change. As a resident at this sprawling government hospital, I worked closely with the head of the department, who had settled into a comfortable, low-stress job that usually didn't demand much of him. It was in many respects an easy job for all of us. We worked regular hours and went home at 5 o'clock just like most office workers. Yet in my idealism, I thought there should be more to medicine. As doctors, we were there to help our patients as much as we could, using whatever tools and knowledge we had at our disposal. But that was not the case here. Patients who could have been helped were often referred out in order to avoid extra work.

I was frustrated with the apathy and lack of concern for the patients who came through the department. I chaffed at the restrictions that wouldn't allow me to treat patients because the emphasis was on moving them through as quickly as possible. I began to wonder if this was really the path I wanted to follow as a life-long career.

My frustrations grew by the day, and although I didn't grasp it at the time, I was being pushed to become more creative. At this point in my life, I was unable to see beyond these admittedly temporary circumstances. A desire to change my situation, rather than simply endure it, had taken root in me.

From Frustration to Enlightenment

The moment when everything changed for me came during a difficult surgical procedure. I was learning how to perform epidural steroid injections into critical areas around the spine which required that a needle measuring three to six inches in length be inserted at precisely the right location and with the exact trajectory, with no room for deviation.

The injections are done in a special suite equipped with a digital fluoroscope, called a C-arm (for the shape of the instrument), which provides radiographic guidance to the precise area. To ensure that the needle reaches the correct location, the usual practice is to take an X-ray. Then the skin is marked in preparation for advancing the needle in a specific trajectory, one that is in line with an imaginary beam, known as the image intensifier that extends perpendicular to the undersurface of the C-arm.

The physician then marks an entry point with a pen. While marking this point doesn't require particular coordination, it does require an extensive knowledge of anatomy. The next phase of the procedure, advancing the needle, requires experience as well as precise eye/hand coordination in order to move the needle from the entry point into the specific anatomical structure.

While an experienced physician could usually find the correct spot with no more than three or four needle adjustments, a resident might insert and reinsert it a dozen times or more. Each attempt is made in a patient who is awake but under local anesthetic. Each additional pass increases the risk of inflicting pain in unanesthetized areas, or even damaging adjacent structures.

I remarked to the attending physician, "They should have something that guides the needle to the correct location. Why don't we go out and get a device that helps you move the needle in line with the beam?"

The attending physician testily asserted, "There is no such device. Now do the procedure."

I assumed that since there was such an obvious need for it, the device must exist somewhere. Like many other first-time inventors, I found that it didn't.

My creative thinking was being fostered in an oppressive atmosphere that was generating considerable frustration. I was actually hoping to go home and find a device that could make this procedure easier. That evening, I spent hours searching the Web trying to find a medical device that would allow you to align the needle with the beam.

I was disappointed I couldn't find anything, and began talking about the situation to my girlfriend, my father, and anyone else who would listen. It was inconceivable to me that someone hadn't already invented a device with such an obvious need. I even sat down with a pad and began sketching out what I thought such a tool should look like.

At this point, my driving motivation wasn't so much about the idea as it was the passion that welled up inside me. I had the desire and I had recognized the problem, but I hadn't yet created the device. I had simply perceived an opportunity.

As a young resident who found aligning the needle to be the most challenging part of the procedure, I just knew there had to be a way to improve it. I was also motivated by a desire to carve some small bit of autonomy in a situation in which I felt controlled and restricted.

Since I couldn't find what I was looking for, I resolved to invent the tool myself. The wheels began to turn. I devised a way to attach a laser to the image intensifier (the undersurface of the C-arm) and reflect the light off of the needle towards the light source. My initial delight turned to disappointment when I found out that this approach had already been patented. A company was already marketing a device that used a similar concept of directing light from the C-arm toward the needle.

This unfortunate development did not extinguish my passion for the project. I was beginning to realize that the most important element is not so much the idea itself as it is your passion – your recognition that you can find a better way. If this device was so good, why was it that seemingly nobody knew about it? It turned out that this process was too cumbersome and inferior to what I would eventually design.

Instead of giving up, I reversed my approach, and attached a small device containing a laser pointer to the back of the needle itself. The light was projected in the opposite direction from the needle back to the C-arm located about two feet above the patient. It then bounced back off the mirror on the undersurface of the instrument and was captured on the top surface of my device. Then the two points of lights could be manually aligned, much like a carpenter's level. In effect, the light bounced back on itself, and the needle became perfectly perpendicular to the underside of the C-arm.

It proved to be a novel and more effective solution, and I knew then that I was on to something significant. All of the other guidance systems for needles placed the alignment system on the imaging equipment. My approach, simple but untried, was to attach the guidance system to the needle itself and reflect the light source off of the fluoroscope. With more than 10 million epidurals performed each year, the potential for saving time and reducing patient injury was enormous.

What Next?

Now I was at the turning point at which many inventors find themselves. Here was a great idea that answered an obvious need. But the central question became "where do I go from here?" I could simply put it away and go back to finishing my presently unfulfilling residency, or I could move forward with the development of the device.

Many people arrive at this critical point and then, for various reasons, make an uninformed decision. More often than not, they never do anything with their idea and it's left for someone else to develop. And those who do carry it forward don't always protect their property, and thus lose it to someone else later on.

At that point in time, I knew little about intellectual property and how it could be legally protected through the patent process. Yet, I realized that if my invention had commercial potential, I wanted to be able to sell it to a company that specialized in medical devices. In order to do that, I needed to actually own the idea.

My girlfriend's father, himself an engineer and an attorney, suggested that I visit a law school friend who was one of the best-known patent attorneys in the city. It turned out that one of his clients was the local research university – where, coincidentally, I was working as a resident.

The patent attorney informed me that he couldn't represent me because, at that time, the institution had a very restrictive policy that specified that they would own almost anything produced by its employees. He advised me to keep quiet about my idea rather than risk losing it. As it turned out, however, since I had never actually signed an agreement with the university, I wasn't subject to that policy.

I soon found a young patent attorney, Ryan Schneider, who was with the Atlanta law firm of Troutman Sanders LLP. Just a couple of years older than me, he was bright, aggressive, and service oriented. As a skilled intellectual property counsel with an engineering background, he was quick to appreciate the potential of my device and the steps I needed to take in order to protect my invention.

He also proved to be sensitive to the fact that I was a resident short on cash, and virtually told me how to file my own provisional patent. Schneider was willing to share his own considerable knowledge of patent filings and act as a coach during the initial stages of the process. He appreciated my passion and encouraged me, even while advising me that the odds were against my successfully navigating the many obstacles between idea conception and market product.

Even in the midst of all the disaffection with my professional life at that point, I felt like I was walking on air. I was connected to the long line of inventors who had come before me, whose devices and ideas had changed the world in ways both big and small. I knew that I was on the verge of doing something good that would allow me to make my own contribution.

And then the process was finally underway, and I was moving in a direction that just a few months earlier would have seemed inconceivable. The process of inventing and marketing this device would prove to be an incredible education for me, and the story of my experiences will provide you with the start to your own road map to success.

Chapter 3

MY PATH TO INNOVATION AND CREATIVITY

Thanks to this invention, my life had taken a totally new, unexpected turn. Suddenly, I was on fire with passion and energy as I began working to develop the idea of a device used to guide spinal injections. I felt a renewed sense of purpose and the black cloud that had hung over me lifted.

My mind had become fertile and my thoughts expansive, virtually every minute of the day. I was dreaming about the device and waking up each morning energized and filled with ideas.

My mental attitude had brightened considerably as I gained this new purpose. I inadvertently embarked on one of the greatest learning experiences of my life as well. The process was like earning a virtual MBA degree, but in many ways it was infinitely more practical.

Over the course of the next year, I gained firsthand experience in developing a prototype, gathering endorsements and recommendations, filing and obtaining a patent, marketing to companies, and finally, selling my invention to a major provider of medical devices. In essence, I went through the entire inventing process from idea conception to product sale.

This process – what you might call the University of Practical Experience, or more to the point, the school of hard knocks – gave me a hands-on view of what it takes to be an inventor. It also convinced me that many people approach this process in absolutely the wrong way. As we'll explain later in the chapter on exit strategies, there are many misconceptions about bringing a device to market and the role you, the inventor, should or could play in it.

A Working Model

I knew that one of the things I had to do was develop a prototype of the device. Although such a working model is not necessary to begin the patent process, it can be a vital step in getting your idea ready for market. In fact, the patent process is based solely on the idea or concept.

I had done numerous drawings and had a clear vision of how the finished product should look. I now had to figure out how to put together a working model that could demonstrate its use for me as well as for others.

I began laboring in earnest to develop a prototype of the device. I devoted many hours to refining the invention, making trips to the hardware store to pick up materials and tools, and then working at night, on weekends, and even during my lunch hour. Sometimes, in between seeing patients, I would go into my office and continue to tinker with what was shaping into an effective model of the original concept.

I bought levels and pointing devices and pasted together materials. Most of the sometimes awkward models still sit on my shelf as a testimony to my passion. Now, you have to understand that I was never the kind of person who tinkered around in his workshop. I wasn't handy with tools, and changing lightbulbs was often the full extent of my mechanical ability. Yet I was so possessed by this idea that I found myself assembling parts like a would-be engineer.

Even while on a rotation in Birmingham, Alabama, with one of the country's leading experts on interventional spine procedures, I continued to spend many evenings going to local stores, buying materials to assemble a new prototype.

One of the items I needed was a laser pointer. I searched through the narrow aisles in vain and then found that the only ones they had were on the hunting rifles sold in the store. I asked an earnest young clerk standing in front of the locked glass cases – containing enough firepower to start a small war – if I could purchase just the pointer. "I'm afraid not," he said apologetically. "It's against state law. Laser pointers are dangerous."

"But they're on these guns," I countered. "You're saying I can buy a gun, but I can't buy a laser pointer because it's dangerous?"

"That's right," he affirmed, with no trace of irony. "The kids shine them in other people's eyes at sporting events. They're dangerous."

It seemed that the state had outlawed laser pointers except for more conventional uses – such as aiming a high-powered rifle. I had to travel back to Atlanta in order to find a store that agreed to sell me one that wasn't attached to a weapon.

When I returned home, I did the initial alignment on a frozen chicken. A friend of mine, who I was later to join in practice, let me do the work in his office. As I set up the quite dead chicken on a table and did the alignment and injection procedure, his office staff gathered around behind me. Afterwards, I heard quite a bit of teasing about my first experimental "patient."

Although I was convinced the device was both highly useful and salable, it hadn't yet been tested in the market itself. In order to show that it had potential, I needed the support and endorsement of experts in my field. With a prototype in hand, I set about contacting doctors who performed this spinal injection procedure, seeking their input and opinion. If their reactions were positive, then I could ask them to endorse my product.

Of course, not everyone who saw the device was impressed with the invention – or my passion for it. Through a family connection, I met noted orthopedic surgeon and inventor Michael Lewis. With just a day's notice, I was able to secure a meeting at his Nashville office. I made the four-hour drive and arrived for what I thought would be, at best, a 30-minute meeting.

After demonstrating the alignment device, he looked at me and said, "You know, I don't quite get it. This isn't my area, but I know someone you need to talk to about it."

He picked up the telephone and placed a call to a colleague, Benjamin Johnson, an associate professor of anesthesiology across town at Vanderbilt University Medical Center. To my surprise, Dr. Johnson agreed to see me right away. Once again I was back in my car, driving across an unfamiliar city, propelled forward by a burning passion for this idea.

I repeated my presentation in Dr. Johnson's office, and when I was done, he said, "This is a great idea. It would be a godsend for my residents."

His reaction was far better than I could have hoped for. Not only did Dr. Johnson like my device, he also agreed to give a written testimonial on Vanderbilt University letterhead, expressing the same enthusiasm that had been exhibited in his initial reaction.

His testimonial proved to be a major impetus in my quest to develop and market my device. At that point, my own family had begun to express doubts about whether I should be putting so much time and energy into such an endeavor. They were telling me I should concentrate on finishing my residency and getting into practice rather than risking so much on an unproven and unappreciated experiment.

My cousin, a highly successful neurosurgeon, took me aside at his son's bar mitzvah and began to assail me to be more practical. Waving his arms around his well-appointed home, he said, "What do you think pays the mortgage on all this? You need to finish your residency and get into practice!"

I smiled and nodded, but still believed that I was right. In fact, I was filled with new energy thanks to Dr. Johnson's endorsement of my idea.

Better still, when I showed his testimonial to others, they were obviously impressed. All of a sudden, I had confirmation that this invention was needed and that people would buy it if it was available.

The Path to Market

As my idea drew closer to fruition, I was consumed with thoughts about how I could get it to market. I was intrigued with the idea of forming a company that could both manufacture and sell the device to the medical community. Starting a company might also prove to be a means for getting out of the practice end of medicine, I thought.

Although it sounds strange even to me, at that time I was growing increasingly dissatisfied with the medical establishment. I didn't know if I really wanted to go into practice after my experiences in residency. The idea of being an entrepreneur sounded appealing, but I knew that I didn't know enough to start a company, and I certainly knew nothing about running one. I had to find help.

I turned to my longtime friend, Ken Hoffman, then an investment banker on Wall Street. We spent many long hours on the phone and in person, talking about the device and its market potential. Ultimately, he declined the opportunity to give up a six-figure income with a major investment bank to become the first CEO of a company that existed only in my own thoughts and dreams.

Through conversations with Hoffman and others, I quickly realized that starting a company was beyond my own ability. It became clear that the next best step was to find a willing buyer who could handle all the tasks, such as manufacturing, marketing, and sales that, as a doctor, I might only learn through difficult – and perhaps costly – experience. So I made the decision to begin searching for a medical device company that marketed a product similar to my own and that might be interested in buying mine.

In order to sell my device, I knew that I had to develop an effective pitch that would at least get me in the door and get me a hearing in front of someone who had decision-making authority. During that time, I was talking frequently with my advisory board, which included Hoffman, best-selling author Brad Meltzer, and my friend and attorney Adam Meyerowitz, who assisted me with both my business plan and sales pitch.

I had realized the value of seeking out the advice of experts who knew more than I did. Just as entrepreneurs know how to use Other People's Money (OPM), I discovered an early valuable resource – Other People's Intellect (OPI). There is no virtue in pretending that you know everything and have the answer to every question. Everyone has their particular area of expertise, and when you venture into a realm in which you are not qualified, the best use of your time and resources is to seek out those whose knowledge you can use to your best advantage. This is a valuable practice that I have followed to this day.

Each of my advisors offered suggestions about how to further refine the idea I had developed down to a few clear, concise sentences that effectively communicated the value of the device. I would be cold-calling various companies, asking for the director of new product development, and then taking advantage of the 30 seconds of his attention I had in order to make the pitch.

Knowing that I had to make every word count, I scripted the presentation out until I was confident that every word would work in my favor. One of your most important challenges will be to develop a presentation that clearly states what you have to sell.

As well-prepared as I could be, I made the first calls to companies that I believed might have an interest in my invention.

"Hi, my name is Dr. Jeffrey Grossman," I would say to the receptionist. "I'm a resident physician at Emory University and I have a patent pending on a medical device to improve spinal injection procedures. I'd like to speak to the head of product development."

I quickly found that simply having an M.D. after my name conveyed a certain air of authority and respectability. Company officials were willing to talk to me because I was a doctor who had a patent-pending invention. Those two facts conveyed the seriousness of the idea and indicated that I was worth a listen.

Once I got the right person on the line, I told him quickly about the idea that I had developed and the potential market I saw for it.

In the beginning, I wrestled a bit with each person I spoke to. I insisted that each one sign a Confidentiality and Nondisclosure Agreement (you'll find a sample one in the Appendix). I became increasingly concerned that someone might steal my idea if I didn't do everything I could to protect it. Many companies refused to sign the agreement, but I shared the idea with the few that did.

Hitting Pay Dirt

One of the companies intrigued by the concept was the Sofamor Danek division of Medtronic, one of the country's largest medical device manufacturers. After a series of conversations, they agreed to fly me to their headquarters in Memphis, Tennessee, for a face-to-face meeting.

I was elated. At the time I thought, "Wow, they're buying a plane ticket and putting me up. They must really be interested." In retrospect, I can see that it really wasn't such a big deal for this $10 billion company to drop a few hundred dollars for a round-trip ticket and a chauffeured car to bring me in for a meeting. They had little to lose if my idea wasn't right for them, and much to gain if it was.

In the meantime, I practiced my presentation on a daily basis in between patient visits at the hospital. To add zip to my talk, I assembled a PowerPoint presentation. I went over it again and again, fine tuning each point until I was positive that it was as good as I could make it.

I even went into the procedure room at the hospital and, using a junior resident as a model, did setups showing how the device would work. I drew markings on his back and using a digital camera, I took photos demonstrating how difficult it could be to align the needle without the device. These materials became a part of the visual presentation.

The meeting was to be on a Monday. Over the weekend, I felt almost like an athlete getting ready for the big game. I was excited and ready to meet the officials of this giant company. I was superbly prepared and ready to answer any questions. I had never felt so confident in my entire life as I did at that time.

Later that day, I was at the offices of Sofamor Danek with my presentation materials, my PowerPoint, a prototype, and everything else I needed. Walking into the impressive, wood-paneled boardroom with its large oak table in the center, I felt like I had arrived. Here was my moment, and I was filled with a sense of purpose and passion. By the time I was done, I could see that I had made an impression. They saw how much I cared about the idea, and in the process, I inspired them as well.

Not long afterwards, they contacted me with an offer to buy my idea. Their first offer was more than I had hoped for, but I decided to negotiate for a better deal. My advisors had cautioned me against seeming too eager and signing the first contract they put in front of me. At the same time, I was pushing forward with the filing of a conventional patent application.

Idea Protection

I had originally filed a provisional patent, which is designed to provide a lower-cost first-patent filing in the U.S. The provisional patent application provides the potential of a one year delay in the requirement to file a non-provisional application on the idea. My provisional would expire in a few months. Since I had shared my idea with several companies, I wanted to make sure that I had the full protection that a conventional or "real" patent would convey.

I did much of the work myself, but by working with my attorney, Ryan Schneider, I was able to file a completed application rather quickly. It was a difficult and labor-intensive process, but in those days, I didn't believe I could afford to turn the entire job over to an attorney. Now, of course, I know better. A professional can save you time and do a much better job than you possibly could, in a much shorter time frame.

With the patent filing and long approval process underway, I continued with my negotiations and finally secured what I believed to be a good contract. It gave me money up front, as well as additional payments based on certain milestones in the development and approval of the device. In addition, I also signed on royalties amounting to a certain percentage of sales. This deal is much the same one that every inventor receives from a large company, and depending on the potential market for your invention, it can be quite lucrative.

My experience gave me a perspective on innovation and creativity and an understanding of what powerful tools they can be in the right hands. I was able to create a much-needed medical device when I applied some basic principles of creativity to the specific knowledge that I possessed as a physician. By actually going through the whole process, I gained an understanding of how creativity can be applied to many other seemingly mundane areas and how it can make your entire life and practice more effective, more efficient, and ultimately more satisfying.

After signing the contract with Medtronic, I often thought about how much easier things might have been if I had had mentors or a guidebook to help me through the process. I also realized that the principles of creativity aren't just for those who want to be inventors or entrepreneurs. They're for all of us who have made medicine our profession, whether you're an orthopedic surgeon looking for a better way of performing knee replacement surgery or an internal medicine specialist who wants to find a way to spend more time with patients without suffering a significant loss in income. Those thoughts, in turn, gave birth to the book you're now holding in your hands.

Chapter 4

INNOVATING YOUR LIFE

When we think of creativity, it seems to be a rare process that magically spawns spectacular innovations that change our lives and enrich their inventors. While that is part of the story, I'd like you to consider another side of creativity that should be applied to your life and the way you live it.

Creativity is a natural part of the human condition. It is a path to new solutions for the challenges you face that can be used throughout your day in many unexpected and satisfying ways. All that creativity demands is the perception of a problem that generates enough frustration to motivate you to pursue a solution.

At its most basic level, creativity seeks a new way of viewing a situation and a better way of doing something. It is a process I apply to my practice – at first unconsciously, but now with careful and deliberate action. It motivates me to seek out the best solutions to the myriad situations I face everyday as a professional healthcare provider.

Cultivating creativity in daily life is a means to an end. For me, it is a commitment to being more effective and efficient in the way I perform procedures, relate to patients, and manage my office and staff. It has been a process that has not only greatly increased my personal effectiveness, but raised my office margins as well. It has built a practice that serves patients, and at the same time has created a high level of satisfaction for both me and everyone else who comes through my door.

One of the most important benefits you can gain from applying creative principles to your work is to carve out more time for the things you most want to do. For some doctors, this might be more time spent with individual patients rather than rushing from one examining room to the next in a grueling attempt to keep up with a packed schedule. It also allows me to branch out into new endeavors and fields of opportunity such as writing this book.

In this chapter, I will outline for you the events that led me to take this process so seriously, and then show you how I have applied it in the way I run my own practice on a daily basis.

Creative Efficiency

Although medical offices have undergone tremendous changes in recent years, it is clear that many are still managed in highly ineffective ways. This is not to imply that patients receive poor care. To the contrary, healthcare in the United States is without a doubt the best in the world and physicians have reason to be proud. Yet when it comes to applying sound business practices, like automating our offices, we lag far behind much of the rest of the business world.

Many physicians believe the only way to boost their practice's income lies in increasing the number of patients seen and procedures performed. Nevertheless, this process can reach the point of diminishing returns as the physician works harder and harder, filling his schedule with patients and procedures until he finds himself exhausted and perhaps even bitter at the hectic pace he has set for himself.

A more productive approach might lie in negotiating better contracts with managed care providers or outsourcing time-consuming activities that can be done better and cheaper by other service providers or finding other means to work more effectively. By adopting a more innovative approach to your practice, you can earn the same income but have more time for patients, friends, family, and, most of all, yourself.

Soon after finishing my own residency, I worked in another doctor's practice that I was considering joining as a partner. While he was a fine practitioner, a lot of work was performed in inefficient and ill-conceived ways. Nearly everyone in my colleague's office was either doing things that weren't their strong points or performing them in a less than efficient way.

Unfortunately, shortcomings such as these are all too common. Yet they have little to do with the talents of physician and staff. Even though most healthcare practitioners are extremely hardworking, hard work is not the only secret to success. In fact, a commitment to work hard alone will only succeed in getting you more deeply into the rut of inefficiency.

Perhaps one of the best decisions I made regarding my practice was to spend more time with each of my patients. Many of my colleagues constantly reduce patient contact time in order to complete more office visits in exchange for greater income. Yet I determined that I could not only achieve greater satisfaction for both myself and my patients, but also earn the income I desired at the same time by seeing fewer patients.

As research shows, reducing time with patients increases the probability of being sued. I decided to take the opposite approach, which was to increase the time I spent with patients. As a result, the level of satisfaction they exhibit is quite high, because they're getting more time with their care provider, and I'm able to answer questions and provide them with the reassurance they sometimes seek.

Many doctors already see large numbers of patients each day, but aren't making very much money in the process. So they often hire marketing experts to generate even more referrals to fill their already overworked schedules.

The problem is that more patient visits – and more hard work – aren't the answer. Often, the contracts doctors negotiate with managed care and other third party payors simply don't provide the level of compensation that they could and should. We're doing more for less, when we should be earning more for the knowledge and skill we bring to our profession.

The Real Problem

A big part of innovation is simply the willingness to look beyond the conventional wisdom of how things have always been done and see the actual goal that you need to accomplish. This realization prompted me to engage in the innovative thinking that recognizes the true nature of the problem and then seeks a solution that is outside of the traditional ways of doing things.

I needed someone to run the office who was not weighted down by conventional and now largely outmoded ways of thinking. The best solution for this particular situation was recognizing that technology, managed care, and HIPAA requirements have drastically changed the landscape of healthcare and so I needed someone who understood just how different our reality had become. In selecting an office manager, most practices look to retired nurses and others who often no longer want to practice their original profession.

The most valuable job that a manager performs is negotiating better agreements with managed care companies. Having someone who could purchase the best software package or organize a filing system might be nice, but it wouldn't make the office profitable. I selected someone whose background wasn't in office management, but in the intricacies of managed care contract negotiations.

The need for a person with these skills was obvious. While preparing to open my own practice, I fell into a pattern of signing contracts without really understanding their implications, simply because we were in such a hurry to get the office up and running. It soon became clear, however, that many of these agreements were not in our best interest, and that they offered considerably less compensation than could be negotiated by someone skilled in these procedures. A contract that had a more favorable and prompt payment schedule would allow me to accomplish the goal of seeing fewer patients yet giving each one more individual attention. It would free me from the feeling that I needed to compress my schedule to work more and more new patients in as I sought to reach the same level of compensation.

Creative Mistakes

Another vital element in creating an effective office and practice is building a culture that tolerates – and even encourages – mistakes. For those of us in the medical profession, the idea of allowing error seems foreign and unacceptable. After all, we're trained to be perfect in our execution of procedures, because often a patient's health and even life may be at stake.

Yet giving your staff the freedom to experiment and fail without fear of punishment can reap tremendous rewards in the long run. I'm not talking about tolerating substandard work, but rather giving them the ability to seek out new ways of doing things, and to allow a certain margin of error as long as they are honest and willing to learn. Like a parent who encourages his child to practice walking on his own and then picks him up when he falls, you build confidence and encourage your employees to stretch and achieve far more than they would otherwise. You also increase the possibility of new breakthroughs that can benefit not only your practice, but your staff as well.

Being intolerant in demanding perfection won't reduce mistakes and errors. It will simply increase the likelihood that the ones that do take place will be covered up and create greater damage. It may also eliminate the possibility of quickly correcting an error that will cost more the longer it goes undiscovered.

The Help You Need

Many books on management point out that one of the prime avenues to success is the efficient use of resources. I discovered that one of my most valuable resources is the people who I surrounded myself with and worked with on a daily basis. No one reaches goals solely through his own efforts. The myth of the rugged individualist who does everything himself and needs nobody's help is an attractive and highly romantic notion. Yet, the reality is that collaboration with the right people is far more important than falling into the trap of believing that you are the sole source of your success.

I wanted to find better ways of working with the people who were my closest staff and advisors. Based upon personality tests, I came to understand that I am a producer of ideas driven to pursue them with passion and clarity. However, calling up someone and sharing the idea immediately often wasn't the best approach – particularly if it was 2:00 a.m. Yet, I wanted to make sure that these ideas were not lost in the passage of time and events.

The answer was once again in using technology. I secured private voice mail numbers for each of my closest associates. I could then call their number without disturbing either their work or sleep and leave a message that is forwarded to their e-mail as a digital voice file. They can then listen to these messages at their convenience. I communicate with them as often as I want while creating a permanent record of my thoughts that we can refer back to when needed.

Going Paperless

Efficiency in all areas has always been the central focus of my practice. I wanted not only the best people I could find, but also to equip them with the best tools and train them to follow the most efficient procedures. At the heart of a great practice is a well-designed office that utilizes space in the most effective way possible.

Initially, my practice occupied a relatively small space, and I didn't want to sacrifice any area for medical records storage. Over the years, the dream of the paperless medical office is one that has evolved through fits and starts and wrong turns for many physicians. Expensive, but inefficient office systems have been sold and often abandoned creating a well-deserved weariness among many of my colleagues.

Yet, the future was moving in that direction and couldn't be ignored. It became obvious that by creating a paperless system of electronic medical record (EMR) I would not only minimize my operations expenses but also allow everyone to operate at a much higher level of efficiency.

With more than 600 companies marketing EMRs to physicians, the choice was far from easy. I had to make sure that my office system met certain requirements, such as complying with HIPAA regulations – and whatever else government regulators might demand. It had to interface with all of my billing systems and my Practice Management system. In addition, it had to work the way I do, and change as quickly as I change. I wanted to be able to customize it without a lot of training. Knowing the sad history of so many doctors who had purchased systems from companies that soon disappeared and left them high and dry, I needed to own it.

I started looking for an expert who could design the kind of system I wanted using off-the-shelf software and equipment. I found the system I needed in the person of a medical supply vendor named Tripp Weeks. We talked about my practice and I explained to him that what I really needed was a low cost EMR, configured using Microsoft Office. Tripp said he could do it.

He and his staff constructed a ground-up system that included an internet connection with a wireless network. Charges and records are stored on Microsoft Exchange Server, providing secure interoffice e-mail. Print jobs and faxes can be sent from any desktop to any of the office's multifunctional devices through the office's shared network. A separate hard drive backup system ensures all records are protected from loss.

After a short time we were up and running and Weeks transitioned support of the system to a local IT firm and moved on to other projects. As he continued to develop the basic EMR that he had constructed for my office, it expanded to include a highly integrated medical office environment that produced exceptionally high quality chart notes in 40 seconds or less. These notes can be distributed via fax to as many as ten different locations – all from a simple drop down menu with just seven buttons. The system interfaces with MRI, x-ray and other digital imaging devices, as well as lab and various billing systems.

In my office, records can be accessed from a computer terminal, freeing up staff from the need to pull records. Files are stored as a locked Microsoft Word document that is password protected. Not only are they easier to manage this way, they're also far more secure than a paper file folder on a shelf could ever be.

In addition, when I receive a call from a patient, I can easily access the right file before picking up the phone. By scanning this record on my computer screen, I get an instant refresher on the patient's condition and treatment, which saves precious time for everyone involved. This process has become essential in providing the high level of care and customer service that I wanted to make a hallmark of my practice. The result has meant greater satisfaction for both me and my patients.

Of course, converting all those paper records to digital files required investing in a high-speed scanner. Initially, I purchased a lower-end device that only processed six pages per minute, which required a great deal of staff time – five hours a day – to scan a significant number of documents. Instead of sticking to my original misguided decision about hardware, I quickly realized a costlier, but more powerful scanner was in order.

To speed up the process even more, I traded in our traditional fax machine for an Internet-based fax service. When a referring physician faxes me a document, it arrives as an electronic file that can then be easily added to the proper network folder.

I also established systems and procedures to ensure that when a staff member was absent, his work could be carried out by someone else with the help of a well-documented procedure manual. Writing this manual, of course, required time and effort from both my staff and me. Yet, this initial investment of time paid dividends later whenever someone was absent, because the office was able to carry on effectively.

Playing to Your Strengths

Encouraging staff members to work using their strengths rather than trying to overcome their weaknesses has also resulted in a higher level of productivity and greater satisfaction for both them and me. Take the example of my front office coordinator, who I regularly sent on marketing visits to the offices of referring physicians to receive feedback on how we can improve our overall service to them. I wanted her to collect information on things such as the names of their staff members, so that when we placed a call, we'd avoid the embarrassment of not knowing a referral coordinator's name.

At first, I suggested she take a notebook and fill out the information immediately after the visit. That idea proved unsuccessful, because she simply didn't work that way – writing things down was not her strong point. She was more verbal, so we hit upon the idea of letting her dictate the information instead. So now, immediately after leaving the doctor's office, she picks up her cell phone and calls a dictation service. Her comments are transcribed and then e-mailed to me. Thus, we not only have complete and up-to-date information on each of our referral offices, but this particular staffer is happier because she works in the manner that best utilizes her talents.

This technique made sense to me since I was already dictating patient notes. While I'm in the examining room with a patient, I dictate into a digital recorder in front of the patient. It not only saves time, but serves to answer questions before they're asked and fosters a greater feeling of involvement by the patient. My notes are then uploaded to the website of a transcription service for processing.

Brainstorming

You should also realize that there are small investments you can make that may not produce an immediate payoff but which will in the long run produce a better, more efficient and more profitable office. Making full use of the wisdom and experience of your own employees is an often overlooked area of innovation that can help you develop new ideas while also testing your own concepts and innovations.

I hold regular brainstorming sessions in which everyone is encouraged to come up with as many solutions – even seemingly strange ones – to a particular problem as possible. While I still make the final decision, having this input can lead to insights that might not otherwise have come to me.

You probably don't need to have a session like this every week, but you should do it on a regular basis and particularly when you're faced with a new challenge or need a solution to some nagging problem. The benefits of this process go beyond simply opening up new avenues for ideas. It also allows employees to participate and become invested in a solution to the organization's problem.

In order for brainstorming to be effective, everyone must agree on the problem or question to be answered in advance. Have everyone write the question out on paper or put it up on a flip chart at the front of the room. It's essential that everyone understand what the group is going to focus on during the session.

Set a time limit and have everyone agree in advance that there will be no belittling or ridicule of anyone's ideas. As the leader of the session, you have to set the standard and make sure these rules are enforced. The goal is to generate as many ideas as possible during the allotted time without necessarily examining each one to see if its not feasible or similar to others. The most essential element in this process is open mindedness.

Just as the first phase of the session is simply idea generation, the second phase involves sifting out the best ones for further consideration. Dispense with unworkable ideas and pare down similar ones till you get to the best suggestions.

Now you're ready for the second phase of the session. As participants generate ideas, the group then subjects them to a form of natural selection. The environmental conditions that produce mutations are the insights and criticisms from those in the room. The group becomes the naysayer who questions the idea and forces its originator to defend and reshape the solution in the face of questioning. The idea evolves and becomes stronger as it is able to withstand these strains.

The eureka moment when an idea first appears is a beginning and not an end. It's like the seed planted in a garden. Within the seed is all the genetic information needed to produce a beautiful rose. Yet, unless it develops and takes nutrients from the soil, the rose will never appear.

The best approach to idea generation is avoiding over attachment to the original concept. Ideas alone are worth very little. They only become worthwhile as they are developed and nurtured and given tangible form. The new drug or medical device is of great value to the inventor, the company that markets it and most importantly the patient whose life it improves. The first conception, if never carried forward to the market, benefits no one.

The Power of Questions

One of the most powerful creative tools you possess is asking questions that motivate and empower people to find their own solutions to problems. This tact can be difficult for physicians, just as it is for many teachers, as we are expected to know the answer to every question. The reality is that no one can really know the best solution to every problem and pretending that you do can lead to disaster.

History is filled with examples of disasters that could have been avoided if leaders had only asked the right questions. After the ocean liner Titanic sunk in 1912 it was discovered that a number of engineers and designers had doubts about her reputed "unsinkable" status. No one in authority asked them for their opinion. Many years later, a similar situation occurred when the space shuttle Challenger exploded soon after launch. An O-ring failure caused the explosion, but it didn't come as a surprise to some involved with the project.

These are extreme examples of the consequences of not asking questions and getting the information needed to make good decisions. Many smaller mishaps take place every day with less noticeable consequences. Opportunities are lost because you didn't realize there was a different way of doing things.

It doesn't have to be that way. The right kinds of questions can spawn innovation both in formal brainstorming sessions and in many situations where a staff member comes to you with a concern or problem. Instead of instantly providing the answer – even if you think you know the best course of action – let them develop the solution on their own or in concert with others. A simple way of moving in this direction is first ask what they have already done to solve the problem on their own. Encourage your staff to exhaust their own possibilities first. You'll also discourage the kind of upward delegation of authority and responsibility that can burden a leader and prevent them from concentrating on higher value goals and activities.

Often when someone such as a staff member appears with a dilemma, we feel compelled to provide a solution. Employees are looking to us for leadership and aren't leaders supposed to be decisive and able to make decisions on the spot? While that may be the popular myth, it's often not the best approach to leadership. In fact, it may sometimes be quite dangerous – especially in medicine.

It's easy to become so attached to your own answer that you are blinded to other – perhaps better – solutions. This resistance to other people's ideas may arise from a lack of self-confidence that compels a leader to take charge and always look as if he's on top of things. It takes a good bit of courage to say you don't know or to be willing to accept someone else's ideas as perhaps better than your own. Many find it difficult tolerating the uncertainty and sometimes chaos that may ensue while your subordinates search for a solution.

Well crafted questions engender excellent responses. By asking the kinds of questions that guide your staff toward finding their own answers you engage in the essence of true leadership. By working through problems, you help them to become better at their jobs and you open the door to innovations that you might never find on your own.

It's important to understand that in order to ask the right questions you must also ask the right questions. There are three kinds of questioners and three approaches to asking questions. The first kind of question comes when you truly don't have an answer and are seeking information. The second type of question arises when you have an answer, but need to seek either additional information and want to keep yourself open to other possibilities. Both of these approaches to questions open you to new ideas and insights that can help you find solutions, or avoid problems.

There is a third type of question in which the questioner is already decided that he has the answer and doesn't require any input. He is making a statement that demands a reaction, not asking a question that requires an answer. These statements may demand a response, but that is a very different thing than actually soliciting input from another.

Unfortunately the people who ask this third type of question are those are who deeply wedded to their own concepts and unwilling to consider any other solution. In reality, they already know all the answers and much like closed minded fundamentalists aren't willing to consider any other perception or point of view. To admit that someone else has a different truth can only mean that you're wrong and that represents a challenge to your entire belief system. The person who shuts out all other sources of information has taken a step beyond reason to a position of faith. At that point, facts become truth without verification or challenge.

This is a very dangerous position for anyone in medicine where the consequences of a bad decision can have deadly consequences. Just as the owners of the White Star Line had blind faith in the unsinkable Titanic, it becomes easy to ignore contradictory information that indicates a course change.

Listen First

An essential element of asking questions – of even of creativity itself – is the ability to truly listen to the words of others. When you're in a conversation with someone the temptation is always to think of something else – often what you want to say next. Your own words fill your mind and you don't really hear the words and thus don't truly understand what she is saying to you.

It is only when we truly listen to a person's words – not our own – that we are able to understand that person. To truly understand and be able to communicate you must quiet the inner dialogue and focus just on the person in front of you with both attention and empathy.

This rule applied just as surly to good doctoring as well. When you walk into the exam room and engage the patient do you truly listen to what they have to say? Perhaps their words won't change your diagnosis or method of treatment, but they will know that you truly hear them and understand. In the process, you have given them a quality of empathy that will make them better patients.

Inside Customer Service

While a growing number of hospitals today are placing increasing emphasis on customer service, there's very little emphasis placed on what may well be the central key to success – internal service. Just as important to me as knowing how satisfied my patients are, I also need to understand how my own staff is thinking and feeling. When the practice was new and I was managing a staff of three rather than 15, it was perhaps easy to ensure that patients had a good experience. As the number of employees increased, however, the only way to maintain this level of service was to empower staff members to deliver the same level of service. Not a day goes by that a new patient doesn't tell me that this is "the nicest office" or "the most caring staff" or some similar compliment.

Granted, I spend a great deal of time handpicking my staff to ensure they have both the right hard and soft skills and that they are compatible with the philosophy of patient care and customer service I expect. To ensure that they will fit into the system, I use various psychological tests, such as those produced by the Gallup Organization. Yet, once they are onboard, I also work hard to ensure that they not only perform well, but that they are satisfied with their jobs. In order to find the answer to that question, you have to ask.

Most healthcare organizations sample the opinions of their patients and want feedback on how well the staff is taking care of them. Yet, few do the same for their employees. Essentially, they wait until a problem develops to find out that staff members are unhappy or chaffing under some ill-conceived work environment.

To this end, I have instituted a regular program of obtaining feedback through what I call the Q-12, a survey consisting of 12 questions that seeks to determine whether staff members believe they know their job responsibilities, have the resources to do them, and whether their talents are utilized in the best way possible.

In addition to developing my own internal staff, I also worked to outsource all functions that can be done better by others. I've applied that process not only to things like dictation and faxing, but also to more complex jobs such as bill paying. Invoices are scanned and placed on my own computer network. An outsourced CPA in California accesses the network on a weekly basis, downloading the bills for processing and payment.

Differing Opinions

Perhaps one of the most beneficial procedures I've adopted has been to make use of professionals who have expertise I do not. When I'm getting ready to make a major financial decision, I will consult two very different advisors. One is a conservative CPA who believes in taking a careful, measured approach, while the other is more aggressive and sees the potential in moving fast. They often produce widely varying advice on many subjects, but out of their differing points of view, I'm able to better formulate my own path. In the end, I must make the decision, but their consultations are invaluable in giving me the information and insight I need to consider all sides.

Each of these processes was worthwhile, because they increased my own efficiency and allowed me to do a much better job as a physician and as a businessperson. Yet, I know that many of the most useful ones might never have been adopted without a commitment to creativity and innovation.

Chapter 5

TIME AND VALUE

If you want to be a successful innovator – or a successful anything, for that matter – you have to encourage creativity and innovation. These two qualities are the engine that will power your success. Yet in order to nurture and develop these qualities, you must have an overflow of time and energy that goes beyond the demands of your job or profession and the grind that daily life often places on us.

Creativity in particular begs for time in order to be truly realized. In order to nurture those precious reserves of time, you must be able to carve them out of what is probably an already busy and full life. You must be able to make choices about how you spend your most precious resource just as you would the money in your bank account.

There are only certain things that are truly worthy of the time you spend. Yet, just as you can waste money on things and experiences that don't serve you well, so can you waste your time as well. Just as with your money, you may find yourself being committed to activities that consume your time. In the first two years of medical school, most students are nearly overwhelmed by the sheer volume of facts they must learn. As Dr. Neil Shulman put it, the medical student is "renting out his brain" for those intense two years. Many doctors may also feel that they have little or no control over their schedules because their work dictates that they go here and do that. As employees, they may be seeing patients and practicing in a manner prescribed by someone else.

No matter what your status, everyone has only so much time – those prover-bial 24 hours in a day – and how you use it determines what you accomplish, and, just as importantly, what you don't.

Yet, even at this point, you can begin to set aside small portions of time that become your own. As you get in the habit of taking control of your life, you'll find that these opportunities grow. In this chapter, we'll explore the secret to creating more time for your more worthwhile endeavors.

I'm sure that you've read a book or two on time management, or at least been offered one by some well-meaning soul who thought you were wasting too much time doing something you shouldn't. So relax, I'm not going to get into the intrica-cies of time management, list-making, or anything of that sort. However, if you want to read books on time management, there are many good ones – I highly rec-ommend Brian Tracy's Time Power for its inspiration and clear, simple ideas.

You can make lists, multi-task, and other tricks for increasing efficiency if you want. The techniques are readily available when you want to pursue them. Time management is a tool, and its usefulness is determined by how well it helps you reach your goals. A hammer can be used either to drive a nail or pound your thumb with equal force. Efficiency in the pursuit of inappropriate or misdirected goals is useless. The best time management techniques will get you nowhere if you don't know where you're going.

Folk singer Jeff Talmadge put it this way:

She's lost, she's lost, she's lost
But she's makin' real good time.

As the song says, moving fast isn't particularly valuable if you don't know where you're going. You have to find direction – the right one – first. And the best way to do that is by looking at your values. What do you most want out of life? What gives you the most pleasure? When you're at the end of your life, what will you look back on with the greatest pride and satisfaction?

This process of prioritizing and goal setting is the best place to start, and it is definitely the place where you should put real effort. The saddest people are those who climb the ladder of success only to find it's been placed against the wrong wall. Next, you must dedicate yourself to doing your absolute best to reach your goals and to perform every task in a professional manner. Finally, formulate goals that are in alignment with your most deeply held values. Never do anything that is inconsistent with those values.

Then put whatever time management techniques you like to work for you. They're all good ideas, but that's not what this chapter is about.

Tactics for getting tasks done more efficiently are valuable and you should develop them. Yet before you start trying to be more efficient, adopt a guiding philosophy and a criterion for selecting the activities in which you want to be involved.

I want you to consider the value of your time and the best ways for you to spend that time. I want you to be able to quickly and easily determine within every minute of the day what you should and should not be doing. Your time is of great value and you must protect this scarce resource.

The old cliché "time is money" is perhaps the best – if a rather arbitrary – maxim to keep in mind when contemplating what activities are worth your time and energy. You must move from a situation in which your time is controlled by others to one in which you begin to control it yourself. Only then will you gain the time and space to be creative and proceed along the path of invention.

Let me offer here a word of caution. While I do advocate attaching a monetary value to your time as a convenient means of sorting among the many conflicting demands and temptations that will be presented, it's only that – a guide. There will be instances in which you should use it and others in which you should discard it. For example, you could pay a nanny to take care of your child, but would you do so? The intrinsic value of those parental encounters is priceless. There is a long history of the well-to-do hiring others to be substitute parents and in the process producing maladjusted, resentful children who believe they didn't have real, loving parents. So tread carefully here.

Money is very important because it is a wonderful tool for getting things done. Admittedly, it's not the key to life, but it can buy you many resources that you can use to reach your goals. It can help you to "purchase" the time you need to think and be creative and produce the ideas that will make your life, and perhaps the lives of others, better.

One of the best situations to find yourself in is one in which you don't need money. Many creative individuals deliberately live below their means so that they can use their resources to fund their innovative endeavors. Those who allow their wants to continually expand and suck up all of their additional income will always find themselves "resource poor" and living, as the saying goes, "paycheck to paycheck."

Unfortunately, physicians as a group have a reputation for being prime examples of conspicuous consumers. Too many of them seem to be always thinking about getting a more expensive sports car, a flashier Rolex, or a more palatial suburban home. This constant spending can take on a life of its own, in which the possessions and their monthly payments really do own you rather than you owning them.

Knowing Your Personal Value

The process of determining time's value is very simple. Everyone's time has some worth. If you're really going to make the best use of it, you need to be able to distinguish between low value activities and high value activities. One way to do that is to attach a dollar figure to each hour you have available to spend on a particular project.

One way to understand your hourly worth is simply by taking your annual salary and dividing it down to a monthly, weekly, and finally, hourly basis. This gives you a good starting point to knowing your "true economic value" as a physician.

While this may sound crass to some, figuring your hourly rate is the first key to freeing you from your time restrictions. We all have a certain amount of time available to us, and it's important that we choose wisely how we use the time we've been given. The hourly rate provides a quick and convenient guide in making choices as to how you use your time.

Let's say, for example, that you calculate your annual salary and determine that you're making $125 an hour. Once you've determined that, you have to make an agreement with yourself that you will never do anything that you can pay someone to do for less than that figure. Taking your laundry to the cleaners isn't exactly a $100-an-hour activity. Neither are the scores of other activities that can be readily performed by others who are more than happy to work for far less than what you've calculated to be your hourly rate.

An exception to this rule is an activity that brings you self-fulfillment or personal satisfaction and growth or has a direct effect on your family.

Before going into solo practice, I worked in an office in which one of my fellow doctors insisted on doing a great many of the menial tasks associated with running an office himself. They ranged from typing his own patient notes to putting up drywall. While he seemed to enjoy these activities, they were frequently a waste of valuable professional time and were sometimes a morale destroyer.

One of the worst examples of this practice was his refusal to hire a cleaning service. He insisted that the office staff empty trash cans and clean toilets. Nobody liked doing it, and most found it demeaning to end the day with a toilet brush in their hand.

On the weekends, he would often come in to paint, redecorate, or even build walls so that he didn't have to hire a professional to do it. He frequently asked that I join him in these labors, but I usually found something else that I needed to do.

I thought it an enormous waste of time, and when I opened my own office, I resolved to leave jobs like those to the people who were best qualified so I could concentrate on the professional tasks that I could perform best.

I have also resolved never to perform any tasks that can be done cheaper or better by someone else. The first question I ask before beginning any project or activity – particularly if it seems to require a great deal of time – is whether it is truly the best use of my time and resources. Do I have to be the one to do it? Can someone else do it better, faster, or cheaper? Does it really need to be done at all? You must be willing to make those same resolutions and ask those same questions. You must also be willing to say no when the situation warrants.

Perhaps you really don't mind painting the office, designing your own office space, or putting up drywall. There's certainly nothing wrong with any of these activities, but if you're going to be truly efficient, you have to delegate things that don't advance your overall goals.

Saying Yes, Saying No

Jonathan is a physician friend of mine who holds a faculty appointment at a major research university. He professes to love his work, but every conversation with him begins with a recitation of how busy he has become and how many appointments he has taken on. His department head asks him to head up a committee on fund-raising, even though he is already serving on one committee for faculty evaluation and another dedicated to refining the institution's ethics policy.

He's also helping another faculty member with a curriculum development project, even as he teaches residents and medical students, conducts research, and performs clinical duties. As he's quick to admit, every moment of his day and many of his evenings are filled with work for which he is largely uncompensated. Many of the meetings he says are a bore and some projects are simply dead ends that will never get off the ground. Yet he faithfully accepts each task and believes that the group can't really accomplish anything without him.

Projects come to Jonathan because those bearing them know that he won't say no.

"I can't turn this down because it's such a great opportunity," he once said to me. "I wish I didn't have to do all these things, but there's no one else who can do the job."

My first reaction was, "Well, you can always say no."
Yet I saw that he believed that he was really giving something back to the university and that he truly thought he was indispensable. He wasn't able to acknowledge that his chronic busyness was a result of his own ego and inability to set boundaries.

One of the hardest things that anyone – particularly those in the helping professions – has to do is say no to some demand on your time and resources. We feel guilty, as though by not giving the asker what they want, we're letting them down or putting ourselves in a position in which we won't be liked. Yet being able to say no to certain things gives you the ability to say yes to the more important ones.

Those who always say yes to everything are setting themselves up for failure and perhaps, worst of all, depression

Rabbi Philip Kranz, of Temple Sinai in Atlanta and a psychology professor at Agnes Scott College, explains the power you gain by clearly defining where you stand.

"Saying no isn't just a negative answer," he says. "It's an answer that says you stand for something and that you're not simply going along with everything that happens. You put some limits on things and give some shape to your beliefs. So a person has a much clearer idea of what is expected of them."

Each and every time you make a choice between competing demands and differing opportunities, you define yourself and you set your priorities and your boundaries. It's very important to have the courage to define where you stand and what you want to accomplish, and then focus your resources on doing what's important. If you're going to take on an endeavor that's going to require a huge commitment like inventing a medical device, other lesser things must take a backseat. You quickly have to realize that you can't be all things to all people. Don't allow anyone to pressure you into doing things that you know you really don't want to do. Just remember that every time you say yes to a task you don't want to do, you are saying no to the opportunity to spend that time doing something that really advances your goals or brings you true pleasure. Focus your energy on accomplishing your chosen goals and reserve your remaining free time for your family, friends, and those who deserve it.

The Purpose of Efficiency

Being efficient isn't something you do just for its own sake. The ultimate goal is to make enough space in your life to be a happier and more creative individual. But you can't do that if you're bogged down with trivial activities that aren't related to what you do best.

In my own study of highly successful individuals, one of the traits that seems to be common among them is that each maintains an environment in which their own creativity can flourish. A recurring theme in this environment is that it allows them to do the things they want to do and shields them from things they don't want – or have – to do.

Many highly effective business executives have become successful through finding creative ways to protect their time. Richard Koch, author of *The 80/20 Principle*, says that many executives avoid useless meetings by simply not being available. When that bothersome assembly rolls around, they disappear. By not being visible, they aren't caught up in the activity.[1]

A prime example of the power that this act can have is found in the life of noted oncologist Dr. Rainer Storb, who is also one of the nation's most often cited researchers. Even though he heads one of the largest and most productive research labs in the country, he has always avoided the time-consuming demands of business meetings. Instead, he focuses his energy on developing and carrying forth the more valuable activities of making sure research projects are properly developed and executed.

Koch's book is devoted to an often overlooked law that governs human affairs. The 80/20 principle states that 80 percent of our results come from just 20 percent of our efforts. Conversely, 80 percent of everything we do produces just 20 percent of our results. While these figures are only a guide, this principle has proven remarkably consistent across a wide range of human activities. For example, the overwhelming majority of the world's wealth is held by a very small percentage of the world's population. And most crimes are committed by a relatively small number of criminals.

First articulated by Italian economist Vilfredo Pareto, this idea is known as

The Rule of the Vital Few and is applied by anyone who wants to be truly efficient and successful. When you realize that only a certain number of the activities you do are actually worthwhile, then you can begin to remove the meaningless tasks from your life. Give them to someone else or don't do them at all. By doing so, you will be able to accomplish your real goals at a faster rate than you ever thought possible. Eliminating the worthless 80 percent and focusing sharply on the important 20 percent will allow you to make monumental strides – even if you don't increase your ability to perform those tasks.

This is not to say that in all instances you should avoid performing what might be considered low value tasks, because sometimes they yield high value results.

You might, for example, find Thomas Fogarty out shopping for his own light-bulbs because he often finds inspiration at hardware and toy stores. But no matter what he is doing, or how mundane it may seem, he is actively engaged in finding inspiration for his next invention.

We have no resource scarcer or more precious than our time. Remember to say no when necessary. Truly protecting this rare resource requires that you understand the importance of setting priorities, which will sometimes require disappointing others whose goals are disparate from your own.

REFERENCES

1.   Richard Koch, The 80/20 Principle (New York, Doubleday, 1998)

Chapter 6

UNDERSTAND YOURSELF AND
FIND YOUR STRENGTH

One of the greatest secrets to success in the creative process is determining early on what your strengths are and then playing to them, rather than trying to overcome your weaknesses. To many of us raised in an educational system that constantly highlights our weaknesses, it may sound strange to say that you should simply accept that there are certain things you're not good at and let those things go.

We buy into the philosophy that you can be anything you want to be if you just try hard enough. Now it's certainly true that just about anybody can learn to play golf, but if you don't have talent for the game, you won't be able to compete with the likes of Tiger Woods, or even make it to the bottom of the top 200 on the pro circuit. In fact, why would you want to waste your time trying to become a golfer if your true talent lay in, say, chess?

Yet the notion that we should continually try to "fix" our weaknesses is the subject of numerous self-help books, programs, and seminars. Educators, human resource professionals, managers, and motivational gurus of all kinds tell us we can learn to be competent in almost anything. And, of course, since we have the most to learn in our areas of weakness, these are also the areas in which we have the greatest opportunities for growth. Because we're so far behind, we can travel a relatively short distance and seemingly make a great deal of progress.

Yet, while we're concentrating all our resources on our weaknesses, we're missing a golden opportunity to make the most of our innate and acquired talents and abilities. It's from our strengths that we will reap our greatest rewards and our most significant accomplishments.

Gary Lockwood, a well-known business coach, facilitator, and speaker who specializes in helping entrepreneurs make breakthroughs in their business, put the idea of concentrating on weaknesses this way: "While learning new subjects is a great idea, striving to develop weaknesses can work against you. Conventional wisdom says we should work on improving our weaknesses. This is a terrible waste of time, talent, and opportunity. Imagine what would have happened if Chopin, Einstein, Chris Evert, or Pavarotti had followed that advice. All these people devoted their lives to developing their natural strengths. As a result, they each were tops in their field."[1]

And yet millions continue to focus on making improvements in their weakest areas while generally allowing their true strengths to "take care of themselves." The result of this delusion is often failure – either to achieve your set goals or to develop your talents to their fullest potential.

"The reason is fundamental," wrote the late Dr. Donald O. Clifton, chair and CEO of The Gallup Organization, in *Soar with Your Strengths*. "To theorize that 'anyone can do anything' assumes that all people are clones, possessing an identical set of talents. This, of course, is false. We are one of a kind, with a unique set of strengths."[2]

Today, companies spend large sums of money training employees after they've been hired to acquire skills they plainly lacked before taking the job. Workers who complete courses and win certificates in their weak areas are usually promoted, based on these acquired skills.

Employees realize that they seldom are called upon to utilize their strengths. One survey of America's workforce by the Gallup Organization asked how they felt about the following statement: "At work I have the opportunity to do what I do best every day." Only about 20 percent said they "Strongly agree." We can assume that the overwhelming majority are not being given the opportunity to play to their strengths and make the most of their talents. Workers suffer because they're not getting to realize their full potential, and companies suffer because they're not getting the most from those they employ.

It becomes a vicious cycle, as customers are confronted with discontented and low-performing employees and often take their business elsewhere. Sales slide and this lackluster performance is reflected in poor balance sheets, missed earnings projections, lowered stock prices, and unhappy investors.

We see this same scenario played out in medicine as well. Certain specialties require specific skill sets and personality types. A general surgeon must be able to pay great attention to detail. A family physician, on the other hand, needs good people skills to be truly successful with patients.

This scenario is the dire result of our obsession with overcoming weaknesses, and it is reflected far more often than you might think in unhappy people and poorly performing businesses.

As an innovative doctor, you are also faced with the choice of making the most of your strengths or spending time and energy trying to overcome your weaknesses. The decisions you make and the approaches you follow will determine just how successful and how happy you are in your career of producing creative ideas. If you're already well established in your career, it may be too late to change. However, if you're still in medical school and weighing your options for practice, now would be a good time to take a hard look at where your natural talents and inclinations lead you.

Built for Success

We are all born with certain talents, which form the basis for our array of strengths and weaknesses. The amount of talent you possess in a certain area determines how well you will be able to build upon that particular strength. Certain people have so much innate ability that they may even be called "naturals." These talented people are perhaps most apparent in sports, but they can be found in every area of life. Some people have a natural ability for mathematics, others for repairing gas engines or playing the violin. Skills can be acquired through knowledge and practice, but how far you can go with them depends on your underlying talent.

We all have some area of strength, and the more we understand and cultivate our natural abilities, the more successful we will become in everything we do.

Before I go any further, let me say that I don't think you should completely ignore your weaknesses. Instead, I suggest recognizing and managing them. A weakness may be a result of lack of skills, knowledge, talent, or interest in acquiring mastery. You must first determine which of these areas causes the weakness and then set about mitigating it.

As a physician, perhaps you can benefit from working with another specialist. You could join forces with another surgeon who specializes in the type of procedure you want to do and learn from him. In effect, you can create a support system that helps you with your shortcomings. Or you could stop performing the function altogether.

As the saying goes, "Don't try to teach a pig to sing – it wastes your time. And, besides, you will only annoy the pig."

Capacity for Creativity

As I mentioned earlier, our strengths and weaknesses are like our personality traits. They're hardwired into our brains and can only be changed a little, if at all, through hard work. When you understand your strengths and weaknesses, you better utilize your time. It will also produce more informed judgments about how you want to approach the process of introducing creativity into every aspect of your professional and personal life.

When I was developing my own invention, I was at first convinced that I should form a company to develop and market it. I soon realized that I didn't have either the business skills or the access to venture capital to found and run a start-up enterprise. The number of physicians who can do so successfully can probably be counted on one hand – maybe even with a finger or two left over.

At the time, I realized that I didn't yet have the type of personality that makes for a good CEO. So I reached out to a few friends and mentors who actually possessed some of these skills.

Others have made those same critical appraisals. For example, Dr. Thomas Fogarty has become famous for starting numerous companies built around medical devices. Yet he has always had the good sense to hire management talent to actually run the operation once it got going. He realized early on that his talent was in creating ideas, not in the day-to-day rough and tumble of management.

Harvard researcher Joseph Sodroski trusts the critical bench work needed to obtain advances in the fight against AIDS to others, because his strength lies in management and writing the grants needed to obtain funding.

The Inventor's Personality

Personality also dictates whether an inventor has the capacity to be a successful entrepreneur, or whether inventing arises solely out of a love for research. There is nothing inherently right or wrong about either. The only thing you can do wrong is to try to be something that you're not. Along that path lies stress and unhappiness.

James Wynne serves as director of research at IBM's famed Watson Research Center. It was there, while he was manager of the laser physics and chemistry group, that Wynne and Drs. Rangaswamy Srinivasan and Sam Blum hit upon the idea of excimer laser surgery.

They discovered that a short-pulse ultraviolet laser could etch tissue in a minute, highly controlled fashion. Cuts could be made to a precise, predetermined depth without damaging surrounding tissue. An immediate application was in refractive eye surgery, such as LASIK and PRK, which permanently changes the shape of the cornea and restores normal vision.

As a researcher working for a major corporation, Wynne is very proud of his accomplishments and the dramatic changes his discovery has brought to the field of ophthalmology and vision correction. Yet despite the fact he has achieved numerous awards and recognition for the discovery, the patent to it is owned by his employer, and he hasn't profited from the huge market the procedure has created.

"We didn't get any huge amount of that money at all, but we got some nice recognition," says Wynne. "I'm quite happy with the recognition that I got, but Srinivasan and Blum have both retired from IBM, so they probably have a different perspective. In any case, I'm still here, and I've recently won a second award with my two colleagues – a second major award. We also got into the National Inventors Hall of Fame."

Wynne recognizes that as an employee who conducted research on company time and using company resources, his work and discoveries belong to IBM, and not to him or his colleagues.

"It's not anything I ever questioned," he remarks. "The only contract I ever signed with IBM when I was hired was an agreement signing my intellectual property to them in exchange for a job. I came here because I wanted to do science. I wanted to be surrounded by an infrastructure of good people – great people hopefully – and not have to worry about writing contract proposals to get my tools."

Clearly, Wynne didn't go into this field because he hoped to one day reap riches from royalties on the sale of products. His motivations are simpler – and perhaps purer. They are firmly based in the love of knowledge and the joy of discovery. For him, that is enough.

"I just felt that industrial research was the right place for me," he says. "And I've never had any regret that I don't own the intellectual property."

Over the years, he's gotten bonuses to complement the recognition and rewards, but he realizes the money is quite small in comparison to the financial rewards reaped by others. "But I'm not unhappy with that," he says.

Obviously, the corporate path is right for some inventors, but not for others. In contrast to Wynne, who works in the safety of a large corporation, others are able to flourish only after leaving the ivory towers and relative of a large company with its steady paycheck and retirement plans.

A good example of this opposing personality type can be found in a fellow member of the Inventors Hall of Fame, Dr. Al Langer. An electrical engineer, he was on the team that invented the automatic implantable defibrillator. In fact, the daunting task of building the device that many doubted could work was his very first job out of graduate school.

At the time, no one had ever built such a device, and a number of engineers declined the job because of the dangers it might pose to patients if it failed.

"We had to do a lot of testing, because nobody had ever done that before," says Langer.

The device went on to become one of the greatest successes in the history of medical devices, but Langer wasn't willing to settle for a corporate job. Instead, he used the experience he gained on this project to found his own company – Cardiac Telecom Corp. – a pioneer in providing in-hospital-grade cardiac surveillance over telephone lines for homebound patients. He has also won more than 30 other patents for a variety of devices.

Today, he continues to work on developing new devices through his own company. A big part of the challenge is in bringing everything together, from the idea to the right technicians to the right financing. Yet his motivation remains the same as when he was one of the pioneers in his field.

"The thing I like to do is build something that nobody's ever made before and make it work," he says. "When you put everything together and it starts doing what it's supposed to do and everything just comes together as you envisioned it, I just love it."

Determining Your Own Personality

The more you understand whether you're a James Wynne or an Al Langer, the more you'll be able to plot the best course for yourself. This is not to say that everyone is either totally a company man or an entrepreneur. Some of us are a little bit of both. It all comes down to your own particular personality, your strengths, and your weaknesses. It's important that you determine your personality type and characteristics.

I've made personality testing an integral part of my office procedures. All of my staff – including myself – have taken tests like those administered by the Gallup Organization. While you must regard any standardized test with at least a grain of salt, they are generally good indicators of your traits, and taken together, they form a road map for the path you should follow.

One of my own personality traits I discovered through this testing is that I have a difficult time completing tasks. I recognize that tendency now, and work to mitigate it by using other people to help me bring closure to the final stages of projects. The fact that you're reading this book now is an indication of how I've successfully managed this particular weakness.

Deadlines are often a good means of forcing your mind to focus on a particular task. Silicon Valley inventor and entrepreneur Mir Imran notes that he creates artificial deadlines where real ones don't exist. He may call up an investor or colleague and tell him that he will show him a completed project on a specific date. From then on, he's forced to get the job done in a particular time frame, because someone is waiting to see it.

The 18th-century writer and wit Samuel Johnson acknowledged the motivation that the stress of deadlines produces when he said, "Depend upon it, sir, when a man knows he is to be hanged in a fortnight, it concentrates his mind wonderfully."[3]

There are a number of good personality tests and I suggest that you take advantage of the insights they can provide you.

As you move through the process of innovation, you will have many opportunities to build your strengths and manage your weaknesses. Finding the right balance of both will enrich your life and make your daily life and work easier and far more productive than you ever thought possible.

REFERENCES

1. Gary Lockwood, Finding the Magic. (Accessed November 12, 2005 at http://www.bizsuccess.com/articles/findmagic.htm)
2. Donald O. Clifton and Paula Nelson, Soar With Your Strengths (New York, Dell Publishing, 1992)
3. James Boswell, The Life of Samuel Johnson (New York, Alfred A. Knof, 1992)

Section II

The Building Blocks
Of Creativity

Chapter 7

THE MAKING OF AN INNOVATOR

The secret to innovation isn't whether you are creative, but whether you're willing to do the work necessary to develop your creative skills and then step up to the plate to put them to work. I've encountered many people over the past few years who have talked to me about innovation and inventing. They usually ask how they should go about developing an idea and getting it patented. They seem poised to move forward, but then somehow they just can't seem to take that next step. They don't do it, and the opportunity is lost. As Horace, the poet of ancient Rome, noted so well, "He who has begun has half done. Dare to be wise; begin!"[1]

If you don't transform your ideas into reality, it's almost as if you never had them. Author and motivational specialist Robin Sharman notes correctly that, "Ideation without execution is nothing more than delusion."

Obviously, just coming up with an idea isn't enough. You must also put it into action. As Tad Simon, healthcare practice leader for the Palo Alto, California, design firm IDEO put it: "It's not how many ideas you have, but how many ideas did you try?"

This truth applies to any kind of creative endeavor, whether it's inventing a medical device, modifying a surgical procedure, instituting a new office management system, or marketing a new product or service. For the purpose of this chapter, I want to focus on the creative processes inherent in the invention of medical devices. However, these methods of recognizing a problem and then defining and creating a solution are the same for any creative endeavor large or small.

Two Kinds of Inventing

Creativity often follows very predictable paths, even though some ideas seem to spring forth fully formed, like Athena from the forehead of Zeus. Your own path of inventing will be easier as you figure out which creative process works best for you.

The first approach is what might be called incremental creativity. This is the most common and perhaps the easiest approach in that it involves adjustments and improvements to already established ideas. This is the type of innovation that you will most often seek in your own life. Perhaps you'll make a small adjustment to a procedure that will make it easier and more successful. Or perhaps you can make an improvement to an already existing medical device, just like Dr. Robert Sinskey did with the Sinskey Modified J Loop Intraocular Lens. He took a device used in ocular surgery and made a small but highly significant change that greatly improved its ease of use. As is often the case, critics said, "That was simple. Anyone can do that." Yet no one else had.

Like many other incremental inventors, Dr. Sinskey took an already established invention – the intraocular lens – and made an improvement that created something more useful, although not necessarily revolutionary.

On the other hand, the creation of the heart stent is a good example of a rarer form of creativity – the market disrupting kind. This type of invention is totally revolutionary and brings into existence something previously never seen. It takes a great deal of courage for an inventor to tread – literally – where no man has gone before.

"Before the first innovation, there was nothing," explains inventor Mir Imran. "I think that is a higher level of innovation than the incremental innovation. The incremental innovation is a more conscious process. The other is more of a subconscious process."

These two types of innovation illustrate the fact that while creativity is a very conscious process that you can control, it also involves extensive use of the subconscious mind. You must want to be creative, and you must work to be creative, but then at the most important moment, you must be able to let go and allow your subconscious mind to produce creative ideas. In the coming chapters, I will explain this important link and show you how to use a five step process for consistently producing useful, innovative ideas.

In other words, don't be limited by the notion that you have to come up with something that is totally new. Modifications of old ideas may not only make a big difference, but can evolve into even more ideas themselves. As noted earlier, most of what we call innovation is incremental in nature and involves improving what already exists.

Throughout most of medical history, operations have been performed with doctors standing over their patients for hours at a time. With some surgical procedures going on for eight hours or more, physician fatigue has always been a problem. Fortunately, technology has been vastly improved, and today's operating tables are being built to allow the surgeon to sit down during the procedure. This seemingly simple idea has made a huge impact in healthcare, but like the early practice of hand washing, it took a while for it to be accepted and implemented.

Clearly, innovation is the vital factor that produces all kinds of progress. The results can be tangible, such as a new book or work of art, or they can be practical, like when I set up a paperless office by transforming stacks of files and documents into electronic bits of information on a computer hard drive.

First One Idea, Then Many

In the course of writing this book, I interviewed many highly creative people and studied much of the literature on the creative process. One of the most important facts that I discovered along the way is that being creative is very much a learned process. Anyone can be creative if they're willing to invest the necessary time and effort. While some people may have more natural ability than others, everyone possesses the innate capacity to conceive new ideas. What separates those who create from those who don't is desire.

Nearly all of the great innovators share certain personality traits and characteristics and exhibit specific behaviors that help them generate new concepts. In fact, once you understand and utilize these characteristics and behaviors, you'll not only come up with that all-important first idea, but you'll also continue developing ideas throughout your life.

You can train yourself to become a fountain of new ideas that can improve not only your own life, but perhaps society and the world as well.

The late Andrew Toti is a good example of productive invention at its best. With more than 500 patents to his credit, he is perhaps best known as the inventor of the "Mae West" life vest. This inflatable life preserver saved the lives of literally thousands of downed pilots during World War II. Among their number was a young man named George H.W. Bush, the future president of the United States.[2]

Toti found fame within the medical device industry when he invented the EndoFlex endotracheal tube – a breathing tube used during surgery. He developed the device after a surgeon told him of the problems he experienced with placing a tube down a patient's throat and the harm it often did to delicate throat tissues. His version featured a flexible tip that made it easier for the physician to insert and which posed less chance of harm.

Toti described his approach to inventing as first identifying a problem and finding an "elegant" solution. He also didn't believe in the cliché that "necessity is the mother of invention." In fact, he declared that "invention is the mother of everything."

For many people, particularly those who have attended medical school, getting into the right frame of mind for the creative process can be particularly difficult. Rigorously trained in the hard science of "see one, do one, and teach one," doctors strive for mistake-free perfectionism. Even in school, we are always pressured to get the highest score on the test and be perfect in everything we do as physicians-in-training.

It is important to realize that creativity is a combination of both intuition and design. Many great inventors talk about that sudden flash of insight that gives rise to a new idea, but they can't say with any certainty how they got to the point of inspiration. In fact, even though they might sound almost like artists connecting with their muse, the insight would never come without preparation and training.

"The equation of science with logic and reason, or art with intuition and emotion, is a blatant popular fallacy," says British author Arthur Koestler. "No discovery has ever been made by logical deduction; no work of art produced without calculating craftsmanship."[3]

First Error, Then Perfection

The problem with always striving to get perfect test scores is that it doesn't allow for mistakes. Although it might seem counterintuitive, mistakes are often the path toward learning and improvement. The poet Nikki Giovanni sized it up perfectly when he said, "Mistakes are a fact of life. It is the response to error that counts."[4]

The reason for this is simple. While in school, we're taught that there is a constant body of knowledge that can be mastered to the point of perfection. In reality, we live in an ever-changing environment that virtually ensures that you can't avoid making mistakes. As you confront your errors, you make changes that allow you to better deal with this new set of circumstances.

As business consultant Marshall Thurber put it, "Anything worth doing well is worth doing badly in the beginning."

Of course, it's not that we set out to do things badly, but mistakes represent the natural process through which we find our way through unfamiliar territory. The intrinsic value of error can be seen in nature as well. Through his theory of natural selection, Charles Darwin expressed the profound significance of mistakes. There are biological variations within every species. Some of their most adaptive traits have arisen from genetic mutations or random errors. Without these genetic mistakes, evolution as we know it would not be possible.

In *Built to Last: Successful Habits of Visionary Companies*, noted business writer Jim Collins explains that companies don't make their best moves by design, but through trial and error. What in hindsight looks like brilliant strategic planning is often the result of a "let's just try a lot of stuff and keep what works" approach.[5]

A good example of this approach can be found in the many successes of IDEO, one of the world's best-known product design firms, with innovative creations such as the Palm V and Handspring Visor handheld computers for a lengthy client list that includes AT&T, Samsung, Philips, Amtrak, and NEC. They have also participated in film projects, including creating a 25-foot mechanical whale for *Free Willy*.

The *San Francisco Examiner* declared that IDEO "has designed more of the things at our fingertips than practically anyone else in the past 100 years, with the possible exception of Thomas Edison."[6] Their record-breaking success is attributed to the concept of "fail often to succeed sooner." This approach to generating new ideas may admittedly look like "spinning wheels" according to company leaders, but it is designed to produce "a fountain of absurd-appearing but innovative ideas before the final answer and products miraculously came through a process of discipline and fast decision-making," said a Harvard Business School study of their company.[7]

Perfectionism has little place in this innovation-driven company, which business writer Tom Peters once described as a "zoo."[8] Experts from many different disciplines – none of whom have fancy job titles – mingle in open offices that sometimes resemble nothing less than a kindergarten classroom. Freewheeling brainstorming sessions create an open atmosphere that encourages even the most introverted to speak their mind and come forth even with the most absurd or far out concept.

While some might view such a process as wasting time and producing too many unusable ideas, IDEO has found a way to produce a long and virtually unbroken string of winning concepts and innovations. At the heart of the process is the drive to find the unknown and the unanticipated solution that will change everything.

As company CEO Tim Brown said in an interview: "It's a delicate balance between process and innovation . . . It's no good if you crank the handle and you know exactly what is going to come out the other end. You have to be prepared to fail a lot. The great thing about a prototype culture like ours is that we have lots of spectacular failures. We celebrate that."[9]

Amidst all this "wheel spinning" and "blue sky" idea generation, there is a clear method to the seeming madness. The goal of the creative process is to give free reign to innovation so that the obvious and mundane can be replaced by the new and better.

"We have a process that we use and it has its variations, but the themes of our process are pretty standard," says Simon, who has been with the company for nearly two decades. "It always involves us trying to understand the users at the end of whatever we do, and we usually have a process that is about understanding and observing and then using those observations [to create designs]."

Simon admitted that this creates many ideas that are unworkable and many others that fall into similar families, but he drew the line at saying any of this effort represented mistakes or failures. A failure would be carrying a particular design all the way to the manufacturing stage and only then discovering that it didn't work. At IDEO, the unworkable is tested out and improved or discarded early on.

Yet in many cases, what some might call failure – or trying to see whether something works or not – is one of the most necessary antecedes to successful innovation, and that can be scary for many of us trained in the exacting discipline of medicine.

As physicians, we strive for perfectionism because, in many cases, the life and health of a patient are on the line, and doctors are often threatened with malpractice if they deviate from accepted practice and things turn out badly. So we do things the way we are taught – the approved and safe way. In some cases it doesn't always work as well as we would like, but we remain safe by adhering to approved standards of care.

Unfortunately, that approach can stymie creativity. As painful as it may be at times, making mistakes leads to new insights and points you down new roads of endeavor.

Perhaps the most famous example of this approach can be found in the work of Thomas Edison and his quest to invent the lightbulb. Many don't realize that this man, who is considered the epitome of successful inventors, failed more often and lost more money than perhaps any other would-be inventor in history.

After trying and failing more than 5,000 times in his quest, many in the scientific community regarded his obsession as crazy, to say the least. A young reporter interviewed Edison and asked him, "Mr. Edison, how can you continue to try to invent the light bulb when you have failed more than 5,000 times?"

Edison replied, ""Young man, clearly you don't understand. I have not failed 5,000 times. I have successfully discovered 5,000 ways that do not work, and I do not need to try them again."

Each failure put him that much closer to ultimate success. Edison realized the secret that was later expressed so well by baseball's home run king Babe Ruth when he said, "Every strike I make gets me closer to a home run."

In nearly all forms of education, there is an emphasis on doing things by rote, although history shows us that the great change-makers are often those who looked for and found a shortcut, or a different way of getting to the same point.

The Rough Side of Creativity

Deviating from the so-called approved way of doing things can take considerable courage. Not only do we risk repeated failure, but like Edison, we may also face the ridicule of our peers.

Many of the inventors with whom I've spoken invariably talk about how rivals, and sometimes colleagues, challenged or denigrated their work. I point this out to help encourage you as you embark on this journey. Developing and then introducing new ideas is not for the faint of heart. You must expect to be challenged and questioned. As your creation moves toward success, there will be those who are jealous of your progress or simply can't believe your idea is that important because they didn't think of it themselves first. You should be inspired by these naysayers and revel in their criticism, because often it is a strong indication that you are on the right track.

As Albert Einstein once said, "If at first an idea doesn't sound absurd, then there is no hope for it." You can be sure there is always an overabundance of those willing to call any truly great idea absurd. In fact, it sometimes seems that the vision to see what could be rather than what already exists is one of the rarest commodities in existence.

Dr. Morty Mower, coinventor of the implantable defibrillator, recalled that the device met heated opposition when it was first proposed. A leading Boston cardiologist wrote editorials in medical journals asserting that the device could not work and was of no use. When he and his colleagues met with the doctor to discuss his opposition, he was pleasant up to the point where they began talking about the device, and then he became angry and irrational. Dr. Mower guesses that his vehement opposition came from "the fact that he didn't think of it."

Today, the device is widely used and has revolutionized the treatment of patients at risk for sudden cardiac death due to ventricular tachyarrhythmia. One of these devices is even monitoring the heartbeat of Vice President Dick Cheney.

Opposition to new ideas is so commonplace as to be considered a normal stage of the inventing process. You might say that you can't create anything new without also creating naysayers. Some of them will be motivated by jealousy or other negative reasons, but many people – including fellow inventors – simply react negatively without really considering the worth of the idea.

Paul Yock, another prolific inventor, insightfully admits that when he would hear an idea from somebody else that really was pretty good and fairly novel, that his first reaction was to dismiss it. "If it's a simple idea, and different, and somebody hasn't thought of it," says Yock, "it's almost an instinctual reaction, a 'Why didn't I think of that?' sort of response."

Yet over the years, he's overcome that reactive part of his nature and developed a clearer understanding of the value of someone else's "simple" ideas.

"I've learned over time," says Yock, "when I have that kind of reaction – it feels like almost a jealous response – those really are the ideas that I actually have to stop and say, 'Okay, this one is really a good one.'"

It has been said that there are two types of critics. One has never attempted something yet delights in telling you why it can't be done. The other is someone who has done what you have done, or something similar, and genuinely wants to be helpful to you in your quest for innovation. Moving forward courageously with your idea in the face of blind opposition is one thing. Accepting insightful feedback and legitimate criticism is another. As Kenneth Blanchard noted in *The One Minute Manager*, "Feedback is the breakfast of champions."[10]

You must not be so blinded by your obsession with an idea that you can't accept constructive criticism or let go of a bad concept that just doesn't work. Sometimes the naysayers do have good intentions and may be right. Not every action you take will be perfect, and even as you move closer to your goal, you'll make mistakes and take wrong turns that need to be corrected. The challenge is in knowing when to stick to your ideas and when to be willing to modify or drop them.

A New Way of Seeing

German philosopher Arthur Schopenhauer once said that, "Our task is not so much to see what no one yet has seen, but to think what nobody yet has thought about that which everyone sees." Much of inventing is simply the process of taking old ideas and putting them into a new framework.

Dr. Julio Palmaz, for example, made a critical breakthrough with the heart stent after noticing the design of a common tool used in building construction. Like many others, he took an idea or principle common to one field and then applied it to something totally different. He possessed the insight to discern how this principle could be used in his own work in medicine.

Noted developer of AIDS vaccines Dr. Raymond Schinazi was able to bring a wide variety of talents to his creative work, ranging from being able to do the detailed bench work to translating ideas into winning National Institutes of Health grant proposals.

Every field of invention has taken inspiration from seemingly unrelated tools and concepts. Consider *SpaceShipOne*, the creation of designer Burt Rutan. When the small combination rocket and glider broke the bonds of the earth's atmosphere in August 2004, it opened up a new era in spaceflight by becoming the first privately funded spaceship. It also brought the idea of commercial spaceflight within reach.

Rutan's wife, Tonya, relates how six years ago, her husband woke her at three in the morning, bubbling with excitement. He told her that he had hit upon the concept he needed for the spaceship design – a badminton shuttlecock. The shuttlecock, a lightweight cone with a rounded rubber nose crowned with feathers, falls slowly and always in the same position – no matter how hard you hit it.

By designing a ship with stubby, adjustable wings like the shuttlecock, Rutan was able to solve the problem of reentry into the earth's atmosphere. The ship employs an unusual technique called feathering for minimizing reentry temperatures and stresses, and eliminating the need to precisely control the craft's entry orientation.

With its rear wings steeply tilted, the spacecraft experiences tremendous aerodynamic drag, which forces it to assume a cabin-level orientation that doesn't require a precise angle of attack.

A former civilian test pilot for the U.S. Air Force, Rutan conceived and created Voyager, the first plane to fly around the world without stopping and without refueling. He is also the founder and CEO of Scaled Composites, the aerospace development company that built the spacecraft with funding by Microsoft cofounder Paul Allen.

The Courage of Your Creation

Innovative ideas come to people all the time, but most people simply never do anything with them, and they're lost until developed by someone with more drive and conviction. Famed entrepreneur and former General Electric CEO Jack Welsh relates in Winning, his book on the secrets to management success, how he conceived the idea of an open MRI (magnetic resonance imaging) device. Up until that time, MRIs were small, closed tunnel-like tubes that produced claustrophobia among many patients.[11]

When he conveyed the idea to the executives in GE's medical device division, they didn't believe that hospitals would be willing to buy such a device because of the lower quality of images it produced. He told them to push ahead, and their reply was, "We'll look into it." Yet they never did, and not long afterwards, a rival company came out with the same device to great success. Welsh's company was left playing catch up because he hadn't pushed hard enough to get the project rolling.

A little more than a hundred years ago, hospitals were considered places where people went to die – not to get well! But hospitals improved, because people asked questions about how things could be better. In that early era, a physician might go from performing a surgery to delivering a baby without either changing his clothes or washing his hands.

Then, in 1847, Ignaz Philipp Semmelweis, a Hungarian doctor in a provincial Austrian hospital, asked a simple question: Why were so many babies being delivered by doctors dying, while those delivered by midwives were not? The midwives, it turned out, washed their hands before the delivery, while the doctors did not. His observations concerning basic hygiene went against scientific opinion of the time, which blamed diseases on an imbalance of the body's "humours."

Semmelweis' peers in the medical establishment did not take well to his ideas, and he was attacked and ridiculed. He discovered just how hard it is to overcome rigid, conservative thinking, as well as the reluctance of doctors to admit that they had caused so many deaths. Semmelweis died in disgrace, after suffering a nervous breakdown and being committed to a mental institution. Ironically enough, he died of blood poisoning.

Yet nobody could deny that in the mid-nineteenth century, postoperative sepsis infections accounted for the death of almost half of the patients undergoing major surgery. Semmelweis was ultimately vindicated, his ideas caught on, and medicine entered a more enlightened era in its treatment of disease.

As Semmelweis demonstrated, the first step toward invention is always asking the questions: Is there a better or a simpler way? What am I missing? Should I take another look at the obvious? Too many people simply accept the way things are done and don't challenge the status quo.

Norman Podhoretz, the famed writer, literary critic, and longtime editor of *Commentary* magazine, said, "Creativity represents a miraculous coming together of the uninhibited energy of the child with its apparent opposite and enemy, the sense of order imposed on the disciplined adult intelligence."

In fact, one of the keys to tapping into your creativity can be found in getting out of your current everyday rigid thinking and adopting what might be called an almost childlike attitude of wonder and open-mindedness. If you've ever watched children at play, you quickly realize that they bring few preconceived notions to their view of the world. They see things as they are and react to them without coloring the event with fears and anxieties that are unrelated to the current situation.

Failure often results more from inaction than action. You can spend too much time deliberating whether an idea is totally right or a decision is completely correct. We fear being perceived as impulsive, because society gives such positive support to words like prudence, caution, and conservatism. You don't want to make a mistake and lose everything. Better to be cautious and wait until you have more information, so you don't lose the farm over a harebrained idea.

The truth is that those who wait until they have every question answered almost always lose out. A patient may die while doctors wait for complete proof that the drug is safe and effective. By the time your start-up proves it's a market-beating company, you've lost the opportunity to invest and make millions.

Instead of being obsessed with "Ready, aim, fire!" it's sometimes better to simply get ready, fire, and then aim. You acquire more information from simply taking action than you do from getting it right the first time, assuming that you can manage the risks associated with a failure. Until you pull the trigger and actually take a shot, you'll never learn from that action. In addition, you'll also learn more from that mistake than you would by deliberating about what might happen or what might be true. You can't predict what the environment's response will be.

In order to become creative, you have to get away from the mental constipation that perfectionism breeds. You have to be open to seeing things in new ways without the filters that are created through years spent trying to write "A+" papers.

Creative Action

There are several steps you can begin taking today that will make you more creative and help you to start generating the ideas you need. In the next chapter, I'll discuss a five step process for generating new ideas that takes creativity from the theoretic and academic to the practical and everyday. In order for those steps to work for you, however, you first have to accept the notion that you have the ability to produce great ideas.

When I first began coming up with new ideas, I initially avoided referring to – or even thinking of myself as an inventor. On the one hand, it seemed too arrogant to put myself in the same category as someone like Thomas Edison; I certainly wasn't in his league. Worse still, the stereotypical image of an inventor was the slightly absentminded, wild-haired genius – like Albert Einstein.

Like me, you'll have to get over these unfair stereotypes. While you may not yet be on a par with such successful inventors as Thomas Fogarty and Mir Imran, you are part of their league simply because you're doing the same thing they're doing – coming up with new ideas. Just like them, you have the courage to challenge the status quo and the courage to continue when critics crawl out from beneath whatever rock they're hiding under. Success is a matter of time, effort, and perseverance.

As for the stereotype of inventors as absentminded professors, consider researchers such as Ron Crystal, who in his spare time is an ice climber. Or better still, think of Dr. Rainer Storb, who while just a few years shy of being an octogenarian, is a competitive rower. In fact, he commutes to work in Seattle each day in a sleek single scull racer across the icy waters of Lake Washington. Maybe they are better stereotypes for creative innovators, not to mention much better role models for young people today than the arrogant pro athletes or scantily clad pop singers they seem to idolize.

The Characteristics of an Inventor

What characteristics do inventors have in common? Perhaps the most obvious one is that they have made the commitment to innovative and unconventional thinking.

It is helpful to study and emulate people who are highly creative and original in their approach to life and work. If you want to be a great inventor, you should carefully study the life and works of people such as Benjamin Franklin, Marie Curie, George Washington Carver, or more recently, Steve Jobs and Dean Kamen.

Walt Disney, for example, built an entertainment empire around simple stories about a talking mouse that appealed to the child in everyone. At a time when central Florida was a mostly uninhabited rural backwater, he saw the possibilities for a theme park built around the cartoon characters he had created.

Everyone told him the idea was crazy. Nobody would come to central Florida, they said. Look at how cheap and plentiful the land is there. That should tell you something, said the naysayers. But where his critics saw a vast wasteland, Disney saw gleaming fantasy towers and unending crowds of happy people. Today, Disney World in Orlando is one of the all-time great vacation destinations.

Even though conventional wisdom might have been to hold back from this massive venture, Disney plunged in with both feet, made waves, and then emerged successfully on the other side. Long ago, I devoted myself to reading biographies of people like Disney, who demonstrated the kind of creative thinking that I wanted to develop.

In whatever you want to do, surround yourself with people who embody the qualities you want to possess and who have accomplished the kind of goals you want to reach. Stay away – far away – from destructive and uninformed critics. There are no limits to the number of people who will tell you that the goal you're striving for can't be reached and that you're wasting your time. They will ridicule your efforts and question your ability. If you listen to them, pretty soon they will have transformed you into just what they are – safe and uninspired. If you're confronted by doubters, simply gain strength from the fact that you're in good company with great innovators, like Ignaz Semmelweis, who were assailed by their critics.

In the meantime, don't be discouraged or sidetracked by narrow-minded people who can't understand what you're trying to achieve. They may try to tear you down and leave you questioning your own ability. When your ideas have reached fruition, you can feel a deep sense of accomplishment that, unlike so many people whose names are now lost to history, you didn't give in to negative peer pressure.

Unfortunately, some of the worst enemies of your creative endeavors will be found among your own family and close friends. Creativity produces changes in your life, and family members are often unprepared and frightened by these changes. Those who care about you can get very nervous when you start investing your savings in developing a prototype of your device, so you have to figure out a way to bring them onboard early.

Once again, this is not to say that every critic is wrong and can't make a valuable contribution to your invention. The most successful inventors know who to listen to and who to ignore. The two biggest mistakes an inventor can make represent opposite responses to criticism. The first is to be easily discouraged by the naysayers and give up without ever really determining whether your idea is viable.

When Alexander Graham Bell offered the rights to the telephone to Western Union, company president Carl Orton rejected the offer with a cutting remark: "What use would this company make of an electric toy?"[12]

But Bell didn't give up and went on to revolutionize the world. The history of invention is filled with similar stories of authority figures who rejected or belittled the greatest ideas in history.

Yet an equally inappropriate reaction is to angrily reject all outside suggestions and criticisms. You can become blind to the failings of your idea and never make improvements that could turn it into a marketable product. It becomes all too easy to surround yourself with yes-men who praise your every idea rather than providing honest criticism. You will never be well served by these sycophants, and ultimately you'll only be lead to ruin by their fawning praise. Better to include one or more devil's advocates who can pose the right questions and make you look at the shortcomings of your ideas. Their intent is always to make your idea better, not to tear down you or your creation.

In fact, these friendly naysayers can help you in one of the most important parts of developing an idea or an invention – prototyping. Over the course of your work, you may come up with numerous versions of your idea as each one becomes better and closer to an ideal product.

Over the years he spent developing the heart stent, Julio Palmaz made numerous modifications to the design and sought out the advice of experts. He was confident and believed in the basic concept, but realized that he needed to find new materials, designs, and means of prototyping that could make it work. The idea was not created full-blown at the moment of initial conception, but developed over time with each new design and prototype.

Moving Forward

As you make progress on your creative journey, you'll become more confident about simply moving forward with your ideas, even if you have no guarantee of success – and even if you fail at some point. Those failures will bring you closer to ultimate success as you learn from them and keep going.

A vital step in this process is to begin identifying the things you're good at and the areas that interest you. In fact, you can combine your medical specialty with a completely unrelated field. One of the best examples of combining medicine with a seemingly unrelated field can be found in the career of medicine's Michelangelo, Dr. Frank H. Netter.

Celebrated as the foremost medical illustrator of the human body and how it works, Dr. Netter was working as a medical illustrator in the 1930s when the CIBA Pharmaceutical Company commissioned him to prepare illustrations of the major organs and their pathology. Dr. Netter's incredibly detailed, lifelike renderings were so well-received by the medical community that a series of volumes now carry the Netter name – *The Netter Collection of Medical Illustrations*. Even 12 years after his death, Dr. Netter is still acknowledged as the foremost master of medical illustration.

A successful commercial artist in the 1920s, he gave up his art career at the urging of his family in order to find a more "dependable" career. He earned a medical degree, but during his schooling, he found that it was easier for him to take notes in pictures rather than in words.

As a young physician during the Depression, Dr. Netter found that there was more interest in his medical artwork than his surgical capabilities. In 1938, he was hired by CIBA to work on a promotional flyer for a heart medication. He designed a folder cut in the shape of and elaborately depicting a heart, which was sent to physicians. Many of the doctors wrote back asking for more heart flyers – without the advertising copy. Netter went on to design similar product advertisements depicting other organs. When that project was concluded, he was commissioned to prepare small folders of pathology plates that were later collected into the first *CIBA Collection of Medical Illustrations.*

Following the success of these endeavors, Netter was asked to illustrate a series of atlases that became his life's work. They are a group of volumes individually devoted to each organ system, which cover human anatomy, embryology, physiology, pathology, and pertinent clinical features of the diseases arising in each system. These volumes are now found in every medical school library in the country, as well as in doctors' offices around the world, and his work has helped to educate and enlighten generations of physicians. His career has spanned the most revolutionary half-century in medical history. He chronicled the emergence of open-heart surgery, organ transplants, and joint replacements.

If you can identify two fields that might seem unrelated but in which you have knowledge, then you can begin searching for ways to adapt tools and technology from one field to another. Many of the greatest advances in medicine have come through taking technology used in one field and adapting it for use in healthcare.

Not every idea that comes to you will be good, or perhaps ready for commercial application. In fact, if one out of ten comes to fruition, your batting average will be equal to that of the world's leading inventors. The secret to success is to keep working and to continue producing ideas. The old adage that a journey of a thousand miles begins with a single step is really true. You must view your creative journey as a long and continuing path that you will follow for many years to come.

REFERENCES

1. Horace, Epistles (Accessed November 2, 2005 at http://www.quotationspage.com/quote/24357.html)
2. Myrna Oliver, "Flotation vest designer Andrew Toti" Los Angeles Times, Mar. 29, 2005 (Accessed April 17, 2006 at http://www.italystl.com/ra/2036.htm)
3. Maury Klein, The Change Makers: From Carnegie to Gates, How the Great Entrepreneurs Transformed Ideas into Industries. (New York, Henry Holt and Co. 2003) 20
4. Nikki Giovanni, Quoteworld.com (Accessed April 1, 2006 at http://www.quoteworld.org/quotes/5453)
5. James C. Collins and Jerry I. Porras, Built to Last: Successful Habits of Visionary Companies, (New York, HarperCollins, 1994)
6. R. Garner, San Francisco Examiner, May 23, 1994, p. B-1
7. Stefan Thornke and Ashok Ninigade, IDEO Product Development (Harvard Business School, 2000)
8. Tom Peters, "The Peters Principles" Forbes ASAP, September 13, 1993, p. 180.
9. Tim Brown, "Strategy by Design" Fast Company, June 2005
10. Kenneth Blanchard and Spenser Johnson. The One Minute Manager. (New York, William Morrow and Co., 1982)
11. Jack Welch and Suzy Welch, Winning (New York, HarperCollins, 2005)
12. The lazy person's guide to voice telephony-Part I, CHIPS: The Department of the Navy Information Technology magazine, Winter 2004

Chapter 8

THE ENVIRONMENT OF CREATIVITY

One of Silicon Valley's most prolific inventors is an Indian immigrant by the name of Mir Imran. This highly creative entrepreneur has built several companies based on ideas for medical devices that he has nurtured into successful products. Like many of his fellow inventors, he traces the origins of his creativity to childhood and a family that encouraged him to ask questions and explore new ideas.

He spent his early years not just playing with his toys, but taking them apart to see how they actually worked. In fact, when his mother noticed what he was doing, she began giving him two toys – one to play with and another to disassemble. By encouraging his innate curiosity, she was helping him to develop a highly creative nature, which quickly manifested in his building small matchbox-size radios that he sold to classmates. It was the beginning of a lifetime of creative invention.

It has long been recognized that certain external conditions are conducive to helping children develop an innovative mindset. As far back as 1954, Carl Rogers formulated a theory of creativity that included three internal psychological conditions that are necessary to foster this talent. They are:

1. Openness to experience.
2. An internal locus of evaluation.
3. The ability to toy with elements and concepts.

To develop an environment in which these factors predominate, there must be two external elements present as well: psychological safety and psychological freedom. The safety comes when the child's social world accepts him as having unconditional worth, doesn't judge, and provides understanding.

The child must also have the freedom to engage in uncensored and unrestrained expression. For Imran, this meant disassembling toys until he figured out how they worked and then going on to build new ones on his own. His parents were highly supportive of all his efforts. As a teenager, he decided to leave India to seek his fortune in America. To help him out, his father acquired several thousand dollars through a loan on the black market to pay his way – even though his father was not a wealthy man and the practice was then illegal.

When the seeds of creativity are planted in hospitable soil they can flourish, but in the wrong place they wither and die. It is this truth that illustrates why creativity is so much rarer in our world than it might otherwise be. How often are new ideas killed by ridicule and fear of disapproval? How many people avoid doing the work that leads to new ideas, new processes, and new inventions because they're afraid that others may not approve?

There are as many naysayers as there are new and innovative concepts. Just ask any inventor about the reaction to a new device, concept, or process. Those with an entrenched interest in the status quo are likely to oppose it out of self-interest. Others will do so because they don't have the vision to conceive of something new or their ego can't accept that someone else thought of it first.

One often repeated story goes that a U.S. Patent Office commissioner named Charles H. Duell resigned in 1899 because, as he put it, "Everything that can be invented has been invented." While the story itself is likely a myth, it is one of those tales that reflects a great deal of truth – at least about the thinking of naysayers.

It is from these "natering nabobs of negativism," as former Vice President Spiro Agnew called them, that the creative mind must be protected if creativity is to flourish.

As a successful inventor, Imran has created his own idea factory – called InCube – where new products can be conceived, nurtured, and then brought to market in the safety of an environment dedicated to fostering this process. He refers to ideas as living organisms that must be allowed to grow in a nurturing environment if they're strong or allowed to die if they're not.

This environment is good not only for new ideas, but for their parent as well. Imran has turned down offers to join larger companies because he recognized long ago that in a more rigid corporate setting, he wouldn't have the freedom to pursue ideas as he does now.

Research into Carl Rogers' ideas on fostering creativity in children has shown the importance of this environment of approval, understanding, and safety. Studies by Chambers in 1964, Datta and Parloff in 1967, and Dewing and Taft in 1973 – just to name a few – have shown that creativity in children is made possible by encouraging autonomy and self-confidence.

It has often been observed that new start-up companies are more creative and innovative than older, more established companies. Small, early-stage enterprises are many times free of oppressive bureaucracy and a culture of risk avoidance. People are encouraged to take chances – indeed, the company itself is a big risk – that may not be tolerated in an established firm that is consolidating its position.

Like Imran, you must develop your own version of InCube. Perhaps it won't be an incubator for new products in the formal sense, but you must have space in which you can have the freedom to express your interests, to experiment, and allow the creative process to take hold.

Begin to be creative now. I'm not suggesting that you leave medicine to pursue poetry, music, or some other creative art. No, the creativity I'm urging you to utilize is your own creative efforts within medicine.

As I noted earlier, making mistakes becomes a vital part of the creative process. For doctors, the idea of mistakes sounds unacceptable, but venturing into any new area always presents the specter of error. I'm not saying you should experiment with patient safety, but rather that you simply keep an open mind when it comes to better ways of delivering care.

Within your own practice, you can begin building a vehicle that will encourage your creativity. After all, you are the boss, you are the owner, and it should be an expression of your talents and personality. Perhaps you won't devote your time to inventing new devices, but you can make the way you deliver healthcare a creative endeavor from which both you and your patients will profit.

If you're a medical student, you truly have a unique opportunity to begin making choices that will enable you to work in an environment that encourages your own creativity to flourish. The choices you make about the specialty you enter and where you choose to practice will profoundly affect your ability to obtain the psychological freedom and safety that is essential to becoming a creative person.

If you're in the first or second year of medical school and facing a rigid schedule, you can rest assured that you are even now gaining the domain-specific knowledge that will later feed your creative drive. When you're ready to put that knowledge to work, then creativity will give you the fuel to take your practice to new heights of accomplishment.

Chapter 9

EUREKA: THE FIVE STEPS TO CREATIVITY

I realize that many of you doubt your own capacity to conceive and nurture innovative ideas. You look at highly successful inventors and assume they were born with ideas spilling from their pockets like loose change.

Rest assured that while some people may be more inclined to creative thinking than others, the process of creativity is a learned phenomenon. In other words, great innovators are made, not born.

In fact, there is a very clear, concise, and proven five step process to nurturing creativity. Every truly creative person from Einstein to Edison, Dean Kamen to Frank Netter has followed this process, either consciously or not.

If you follow this process, you too will become a fountain of new ideas and ultimately new inventions as well.

The five interlocking steps are:
1. Preparation
2. Frustration
3. Defining the problem
4. Deliberation
5. Illumination and documentation

Of course, you may stumble upon new ideas without following this process, but they will tend to be infrequent and it will be more difficult for you to realize your full potential. Just as there are many paths to a particular goal but only one best way, experience has proven that this process offers the greatest chance for success.

Let's look at each of the steps and how they fit into your life and work.

Step 1
Preparation: Get Ready

The first step, preparation, is certainly the most calculated. It encompasses your education, attendance at seminars, watching procedures, talking to colleagues and friends, reading, and just about any other activity that gives you more knowledge and a better grasp of the field. Before a doctor can figure out a better way to perform a surgical procedure, he has to understand and practice the current method of performing it. You have to be in the game and have the right domain-specific knowledge in order to even know a problem exists.

Throughout this book, I've explored a form of creativity that can be defined as novel, socially valued products instead of processes. For those of us in medicine, this is a definition to which we can easily relate, because we so often see new devices, procedures, and solutions to highly technical problems. Yet creativity can be applied to just about any situation that presents a problem that needs solving.

Sometimes the problems will be big and other times quite small. One noted inventor profiled in this book has scores of medical patents to his credit and is recognized as a leader in the medical device field. Yet he says that one of the problems he's working on is a better way to clean toilets. Why, after developing some of the most successful lifesaving devices on the market, would he concentrate on such a small issue? His annoyed answer: "Have you ever cleaned a toilet? I have, and it's disgusting."

Most of us just accept that little brush sitting there as a fact of life. But this inventor recognizes it as a new problem that needs a creative solution.

Getting into the right frame of mind to start incubating new ideas is the place where we all must start. Great ideas don't just happen. The apple may drop out of the tree onto your head, but first you must be prepared for the significance of the apple and be able to understand the magnitude of what it means. You must be as curious as Sir Isaac Newton and ready to make the right connections.

Louis Pasteur once said, "Chance favors the prepared mind." Those who are prepared frequently make "lucky" discoveries, because luck is simply what happens when preparation meets opportunity.[1]

Those of us in medicine have the knowledge and the ability to put ideas into the proper context. Thomas Fogarty invented his balloon embolectomy while working as a surgical scrub tech – long before he even graduated from medical school. He began working in hospitals when he was just a boy of 14, and he observed the difficulties that surgeons experienced, as well as the high mortality rate of patients. He was challenged to find a better way, and thus revolutionized vascular surgery. Even today, he describes his original idea as "pathetically simple." Edwin Land, the founder of Polaroid, put it another way when he quipped, "Every creative act is a sudden cessation of stupidity."[2]

Fogarty was able to simplify the complex, rather than complicate the simple. He was willing – as you should be – to reconsider the obvious, pay attention, change your point of view, and always be open to new ideas in a childlike yet inquisitive manner.

Step 2
Frustration: The Great Motivator

Preparation leads naturally into the second step of frustration. This is the pain that arises from a particular problem or inconvenience that you encounter. At first, these problems may seem to be a matter of circumstance, but personal action is also required here as well. You must train yourself to look for problems and frustrations in your daily life that require a solution. Many people, including doctors, simply accept shortcomings or poor outcomes of procedures as just a part of life.

"One of the advantages I've had is that I'm not a practicing clinician," says prolific inventor and entrepreneur Mir Imran. "I can see problems much more clearly than the opinion leaders who are so close to their problems that they incorporate the problem into their daily routine and it ceases to be a problem for them."

He brings fresh eyes and a new perspective to ask, "Why are you doing it that way?" Perhaps it's a traumatic procedure or the side effects are deadly, creating poor patient outcomes. Solving these problems can lead to better patient results, greater clinician satisfaction, and perhaps even a company built around a new device.

Those who take their ideas to fruition are often those who find themselves in an uncomfortable or difficult situation. I was an unhappy resident who felt frustrated with the rigid and confining structure of medicine. These feelings drove me to break out of what I saw as a prison through creativity applied within my own rigid environment.

A certain amount of discomfort is often needed to push you toward your true potential. When a winemaker wants to produce great grapes, he grows them in soil that is deliberately deprived of water. In this stressed soil, the vines' roots reach out looking for life-giving water, and the result is better grapes. Great ideas are grown from the soil of frustration, discomfort, and sometimes even adversity.

Some inventors, like Thomas Fogarty, were subjected to real-life stress and deprivation, yet were able to thrive and display great creativity even in the midst of these trials.

Ask yourself the same questions that Imran asks. If you're a doctor and you've been performing the same procedure the same way for the last decade, take yourself back to the first time you performed it. Think about how you learned to do it and what about it was difficult or easy for you. How could the process have been made easier? Look at the whole process through unbiased eyes and think about each of its component parts one at a time. Perhaps you need to work backwards and try to break down the procedure into each of its steps. Is there a simpler or easier way to do something?

Ask yourself if what you're doing is purely out of habit. Are there ways that new technology can make things easier? Can you create shortcuts that can get the job done faster?

Professionals tend to be much better at recognizing problems early in their training than later on, when they've become totally immersed in procedure and result.

"I think from a needs-finding standpoint – at least in your own field – you get pretty comfortable with the way things are done as you get more expert in it," explains Dr. Paul Yock, director of the Biodesign Center at Stanford University and the inventor of such groundbreaking devices as the rapid-exchange angioplasty system. "You don't chase in the same way as a young person who's coming in, and you don't see needs in the same way."

As a young resident learning the art of spinal injections, I quickly recognized how difficult it was to align the needle properly. Veteran physicians who had mastered the procedure didn't see the process as a difficulty. When I developed a device for making the alignment easier and began to show it to other physicians, the older docs often said they didn't see the need for it. They had mastered doing things the old way and didn't need a device that made their work easier and more precise. Yet younger doctors all said it was a great idea and had wished that such a device existed.

Healthcare professionals are in a perfect position to identify problems and create solutions. They don't have to wait for an engineer to recognize that a particular device is needed. The challenge is to recognize a problem, rather than develop a solution. The formulation of the problem is the central idea.

Step 3
Defining the Problem: Clarity Matters

Recognizing the pain and inconvenience of a situation is useless unless it is followed by the third step of stating the problem. Here you lay out the difficulty, its dimensions, details, and ramifications so that you clearly understand what you want to solve. Do you need a better way of aligning the needle? Are you dissatisfied with the results of another procedure that you're performing?

You begin by thinking about the problem, writing or dictating your ideas, and discussing them with friends until the situation is as crystal clear as you can make it. This recognition will push it deep into your subconscious, where the next stage of the process will continue.

These first three stages interlock with each other, and one is not possible without the other. If you're not prepared, you won't know the frustration and the degree to which a frustration exists or the amount of grief or inconvenience that is created by the problem.

Here you must train yourself to look for problems and not simply accept that "this is the way things are."

When Thomas Fogarty recognized that the technique used in vascular surgery was the problem, he was then able to consider a multitude of solutions. In fact, finding a solution is often the easiest aspect. Einstein said, "The formulation of a problem is often more essential than a solution, which may be merely a matter of mathematical or experimental skill." He continued, "To raise new questions, new problems, to regard old problems from a new angle, requires creative imagination and marks a real advantage in science."

Famed psychologist and developer of the Gestalt theory Max Wertheimer noted that the central issue of innovation is actually envisioning that a problem even exists, and that the solution is usually the simpler part.[3]

Charles F. Kettering, founder of the Delco Products Division of General Motors and the holder of 140 patents, noted the difficulty of getting into this mindset when he said that an inventor is "a fellow who does not take his education too seriously. No matter what we are doing, if it is new, we could always find the book that will tell us it can't be done." [4]

True problem solving also means being able to completely change your thinking when confronted with new evidence and insights. Inventor Dean Kamen struggled for years to invent a new kind of wheelchair with little success. Then one day he realized that he had defined the problem in the wrong way. Instead of concentrating on improving mobility, he should instead concentrate on making it dynamically stable – just like walking human beings.

In addition, you must realize that the answer you seek is unlikely to come to you complete and full-blown at first. Solutions develop over time, and the most powerful tool for getting the right solution is the prototype. Some inventors have started down the road to success with a series of models of their device. As each one is created, their thinking changes and the design evolves into a more sophisticated idea.

Product development company IDEO's innovation principle states that, "If a picture is worth a thousand words, a prototype is worth ten thousand."

In fact, no other company has so thoroughly mastered the art of developing ideas through models. IDEO has adopted the practice of "quick and dirty prototyping in order to create a greater number of versions that are less than perfect in every respect. This process allows for the creation of various "straw man" versions that can be examined, their defects discovered and then knocked down to prepare for new and better ones.

In creating a prototype, staffers at IDEO might focus on one specific element that needs development. For example, they might build a dummy telephone receiver just to get the shape of the handset right. Other models would focus on other vital elements that needed to be perfected before they were all incorporated into one final design. The virtue of this rough prototyping is that the answers to various problems are worked out before anyone becomes committed to a single version.

If you're inventing a device or simply modifying a way of doing things, this process can be of great help to you in working out your idea. You might start by committing the idea to paper in words and then drawings. Finally, you move to crude models and eventually more complex working prototypes. At this point, you'll probably move out of your own workshop and retain the services of a professional prototyping organization such as IDEO to get all the features right.

Prototyping isn't simply limited to physical products. It can also be used with business processes or techniques. There's a reason that many new techniques are tried out on cadavers before living patients. It's obviously better to see what goes wrong or doesn't work on the dead than the living while you refine both the technique and your own skills in using it.

Clearly, one of the greatest virtues of constant prototyping is that it allows you to work out the bugs and shortcomings of an invention or a process before it is put into practice or rolls off the assembly line.

Step 4
Deliberation: Let It Simmer

With the problem now firmly in your mind, it's time to simply ruminate or let the ingredients simmer in the oven of your subconscious. Much has been written about this creative state and the conditions that make it possible. Here is truly an area where less is more.

In the first three steps of my process, you were pushing hard to get prepared, to feel the frustration, and to clearly define the problem. Now it's time to switch gears and be patient, as the solution works its way up from the depth of your mind and consciousness. The ideas will come forth when you're in your own optimum state.

How long it takes for the idea to come forth is very much a function of the first three steps. The more prepared, the more frustrated, and the more clearly you define the problem, the faster quality ideas will come forth. Of the first three steps, I believe the preparation stage is the primary component that will allow you to step up and begin to solve the problem. If you see the problem as small and not really worth your attention, ideas will not be forthcoming at the same rate and quality than if you were to see a vexing problem that you very much wanted to solve.

Step 5
Illumination & Documentation: The Big "Ah Ha!"

Creativity can be managed, but it cannot be forced. Throughout history, many inventors have reported that insights came to them during periods in which the mind is detached and unfocused. The great 17th-century French philosopher René Descartes conceived the foundation for the modern scientific method during a dream.

Albert Einstein conceived the theory of relativity during a dream, in which he saw himself riding a beam of light and then looked back to see himself in a mirror. This experience led to E = mc2.

One of the simplest ways to make use of your dreams is to plan to remember them prior to going to sleep. Put a pad and pen or tape recorder by your bed. Then, just before drifting off to sleep, ask your subconscious to solve a problem for you. Perhaps you've been faced with a technical hang-up in a device you're working on. Put that problem into your mind and then let it go. Don't try to force it or even come up with suggestions for solving it. Let your mind take over and wait to see what happens.

Controlling Your Dreams

One inventor after another confirms that the optimum time for coming up with a new idea isn't when you're looking for it, but when you're distracted, focused on something else, relaxed, daydreaming, or even deep in sleep.

Paul Yock found he was most productive when he wasn't being productive. His ideas usually came when he was faced with writing papers or reading materials or doing other work that was demanding and that he really didn't want to do. He would become distracted and begin daydreaming, and then the ideas and solutions he was looking for would come to him. In a sense, procrastination of an undesirable task proved to be a great motivator.

"I let myself wander into thinking about problems and trying to invent at a time when I was supposed to be doing something more productive," he explains. "So for me it was when I was at my desk and I was supposed to be reading six chapters or writing a paper or something and I gave myself permission to wander and invent."

English chemist and physicist Michael Faraday is known for his pioneering experiments in electricity and magnetism. Many consider him the greatest experimentalist who ever lived. Although never formally educated, he is considered the father of electromagnetic field theory, which in turn led to the creation of the vacuum tube, which lead to the creation of radio, TV, and the entire electronics industry.

The idea for his theory came to him in a dream and still stands today as one of the world's most original contributions to science.

While dreaming can seem to be a largely uncontrollable process, many inventors have developed the habit of lucid dreaming, the practice of dreaming while knowing that you are dreaming.

The 19th-century Dutch novelist, poet, and philosopher Frederik van Eeden first originated the idea of lucid dreaming using the word "lucid" to mean mental clarity. Lucidity usually begins in the midst of a dream when you realize that the experience isn't occurring in physical reality, but in fact is a dream. This realization may occur when you notice some impossible event, such as flying or talking to the dead, which prompts you to conclude that it's a dream and not reality. Sometimes people realize they are dreaming and become lucid without even encountering an implausible event.[5]

Research indicates that the quality of lucidity can vary greatly. Dreamers may be fully aware of everything that is taking place and also understand completely that they are dreaming. They may also be able to control their dreams and even alter their dream states to some extent.

For the inventor, the real benefit of this type of dreaming is being able to take away insights and ideas that may come during the dream state.

"The creative process goes on in both the conscious and unconscious mind," says Mir Imran, a frequent lucid dreamer. "Yet when your neural pathways are blocked by external stimuli and other input you get while awake, your internal processes won't come to the surface. Yet in lucid dreaming, [these ideas will] just come bubbling up."

This experience of enhanced creative activity comes about because the brain is highly active in REM sleep and is unconstrained by sensory input. This same novelty allows thought to take on forms that are rare in waking life, manifesting as enhanced creativity. One study found that word associations immediately after waking up from a dream are 29% more likely to be uncommon compared to word associations later in the day.[6]

Another study comparing daydreams, memories of actual events, and dreams found that dreams were significantly more creative than both daydreams and memories.

While some inventors, such as Imran, are quite conscious of using dreams as a path to creativity, others maintain that they don't find ideas during sleep. Thomas Fogarty maintains that he engages in creative problem solving every minute during the day, but doesn't dream of ideas. But then he and other noncreative dreamers may simply not be aware that the idea they think of during the day first came to them in a dream.

In order to learn how to use lucid dreaming, you must be willing to exercise motivation and effort. Many people have spontaneous lucid dreams at one time or another, yet they rarely occur without the conscious intent to do so. There are various techniques you can employ to focus intention and prepare a critical mind. They include mystical exercises of ancient religious traditions and modern mind control techniques such as the popular Silva Method.

Eastern religious traditions describe the process of meditation in which the individual meditating finds God between the gaps of thoughts. Others have achieved this state after drinking alcohol, taking hallucinogenic drugs such as LSD, or engaging in heavy exercise.

I've found that my most creative moments come in the morning when I get in the shower after waking up or while running on my treadmill.

What each of these methods has in common is the letting go of conscious control of your mind and allowing your cognizant mind to be distracted. For those of us trained in the Western approach of logical scientific diagnosis and treatment, it can seem unnatural and maybe even a bit mystical. Yet throughout history, the world's greatest inventors have followed this process and arrived at great ideas in exactly this way.

It is a method that is difficult to measure, although its results are obvious. Although René Descartes formulated the scientific method from a dream, those who use his work as the basis of research largely reject the idea that something so amorphous can play any role in science.[7]

When the ideas arrive, that is the time that your logical mind must take over to ensure the ideas aren't lost. Many people keep a notepad and pen by their bed so that they can immediately write down what has come to them during the night. I've found it easier to dictate into a tape recorder or better still, use my cell phone to call a dictation service.

The virtue of the latter approach is that within hours I can get a typed transcript of my thoughts via e-mail. A dictation company can save you vast amounts of time and energy and ensure that your ideas are quickly converted to written form. Record the ideas immediately, no matter how farfetched or incomplete they may seem. You can come back later and begin to flesh them out.

With the idea now captured on paper, you're ready to move forward with the process of turning it into reality.

Interlocking Steps

It's easy to see how each step in this process is connected to the others and in reality how each one feeds off the other. Yet it's also important to realize that these steps may be repeated many times during the process and that you may go back and forth between steps.

Once you've conceived your initial idea, you're not done with the creative process. In fact, you will at that point move into a process of refinement and prototyping that will allow the idea to evolve.

For example, after first conceiving the idea of the heart stent, Dr. Julio Palmaz immediately began writing down his ideas, making drawings, and in essence, taking the first step toward putting thought into reality.

Many seemingly brilliant ideas may simply be unworkable when they're translated into reality. Putting your ideas down on paper helps you to shape and refine your concepts to overcome any problems that may arise.

Your idea will evolve even further when you begin to create your first prototype, however crude it may be. Each step that you take along the way will bring about new challenges and new opportunities for creativity.

Even after a device has gone into development, many challenges have to be overcome. Inventions don't always work the first time, and sometimes even though it may seem promising, you may never be able to work out all the bugs.

When a problem arises, it may present a new opportunity to experience frustration and thereby help you move through the five steps to a new solution. Each step fosters the others. The more you prepare, the more frustrated you become, which will drive you to become even more prepared. The more you define the problem, the more you will deliberate. The more illumination you receive, the more you will be encouraged to go back through the steps. It is a never-ending process of creativity and invention.

REFERENCES

1. Interactive Concepts in Biochemistry, Visonaries (Accessed April 18, 2006 at http://www.wiley.com/legacy/college/boyer/0470003790/cutting_edge/history/history.htm)
2. Maury Klein, The Change Makers: From Carnegie to Gates, How the Great Entrepreneurs Transformed Ideas into Industries. (New York, Henry Holt and Co. 2003) 21
3. Klein 31
4. Klein 29
5. Stephen LeBerge and Lynne Levitan (2004) Lucid Dreaming FAQ, Verson 2.3, January 16, 2003. (Accessed December 24, 2004 at http://www.lucidity.com/LucidDreamingFAQ2.html)
6. LeBerge and Levitan
7. Willis Harman, Higher Creativity (New York, Jermey P. Tarcher Putnam, 1984)

Chapter 10

THE MEASURE OF CREATIVITY

So far we have examined the creative process and broken it down into its fundamental elements. We've considered how each element interacts and flows into an almost seamless process that throughout history has produced an endless array of discoveries and innovations.

Armed with the Five Step Process, you can now begin to develop your own ideas, which can ultimately lead you to great inventions and financial rewards. It might be sufficient to say that this process is all you need, but there is another factor – you might call it the sixth step – that will transform your inventing career and quite literally put you into overdrive. By implementing the tool revealed in this section, and using it consistently, you will become more effective and able to produce more new ideas than you ever thought possible.

That next step is, quite simply, measurement. Yes, I am talking about measuring your own creativity, just as you would any tangible phenomenon. As scientists, we're familiar with measurement, and the study of a wide variety of things that can be placed under a microscope and observed. I understand that many of you will find it difficult to comprehend how something as intangible as creativity can be measured. But I'm here to tell you that not only can it be observed, recorded, and measured, but it must be if you are to be as successful as you are capable of being.

Your Personal Hawthorne Effect

The process of measuring creativity takes place everyday in business, because as the saying goes, "What gets measured gets done." Measurement is not just a tool for showing you where you are, but a means for helping you to go further than you would otherwise.

By measuring your creative activities, you will be heightening productivity in a manner that was first observed in 1927, during studies performed on workers at Western Electric's Hawthorne Plant in Cicero, Illinois. One of those studies found that better lighting led to significantly improved worker productivity. A second study decreased lighting with the expectation that worker productivity would go down. Instead, they found that it also made productivity go up. The conclusion was that it was not the change in lighting, but the perception by the workers that they were being observed that led to improved performance.[1]

Subsequent studies have validated the reality of what has become known as the Hawthorne Effect. Individual behavior can be altered simply by knowing that you are being observed during participation in a test, trial, or study. So any introduction of measurement, or the perception of being watched and monitored, will in and of itself become an intervention.

The purpose of benchmarking and setting goals is to achieve a certain behavioral modification or a desired outcome. When you set a goal and then measure your progress in achieving it, you are then automatically creating your own personal Hawthorne Effect. You're applying an intervention. You're applying a watchful eye – your own watchful eye. You're assessing yourself. In this way, you're changing or modifying your behavior.

In measuring creativity, I'm asking you to intentionally create your own Hawthorne Effect. You can do this by following my Five Step Process and then keeping track of every action that relates to each particular step, from preparation to illumination and documentation.

Critical Creativity

When we observe the world today, we are aware that there are obviously vast differences between people and nations. Some are incredibly rich, while others reside in abject poverty. Some countries have sophisticated economic engines that produce goods, services, and jobs at a dizzying rate, while others struggle to meet the needs of their citizens.

For decades, the United States has led the world in economic growth and stability, making residence in this country a dream and a destination for people throughout the world. While our streets may not literally be paved with gold, our economy has produced considerable wealth for many people who have the requisite drive and ingenuity. Even many recent immigrants – legal and otherwise – who find themselves at the bottom of the economic totem pole are often much better off financially here than they were in their native lands. Each day, new immigrants arrive with limited resources and perhaps don't even speak the language. Yet within a short period of time, some become highly successful, and within a generation, many do.

What sets the U.S. apart from other nations? Our free enterprise system, while sometimes producing harsh inequities, also allows the talented and motivated to excel and to display their creativity in ways they could never dream of in the rigid social systems of their home countries.

Mir Imran, for example, came to the U.S. as a young man without knowing anyone and with only a few dollars to his name. After enrolling as a student at Rutgers University, he soon founded the first of what would be many companies. Today, he is a wealthy man renowned as one of the most creative inventors in California's Silicon Valley.

While we have distinct advantages in terms of a large continent brimming with natural resources, the central factor is the freedom to create that generates new technology and innovation. Even when manufacturing jobs have been exported to lower-wage countries, they are often replaced in even greater numbers by high-tech positions requiring greater education and training.

When upstart, foreign competitors have overtaken the U.S. in certain areas, such as manufacturing, the U.S. has moved forward into even more complex and innovative realms.

Throughout the last few decades, the real currency has been intellectual property – the results of creativity and idea generation.

The precursor to all technological innovation is creativity. Without it, none of the medical devices we take for granted –some of which are described in this book – would exist. The quality, for example, that makes Microsoft such a dominant force in the computer industry is not Bill Gates' adept management style, but the Windows operating system itself. It is a product of innovative genius.

Throughout the business world, this high level of achievement is produced to a great extent because everything gets measured. Managers evaluate employees. Investors evaluate companies. Customers make judgments through their purchasing decisions.

Achieving your maximum level of creativity will ensure that you achieve the most that you possibly can. You may not create a product that rivals Microsoft Windows in market dominance, but every successful invention will add to your wealth and the wealth of our nation.

Keeping Tabs and Records

Keeping a record of your creativity is the first step in making sure that you're getting the most out of your use of the Five Step Process. You can do this with a simple logbook in which you write down each step, as well as the activity that arises from each of the steps.

Suppose you attend a seminar to enhance your abilities to perform a new procedure. That's part of preparation. Or perhaps you observe a problem with a patient that results in a less than perfect outcome. That classifies as a frustration, so you should write it down in your log. As you begin to formulate and define the problem, you record each step along the way. This makes it possible to relive the frustration intentionally. I suggest that you use something like an Excel spreadsheet that will allow you to link this category to Word documents containing your written explanation of each problem.

Although recording each of these events is important, it's not enough to achieve maximum creativity. To truly create your own Hawthorne Effect, you must also find a way of measuring, benchmarking, and keeping score.

An idea for an invention is truly a living, growing organism. With each step, a new embryo is produced. As it grows, it must be carefully nurtured and cared for until it finally comes of age. When its own offspring are born, they in turn give birth to other children, as the idea moves through this interlocking, nonlinear process. It becomes, in effect, a self-propagating machine with a positive feedback system.

An effective measure takes into consideration that each step is connected and interlocking. Recognition of a frustration leads to developing a clear definition of the problem. It then becomes necessary to deliberate before you can achieve the desired illumination and documentation of the idea. Surrounding each of these steps is an ongoing field of preparation that becomes, in effect, almost your basic essence.

Keeping a close record of your creativity is your first step. As stated before, some people question whether creativity can truly be measured. Yet, obviously, the tangible outcomes of creativity, such as new devices or procedures, can be observed and measured. So too can the behaviors that are exhibited in the Five Step Process that leads up to creativity.

By using measurement as a tool, you can consistently create ideas and innovations. You will then increase the frequency of the behaviors leading to creativity, and in this way, creativity can indeed be measured.

Measurement of preparation is fairly straightforward in its approach. You keep a log of each activity that brings you new knowledge, deepens existing skills, or opens up new pathways to doing things. However, when it comes to measuring and profiting from the next step – frustration – you must adopt a different way of thinking about just what is measurable.

In essence, you won't be measuring the situation or event that creates frustration. Instead, you must look inward so that you can recognize and measure your own personal feelings that arise from the frustrating experience. To do so requires self-awareness and the courage to observe yourself and your own reactions and behaviors. The longest but most productive journey you will ever make is the one inward.

The first step is recognizing the changes you go through – both emotionally and physically – when you're confronted with frustration. Say, for example, you're a physician whose patient returns to your office following a procedure you performed. This individual is still in pain and hasn't made the kind of progress you were hoping to see. How do you react? Do you see the situation as just par for the course and the best that could be expected? Or do you become irritated with your staff or even the patient himself? Do you feel it physically, experiencing a loss of appetite or even a feeling of dread at seeing the returning patient?

Feelings generated by a frustrating event can parallel those of depression, but they are generated by a particular situation, not your life in general. Because you are developing self-knowledge, you recognize that these are feelings produced by a frustration. At this point, you will enter in your logbook the feelings of anger and resentfulness or other physical reactions and record the time of day and events that were taking place in relation to these feelings.

The importance of measuring your own feelings of frustration as opposed to initially documenting outside events is twofold. First, it teaches you to look closer at your own psyche and how you view and react to events in your life. Second, it will serve as a better identifier of true frustrations. A procedure that takes longer than it should and is costly for the patient may not be a frustration for some people, but may be for others. You have to decide what the true frustrations really are. If you can identify what forms they tend to take, then you will become better at recognizing similar kinds of problems.

Keeping Your Log

As you become prepared, experience frustrations, define problems, deliberate, and finally experience illumination, you must record each event.

I've developed my own log system, which you'll find reproduced in the Appendix at the end of the book. There are three interlocking columns for Steps 2, 3, and 5. Steps 1 and 4 are nonlinear and may take place at any time. You should record developments in these areas to measure how you're doing. I encourage you to come up with your own logbook. The system I have provided in the Appendix is merely an example and a starting point for your creation.

Feel free to make a copy or adapt it for use your own way. I wish that I could tell you that this system is the optimal one, but I suspect that many of you will want to improve on the basic model or even develop your own. As you find ways to refine it or start over, I welcome your comments. Clearly, this tool is itself a prototype that will be refined and developed through time and experience.

This model can be drawn out in virtually any logbook. Try it for a while, and create new prototypes.

Finally, I think it is important to make a commitment to measuring creativity in your own life. It may seem strange and difficult at first, but as you gain experience, it will become second nature.

The process of creativity is a nonlinear movement of stimulus, ideas, and reactions that mesh to create the seeds of insight and innovation that are at the heart of all invention.

REFERENCES

1. Elton Mayo, The human problems of an industrial civilization (New York: MacMillan, 1933)

Section III

The Creative Doctor
Profiles In Innovation

Chapter 11

NEIL SHULMAN
DOC HOLLYWOOD AND THE HUMOR OF CREATIVITY

Someone once said that laughter is the best medicine, but most people today would be hard-pressed to find anything amusing about the modern American medical system. Neil Shulman, however, would strongly disagree. His whole career has been about using stand-up comedy, novels, movies, and video to practice medicine in some of the most unconventional ways imaginable.

Sporting a top hat, bow tie, vest, ridiculously large glasses, and a stethoscope, he appears on stage and in video for public television and cable programs, spreading the message of healthcare in an accessible and down-to-earth format that is laced with humor and one-liners.

Even while keeping busy as a member of a medical school teaching faculty, he found time to author more than 20 books on healthcare-related topics. He's perhaps best known for three novels, including one that became the hit movie *Doc Hollywood*, starring Michael J. Fox. All of his projects – whether fact or fiction – are a reflection of his innate desire to creatively empower people to heal themselves. The real Doc Hollywood isn't your typical physician.

These days he has pretty much left behind the daily grind of patient visits and has dedicated himself to finding new means of expression. One of them is stand-up comedy, in which he seeks to "find doctors who are very serious and try to tickle them."

He tells the story of a conference where he was standing in front of 250 of these very serious physicians. To loosen them up, he asked one of them to share his most embarrassing moment as a doctor. The participant told the story of how he found a lump in a female patient's breast, so he went to the waiting room to get her husband. The doctor explained the situation to the man and had him feel the lump and then asked if he could tell the difference between that and a normal breast.

The man replied, "Yes, I do, but this woman is not my wife."

Shulman was fortunate to grow up in a family that encouraged free expression like this. His matchmaker grandmother was a strong influence on him, and she was instrumental in encouraging the young boy's imagination.
"My grandmother was very funny and very creative in a lot of different ways, and I think I probably inherited some of that," Shulman says. "She was a wheeler-dealer, but she was also creative in how she dealt with things, and I think you can be cre-

ative in a million different ways. So for some reason when I was growing up, I just had the right environment."

His stay-at-home mother and career dentist father were always supportive of their children following their own paths and learning to think for themselves. They were never told they had to be a particular way or aspire to a particular ideal.

"There weren't any 'shoulds,' except for getting good grades and getting an education in an area that you want to have an education in," he recalls.

In this nurturing environment, Shulman lived a childhood filled with things like backyard circuses and sled trains. He remembers calling *The Washington Post* and asking them to come out to cover the world's longest sled train ride. They did, and he and his young friends were featured in the one of the country's premier newspapers.

Several lessons made an indelible impression on him, setting the stage for his later forays into unfamiliar areas. The first, he says, is the idea that you should always try something, and if you get rejected, that's just part of the process.

"When you create something, there's always going to be differences of opinion on what you do," he explains.

That's an attitude sorely lacking in most medical schools, where the overarching goal is to get the highest grade and be able to repeat every lesson and technique perfectly. Yet you don't get an "A," or any other grade, when you create something.

"When [Steven] Spielberg creates a movie, there will be some people who like it and some people who don't like it, and he will never get an 'A' from everybody," explains Shulman. "There will be lots of inventions that will take off and others that won't for lots of reasons that are separate from whether they're any good or not."

Shulman has never been shy about venturing into new territory and trying new things. While in college during the '60s, he embarked on a variety of entrepreneurial endeavors, including a radio talk show in Washington, D.C. that featured draft dodgers and military generals debating the ongoing Vietnam War.

All that came to an end when a friend who was then enrolled in Johns Hopkins Medical School showed him how to deliver a baby. Within days, Shulman had gotten his deposit back from law school and began taking the courses needed to obtain admission to Emory University.

His first two years in med school proved to be a radical departure from the relative freedom he had experienced since childhood. Suddenly, he was faced with the daunting task of absorbing the vast amount of information that is an integral part of every medical student's first two years.

"I was forced to focus on memorizing a lot of useless material," he recalls. "I was renting out my brain for two years, filling it with lots of facts, but most of this material would have no impact on how good a doctor I would be."

It was only in his third and fourth year, when the biochemistry and other basic sciences were behind him, that he could again concentrate on expressing himself the way he wanted. The first of these creative forays came when he started writing a book inspired by the adventures of his matchmaker grandmother. He also began gathering funny stories from his classmates. These tales eventually became his first book, called *Finally ... I'm a Doctor*, which was published by Scribner's.

Like most comedians, Shulman takes his job very seriously. He has dedicated his life to demystifying medicine and finding new means of making it accessible to everyone. That dedication, combined with his unconventional way of thinking, has often cast him in the role of rebel within the medical establishment.

While a resident at a major public hospital in Atlanta, he raised the hackles of officials who wanted poor patients to be processed through as quickly as possible.

"I was really distraught over the fact that people would wait for hours to be seen just for a minute or two, and the doctor didn't know much about them," he says. "The resident who saw the patients the fastest was the one who made the nurses happy. If you spent too much time with the patients, you got in more trouble."

Instead of fighting the system, he came up with the idea of bringing in volunteers and doing screenings while the patients were in the waiting room.

The volunteers' goal was to "find out if [the patients] have blood in their stools, anything, so they could give us that information and maybe we could find things that could be really helpful for them," he adds.

Later, Shulman's efforts to determine the prevalence of treated and untreated high blood pressure among inner-city residents helped to capture an $8 million National Institutes of Health grant. He was soon writing papers on the subject, and eventually published a book on high blood pressure among African-Americans. His work led to the founding of an international society on hypertension.

"Then one day I was lecturing on blood pressure, and I heard somebody snoring – and it was me," Shulman remarks. "That's when I decided I was going to decrease my institutional academic work. So I gave most of my salary back."

Getting free of the bureaucracy and finding the time and resources to carry out his own projects became a driving force in his life. Some of the projects, he conceded, might not make any money, while others might – and some certainly have. But, says Shulman, "I didn't work on a project because it was going to make money, but because I thought it might have some innate value."

He also believed that the most important question you needed to ask about money wasn't "What luxury items can it buy?" Rather, it was "Will it give me the freedom to follow my passion?" He knew exactly what he wanted to do – and it wasn't to continue his career as a traditional full-time academic physician.

Over time, he gradually removed himself from full academic duties and devoted considerable amounts of time and energy to his independent projects. As a social entrepreneur, he knew how to make the money that could be used to fund other projects that, while worthwhile, might have no obvious support.

Some of his efforts have been quite successful. His second novel, titled *What? Dead … Again?*, is the story of a young doctor who finds himself working in a small-town emergency room after his car breaks down on a cross-country trip. Based on true life experiences, it was optioned and eventually became a major motion picture release called *Doc Hollywood*. Although he didn't appear in the film, he has used the Doc Hollywood character and persona to promote healthcare. One of his projects, a national Doc Hollywood Day, is being planned to salute health providers.

The struggle to get the book translated to the big screen was a long and arduous journey for Shulman. After first hooking up with a Hollywood agent, he soon got into a disagreement over whether the agent should sell the rights to TV or hold out for a movie deal.

"[The agent] said, 'You're crazy not to take the TV deal,' and fired me," Shulman recalls. "But I lucked out."

Warner Bros. Studios picked up the rights as a vehicle for *Saturday Night Live* star Chevy Chase, but they soon dropped it. An executive at Warner then pitched the idea to Michael J. Fox, who was intrigued. What followed was a seemingly endless series of screenplay rewrites.

"Warner Bros. hired me as associate producer to go back and forth with [the screenwriters]," says Shulman. "The Hollywood screenwriters called and asked, 'Do you wear shoes in Georgia?'"

To give them a better idea of the setting for *Doc Hollywood*, he invited the crew to go on a tour of rural Georgia. After meeting them at the airport wearing a white coat, and carrying a stethoscope and black bag, but, of course, shoeless, they all climbed into the back of a borrowed ambulance for the journey. Over the course of the next few days, they went through small-town speed traps, talked to moonshiners, visited black churches, and even toured several rural hospital ERs.

Nowadays, Shulman has become the "real" Doc Hollywood. It's a persona he presents on stage and in film and one that is popular with children of all ages.

"Adults are just kids in bigger bodies," he says.

He has kept on writing, often incorporating his own experiences into fictional stories. His most recent novel, *The Backyard Tribe*, is the tale of a doctor who invites a Kenyan girl to America for needed heart surgery. But he doesn't realize she's going to bring her entire tribe and charge the trip to his American Express card. They set up a village in the backyard of his home in an affluent Atlanta suburb. Shulman hit upon the idea after a trip to Africa, where he participated in a health screening program for indigenous peoples. The book is currently being developed as another major motion picture.

Although he might have at first rejected TV, he has since applied his talents to this medium as well. He served as associate producer of the 1985 Movie of the Week *Dreams of Gold: The Mel Fisher Story*, about the life of the famed deep-sea treasure hunter. More recently, he co-wrote, co-produced, and starred in the independent romantic comedy *Who Nose?* He is also producing and performing in two new spots for kids on public television.

Shulman is obviously an accomplished performer, writer, and creator, but perhaps his greatest talent is as a facilitator and communicator. On first meeting, his style is one of asking questions and getting a feel for where you're coming from and how he can connect with you. Always the clown, he will show up at a formal dinner in his comical Doc Hollywood garb as a means of breaking the ice.

While growing up, Shulman says that he was often the object of other kids' snickers. Yet, over time, he realized that it didn't really matter whether they were laughing with him or at him, as long as they were laughing, because "You're making them happy," he says. His ability to connect with other people helps explain why he has spent much of his career collaborating with one person or another, getting projects started and helping to see them to fruition.

For example, one day he was sitting on a plane next to a woman who explained that her son had considerable talent as an illustrator. The only problem was that he had become a doctor, even though she wanted him to be a cartoonist.

"Obviously, you're not a Jewish mother," Shulman told her.

With the mom's help, the two doctors connected, and the result was Shulman's first children's book, *What's in a Doctor's Bag?*

In this story, a young boy who's frightened by doctors turns over a physician's bag and the instruments fall out and become fanciful creatures. Among them are Otis the Otoscope, Woody the Tongue Depressor, and Tempo the Thermometer. The characters eventually became a line of toys and the stars of a half-hour video shown on the cable television channel QVC.

Shulman sees no limit to the mediums that can be used to promote good health. Sitting in front of a computer at his home in suburban Atlanta, he shows a visitor the website — www.redlightwarning.com — based on his book *Your Body's Red Light Warning Signals: Medical Tips That May Save Your Life.*

The website uses an interactive approach to give visitors the top 225 warning signs of disease in various parts of the body. For example, by clicking on the eyes of a digital body with your mouse, you can see all the most obvious warning signs for problems in that area. Shulman gathered the warning signs from the top experts in each medical specialty and then compiled them into an easy-to-follow book, followed by the website. Both are ways of engaging patients outside of the traditional confines of the doctor's office.

"And so far I haven't been sued," he jokes.

Much of his work has been geared to fighting the general medical illiteracy that seems to pervade America. Even well-educated professionals are baffled when you ask them about the difference between normal and abnormal body conditions. The average accountant, for example, could not identify the warning signs of stroke.

He's also using film to teach kids about healthcare as well. As the comic Doc Hollywood, he has starred in a series of short clips – which he refers to as interstitials – that instruct children on brushing their teeth, good nutrition, the role of hand washing in preventing illness, and other basics of good health. The spots air on public television stations. You can also see the video at the website, www.whatsinadoctorsbag.com.

Much like another comic doctor who found movie fame, his friend and colleague Patch Adams, Shulman has devoted much of his time and effort to building and funding charitable organizations. The first of them was a nonprofit called Social Entrepreneurs, which started small, but really struck a chord with its intended audience – undergraduate students. He offered $250 grants to students who wanted to start their own nonprofit. Even though the students were spending tens of thousands of dollars to attend school, these small awards motivated many of them to channel their efforts into helping others.

He also helped found WorldPlay, a toy exchange that encourages children from around the world to trade toys they've made themselves. He has also organized the Atlanta version of Soccer for Peace to use the popular sport as a means of promoting peace and understanding between nations, while also raising funds to help the victims of the Darfur conflict in western Sudan. Another nonprofit called Second Wind Dreams is helping to make dreams come true for nursing home residents.

For Shulman, medicine is far more than just prescribing drugs and viewing patients solely as a condition or disease. It's about using creativity to empower patients with knowledge, and understanding that there are many ways to accomplish the job of the physician.

Chapter 12

THE REAL PATCH ADAMS
HEALING, HUMOR, AND REBELLION

Don't think Patch Adams is just a clown.

It's true that the first thing you see is this very big guy with a glowing red nose, a crazy hat sitting cockeyed on his head, and those huge shoes. He's out on the streets, moving from one person to another and leaving each one laughing.

This clown is like a child – one with Down syndrome to be exact. He comes across as simple, curious, and loving, but ready to get into trouble wherever it can bring joy to those in pain.

"The first 20 or so years, I did many characters. In the last 20, I have done this one because of his effectiveness," explains Adams. "In the old Soviet Union, I'd go up to a policeman, take his helmet off of his head, and put a [clown] nose on his face. Only a fool would do that."

Adams and a troupe of followers were in Sri Lanka in 2004 soon after the waves of the horrendous tsunami had subsided. He's been in Moscow and Beijing and on the dusty and dangerous streets of Kabul after the fall of the Taliban, as well as other not-so-humorous locations in more than 50 countries around the globe.

If he looks altogether comfortable as a clown, it's probably because he's spent the last 25 years wearing nothing but these kinds of costumes.

"I grew up a class clown," says Adams. "A lot of nerds are class clowns because they find that they're not punished and the bullies don't beat up on them because they're funny. There is a huge seduction in the consequences of making people laugh, and there is also a bad-boy quality and naughtiness. I always tell my audiences I am a clown who is a doctor and not a doctor who is a clown, even though their jobs are actually the same – to walk towards suffering and to care about the outcomes."

To Adams, clowning is "a public health gesture to spread joy in a population and to make the public space human again." He has used it in Third World hospitals to bring relief through laughter to suffering children whose screams are familiar sounds.

"Since I started to go to the refugee camps, I have probably been at 10,000 deathbeds," he relates. "A lot of Western physicians have no idea what it is like to be in a hospital where there is no medicine."

His decision to adopt the persona of a Down syndrome character as his clown personality was a calculated decision. Traveling in foreign lands where he didn't speak the language, the character didn't need to talk. His actions and unconditional love, which Adams modeled after those of personal acquaintances with the condition, were more than enough.

"I was looking for something that was disarming and also inviting, and I couldn't look more harmless," says Adams, who at six feet four inches and more than 200 pounds strikes an imposing figure.

But not everyone saw the humor. Some activists for the mentally disabled questioned whether he was making fun of those with Down syndrome. His response:

"Why is 'making fun' a negative thing? It's certainly not as negative as being grumpy or apathetic. So I told them I was honoring [Down syndrome patients]. This was the highest out of all of the possible choices I could make [for a character]."

It's just one approach to healing that Hunter "Patch" Adams has developed over a lifetime of using medicine in creative and often controversial ways.

Adams is a doctor who has spent a lifetime healing both the bodies and spirits of some of the earth's most fragile people. The motion picture bearing his name and starring Robin Williams made him and his work famous, but it barely scratched the surface of this creative and highly complex physician.

He is, most obviously, a doctor, a clown, and an entertainer, but he is first and foremost a social and political activist. He decided medicine was his calling because it allows him to connect with people on the most personal level. But instead of following the professional mainstream, he embarked on a career that has been characterized by relentless criticism of the healthcare system, coupled with a sometimes total rejection of conventional practice.

His rebellious role has been both a blessing and a curse. It has gained him wide acclaim within the popular press as something of a medical folk hero, but his work and ideas have yet to gain him any recognition among the profession at large. In fact, even as the medical community is beginning to recognize the value of a better doctor-patient relationship and the healing aspects of humor, Patch Adams receives little credit for his early advocacy of these ideas, and his work has long been rejected by medical journals.

Yet in many ways, he is an example of creativity and innovation at work. While few physicians would be willing to go to quite the extreme of this rebel with a cause, Adams vividly illustrates the many and varied paths that are available to those who possess a Doctor of Medicine degree.

"I made a choice to serve humanity, to be an activist, and pretty much every second of my life since then has been devoted to that end," he says. "When I entered medical school, I had the idea that I would use it as a vehicle for social change."

Adams' decision to become a compassionate activist was very much a victory of life over death – one that saved his own life. A military brat, he lived in cities from Texas to Germany as his father moved from one posting to another.

A bright but lonely youth, he buried himself in schoolwork, science projects, and competitions. While his mother was close and loving, his father, an artillery officer who served in World War II and Korea, was seldom there.

At 16, Patch spent a week with the older man and finally came to understand and appreciate the torment that his father had lived with all those years. The wars had destroyed his spirit and left him with psychological scars. He felt guilty for surviving when so many of his friends had died in combat – including one who fell on an enemy grenade to save the elder Adams' life – and for not being a better father to his two sons.

Adams never felt closer to or more understanding of his father than during that brief interlude. For the first time, Adams truly understood the pain his father had endured and the losses that had weighed so heavily on him. Then, as suddenly as it began, this idyllic period of friendship came to an end when, just days later, his father died from a sudden heart attack.

From then on, everything changed. During the next few years, the family moved back to the U.S. from Germany, and Adams began to realize that the world was a very different place than he had imagined. He became deeply involved in the civil rights movement, even as a high school student. In school he was a trouble-maker – brilliant but alienated.

"I was a happy kid and didn't want to live in a world of violence and injustice," he recalls.

He couldn't express these feelings either to himself or anyone else, so he channeled his energy into fighting the system – about whatever it might be. He went to marches and sit-ins to protest racial discrimination. With a scientific mind that rejected religion, he often sought out the religious and tried to destroy their faith through his logical arguments. He defied authority. In the process, he alienated himself from nearly everyone. Eventually, the pain that he kept bottled up inside took its toll and he attempted to take his own life. He failed, and committed himself to a mental institution.

There, amidst even greater suffering, he found his purpose in life. He also realized that unless he was able to both give and receive love, he was going to end up bitter and alone.

"I made a decision [then and there] to never have another bad day, to love life," he says. "I am now 42 years into not having a bad day."

Instead of insulating himself from people and immersing himself in books and science, he began reaching out in new ways. For two years, as he pursued pre-med study, he spent his spare hours calling up wrong numbers to sharpen his conversational skills, and riding up and down elevators just to see how many floors it would take to get the occupants introduced and singing songs together. He attended civil rights rallies one day and Ku Klux Klan meetings the next.

Adams applied his brilliant mind to medical school and found it easy – at least when it came to learning facts and getting top grades at the Medical College of Virginia in Richmond. It was there that he became frustrated with the inequities and shortcomings of a system that was costly and sometimes even dehumanizing for patients who were often only called by the name of their disease. He regarded his professors as aloof, arrogant, and devoid of humanity. His clashes with medical authority became the stuff of legend as he began to rebel against the system.

After entering the clinical phase of his education, he rebelled against grand rounds and preferred to visit patients by himself. Most found him funny and vibrant, and he watched them brighten up once they got used to his totally unconventional appearance. Tall, with long black hair in a ponytail, a mustache, and a black patch safety-pinned to the lapel of his white jacket in protest of the Vietnam War, he radiated a warm personality that quickly won them over.

"I was free to talk to the patients, cry with them, massage them, comfort them, joke with them, and inject some exuberance and fun into their lives," he recalled in his book, *Gesundheit!*

While most patients and nurses loved his antics, many fellow students and nearly all of his professors were shocked. In one clash with an assistant dean who threatened to expel him, the offended faculty accused him of being "excessively happy." He survived the battle and graduated, but his view of medicine and his vision for a career had changed dramatically in comparison to that of his fellow students.

Leaving school didn't end his dissatisfaction with the system. Soon after joining a pediatric residency, he quit because of the same practices that he found so objectionable in other settings.

Freed from what he viewed as the restrictions of medicine, he began applying his outrageousness to medicine. He conceived the idea of a hospital where patients and doctors could come and work together for healing. Modeled after a utopian commune, the hospital would be self-sufficient by growing its own food and encouraging patients to apply their skills in the community. Best of all, it would be free.

In what was perhaps the ultimate act of rebelliousness, Adams decided to take one of America's most expensive commodities – healthcare – and give it away.

After dropping out of his first year of a pediatric residency, Adams and a group of associates began practicing his brand of compassionate, unconventional medicine from their homes. In locations ranging from a three bedroom house in Arlington, Virginia, to a rural farm in West Virginia, they undertook what Adams saw as a pilot program for the dream of a free full-scale hospital and healthcare community.

In defiance of medical convention, he and his staff never accepted payment or carried malpractice insurance. They practiced as they saw fit and even invited alternative practitioners to work side by side with them.

Those early efforts became the model for what he calls the Gesundheit! Institute. While he has yet to break ground for this hospital and it remains just architectural plans at this point, Adams believes he is closer than ever to achieving his goals – more than three decades after he first conceived them. He also believes that his failure to build the hospital yet has an upside. Instead of settling into the role of practitioner in a hospital, he has embarked on his clowning work and inspired thousands of others to undertake similar roles.

It also led to the motion picture that bears his name. Adams says that, in the beginning, he cared little for the film or the license that Hollywood took with his story and personality. In the movie, as played by Robin Williams, he comes across as a compassionate and funny doctor. His dedication to social activism and drive to stop violence against the weak, however, is missing. He would have made a very different film if given the chance. Eventually, however, his perspective changed.

"At first I was embarrassed with the film," says Adams. "But now that I have seen that thousands of projects have started up all over the world because of the film, I have come to love it."

The evidence is the thousands of letters he has gotten from around the world, which has proven just how much impact his story has. People write saying they have seen the movie 20 times and have been inspired to start an orphanage or a free clinic or to put clowns in hospitals – nearly 3,000 projects in all.

Proceeds from the film have also allowed him to purchase a large farm in West Virginia, which he believes will one day become the institute he first conceived of so many years ago. Whether that physical structure is ever built or not, Patch Adams will remain a physician who followed his vision and his ideals wherever they led him. His life and career are shining examples of the range of options and opportunities open to physicians seeking to expand their own creativity and innovation.

Chapter 13

JOHN STONE
HEALING FROM THE HEART

John Stone has the soul of a poet – and it is a gift that has allowed him to get to the very heart of medicine, both in the words he uses to paint pictures of emotion and experience and in his day-to-day practice as a cardiologist treating patients.

"The medical career serves as a source of arresting moments," says Stone, sitting at the kitchen table in his modest Atlanta home. "You might even call them epiphanies, which is one of the ways that writer/physicians interact."

Over a long career as a doctor and author, he has consistently transformed those arresting moments into sensitive and deeply penetrating verse that tells the stories of his daily interactions with patients and their families – fathers and mothers, children and grandchildren. In the seemingly mundane activities of daily life, he finds meaning and inspiration. With the understanding of a writer, he discerns the humanness that is sometimes lost in the practice of medicine.

During his career, Stone has published five books of poetry, in addition to a collection of essays on medicine written for *The New York Times*, called *In the Country of Hearts*. His anthology *On Doctoring* – now in its third edition – is annually presented to every freshman at American medical schools by the Robert Wood Johnson Foundation. In this book, he brings together essays that explain what it truly means to be a physician, including the good, the bad, and the ups and downs of a life spent in medicine.

Through his writing and a long career in academics at Emory School of Medicine, he has been recognized as one of the leaders in a growing movement to help the profession become more compassionate and intimate. As much as anyone, he has spoken in his work of what it means to be human in the context of the doctor-patient relationship and the need to listen to and understand those who come to the physician seeking healing.

He brings to his craft a poet's insight into the most basic aspects of life. After all, poets seem to write mostly about a few common subjects, such as love, life, sex, and death. As the son of a man who died at an early age, Stone has always been very much aware of the fleeting nature of time and the ever-present reality of impending demise.

"The time we have is very precious," he says.

Stone may not be the first or only doctor/poet, but he is certainly in the vanguard of the movement. One of his heroes is famed writer and physician William

Carlos Williams, who in a wide body of work wrote sensitively of his relationship to patients and what it meant to be a doctor who observes human beings in their most vulnerable moments.

Like so many writers who pursued other professions, Stone's interest in the craft developed early in life.

"The writing came well before the medicine, when I was in junior high," he says. "Like [Chilean poet] Pablo Neruda said, 'I don't know from where it came. It claimed me, it came to me, it announced itself to me.' I just realized that this is something that I could do. I had the right receptor sites for it."

Stone's path of writing and medicine is filled with the stuff that inspires his poetry. He developed a heightened sensitivity to words and the fine shades of their meanings after his mother encouraged him to study Latin. Yet he only turned to poetry in a serious way after the death of his father.

Growing up in Jackson, Mississippi, Stone recalls coming home one day to find that his father – a big, burly man just 45 years old – had left work early because of chest pains. He had a heart attack and died a few days later in the local hospital.

That became one of those real-life moments that triggered his poetry. Over the course of his career, there would be many more moments – both from his own experiences and those of others – that would inspire words of deep beauty and insight.

"It might be a preoccupation with a rhythm or sound or words, and that becomes the nucleus of the poem, and then, much as iron filings stick to a magnet, you start with a Donne [French for "the given"] and then other lines adhere to it," he explains.

Yet coming from a family in which both his uncle and grandfather were physicians, following in their footsteps seemed an obvious choice. He was deeply impressed by his grandfather, who was himself a gifted storyteller.

As a youth, Stone visited his grandfather's office and sat across the desk where he would have talked with patients. Behind him on the wall were rows of specimen bottles filled with gallstones, gallbladders, a fetus, and "all kinds of amazing things." He was deeply impressed, because in each of them he saw a story and a little bit of magic.

"Physicians depend on magic to heal the patients," says Stone. "We will take advantage of all the placebo responses that we can muster."

He has tried to convey that sense of magic to a long procession of medical students through his duties as assistant dean at Emory and as a popular teacher and lecturer, presenting topics such as The Literature of Medicine and Compassion and the Art of Medicine.

Stone's medical experience and his commitment to understanding patients developed through years of practice in cardiology. In fact, one of his most moving poems describes his relationship with an elderly woman who came to him one day complaining of shortness of breath.

"She came to see me in the clinic one day and said, 'I live at the top of a hill and there's a grocery store at the bottom of the hill, and I go down to get groceries and when I start back up, I have this discomfort in my chest and I feel like I'm going to faint,'" he recalls her telling him.

He diagnosed a massive calcification of her aortic value and recommended a surgical procedure.

"I told her she needed a cath," he says. "I did the cath, and then she had her surgery, and this is not the whole story, because the stories are complicated in medicine. When you start thinking past what you're going to do for a patient, they all get complicated, because all of life is complicated."

A few years after her surgery, the woman invited Stone to come to her house and pick figs. He observed her life, her small house, the little music box on the table, the illuminated 3-D Christ that turns into Mary, and then the angels - all the things that are the accumulated stuff of life.

"At the hospital, a thousand times I've heard your heart valve open and close," he wrote in *He Makes a Housecall*. "I know how clumsy it is, but health is whatever works and for as long, I keep thinking of seven years ago without a faint. On my way to the car, loaded with vegetables, I keep thinking of seven years ago when you bled in my hands like a saint."

In this poem, he discovered what health is really, finally, all about. "Health is whatever works and for as long," Stone repeats. "In the last line, 'when you bled in my hands like a saint,' the poem is on its own hook. I didn't write this; I just wrote it down. It came to me that 'when you bled in my hands like a saint' underscores the relationship between doctor and patient, which is sacred."

For Stone, this elderly woman stands as an example of how physicians are taught by their patients. They allow doctors to lay their hands on their bodies and learn from those bodies.

"In anatomy class, we lay hands on bodies, too, and they teach us perhaps the most impenetrable truths there are, but every patient afterward has this story into which we walk as physicians, into which we are privileged to walk," explains Stone. "If we keep in mind that relationship, we'll be a lot better off in medicine."

Just as Stone has found a wellspring of inspiration for his writing in the lives of his patients, he believes that every doctor can find both motivation and new vistas of knowledge through these interactions. In fact, when doctors make mistakes, it is often because they have not listened well enough.

"The unfortunate truth is that often we neglect the epiphanies that are all around us," says Stone. "We don't pay enough attention to them. We know we have to get to the next patient. You can't do this with every patient, but you can find a patient who teaches you a special way of looking at his or her problem."

Stone hopes that his years of teaching and writing will help other doctors to find their own sources of creativity, and through those endeavors the renewal that it offers each of them, whether that renewal is found in the stories that their patients provide, or in the realization that they have found a new way of doing a procedure that will save lives.

"Who knows what problems can be solved by simply looking at them a little bit harder?" says Stone. "There are so many better ways of doing things in medicine that are simply aching to be discovered."

Chapter 14

RON CRYSTAL
LEADING THE GENE REVOLUTION

Ron Crystal never really intended to become a physician. His true interests lay in the far different field of high-energy physics. Medicine was just what he now calls a side interest until, that is, he began exploring the physiology of the cardio-vascular system.

While attending graduate school at the University of Pennsylvania in the early '60s, Crystal decided to drop out of physics and begin the process that would change not only his career, but would ultimately produce a series of groundbreaking contributions to modern medical research.

"One day I just went over to the medical school and made an appointment with the dean of admissions and said, 'I'd like to go to medical school,' and showed him my transcripts," says Crystal.

Getting into the school proved to be relatively easy, even though he hadn't taken the usual round of biology, chemistry, or other basic science requirements. At first, his interest was purely in the research side of medicine, but as he progressed through school and entered his third-year clinical duties, he became intrigued with the process of treating patients.

It was about that time that Crystal learned the importance of taking risks when the situation seems to warrant it. As a young medical student at Penn, he had his eye fixed on winning an internship at Massachusetts General Hospital in Boston, which was said to have the best internal medicine and surgery program in the country. Thus, winning one of the 16 spots there meant competing with the best medical students in the nation. After placing in the final 20 in the selection process, he was called in for an interview.

"They did it, at that time, with a group of professors sitting around asking you questions," Crystal recalls.

One distinguished faculty member presented a hypothetical case to him: "A man comes into your office with his wife. He turns to her and says, 'Mabel, Mabel, I can't see. I'm blind.' The woman turns to her husband and proclaims, 'Howard, just open your eyes; they're squeezed shut.'"

Turning to Crystal, the professor asked simply: "How would you handle that, doctor?"

With his future career riding on his answer, Crystal thought back to an incident that had occurred just a week before. One day, while wearing his white coat, he dropped by a bike shop in Philadelphia. The owner came over to him with his eyes partially closed and inquired if he was a doctor. When Crystal answered that he was just a medical student, the man said, "Well, I have an unusual medical condition. It's called blethrospasm."

The man then began to give Crystal a detailed description of the causes and treatments for the condition, which caused uncontrollable blinking of the eyes. During the interview, that encounter came back to him and he replied calmly, "That's obviously a case of blethrospasm."

Even though he had never seen a case, he decided to take a chance and make it his answer. He ended up being ranked first among the group of intern candidates.

After finishing his internship and residency, Crystal was faced with another dilemma. It was the late '60s and the Vietnam War was at its height. Since 1942, physicians had been automatically drafted into service. To avoid the prospect of being swept up into the raging conflict in Southeast Asia, however, doctors with a research bent were applying for work with the National Institutes of Health. It was also a highly competitive position – just eight or nine out of more than 1,000 applicants were accepted. Crystal was one of the lucky few, and because of that stroke of fortune, he was able to embark on a research career that has spanned decades of accomplishment and leading a revolution in gene therapy.

While at NIH, Crystal followed several research interests, one of which included setting up a lab for research into lung disease. That effort eventually grew into one of the largest programs still carried on by this leading government research institute.

"There was a mixture of basic science, mostly molecular stuff and clinical medicine," he explains.

The program also led to Crystal's entry into the field of in vivo gene transfer, opening up boundless possibilities for the treatment of both hereditary and acquired diseases such as cystic fibrosis and atherosclerosis. In addition, he has helped lead the charge to develop new means of delivering vaccines that can more effectively protect populations against terrorist attacks involving anthrax and other biological agents.

He was first attracted to the field when he began studying a genetic disorder called alpha 180 trypsin deficiency which is the cause of about two percent of emphysema cases. In the mid-1980s, Crystal and his team at NIH were able to develop a purified version of the F1A trypsin protein, which is now being used to treat thousands of patients with the disease.

"Our group was the first to ever use a virus to transfer a gene to a human," says Crystal. "The actual first human gene transfer of a virus — actually putting a virus into a human — was in 1993, when we used it to try to express the normal cystic fibrosis gene in the airways of people with cystic fibrosis."

The inspiration for using this method came to Crystal following a conversation with a former colleague who was working as a senior scientist with a French pharmaceutical company. The company was in the process of putting a gene into a modified cold virus, but hadn't decided to what uses it could be put, and the colleague wondered if Crystal had any ideas. He didn't at the time, but he assured his friend he would give it some thought.

Like so many creative bursts of imagination, Crystal's moment of brilliance came when he was focused on something entirely different. Out on a wooded trail, lit by the sinking afternoon sun, he was running in preparation for the marathons that were his hobby. Suddenly, in the middle of his run, when his mind was clear and focused on his pace and breathing, inspiration came to him.

"I suddenly got the idea that this would be a way to cure cystic fibrosis, because I knew that it was an airway disease and I knew that if you could transfer the genes in the airway epithelium, you potentially could cure the disease," he recalls. "So that was the idea to use a virus directly. Nobody had done work in that area, and so we quickly learned how to do adenoviruses. We put genes into adenoviruses and then we wrote a series of papers. We were the first to put it into practice in humans."

While the project proved to be only partially successful, it was the beginning of extensive research into the use of gene transfer in the treatment of disease. Today, Crystal sees that the entire development was made possible by taking a question posed by another physician and mixing it with his own background as a clinician, along with his knowledge of recent research into the disease.

"I knew about cystic fibrosis as a clinical disorder, and the gene had just been identified a few months before," Crystal recalls. "So I knew the literature and I'd been thinking a lot about it and, perhaps, going after the gene. But others had done it and I didn't work in that area. And I knew about gene transfer because I'd been thinking about that and working in the field. Then all those things connected while I was jogging."

Crystal was not the first to propose the idea of using a virus in this way, but he became the leader in proving it could be done effectively, and that the method could be used to treat a wide variety of diseases.

Throughout his career, many of his most productive ideas for solving research problems would come while he was engaged in physical activities, be it running or ice climbing. In fact, many of his creative ideas have emerged when he wasn't even really thinking about the problem he was trying to solve.

After spending more than 23 years running the largest research lab at NIH, Crystal left the government to take a post as chairman of the Genetic Medicine Department at Weill Cornell Medical College and director of the Genetic Medicine Institute.

While running large research labs, Crystal has proven to be highly successful at finding talented and highly original researchers to work with him, and he has also mastered the art of winning research grants to fund his work. In the world of academic science, money is the vital fuel that keeps projects going and allows scientists to pursue their ideas.

Despite his success, he hasn't always found himself batting a thousand in his field. He admits that he's had a number of rejections over the years that have pushed him to focus more clearly on what he wanted to accomplish. Most of all, his rejections have taught him to persevere.

For example, when he left the NIH, the very first grant he wrote after going to Cornell was for one of his best projects – alpha 1A deficiency.

"It was trashed," he admits. "It got a terrible score, and I put it in two more times and it also got a terrible score, and I never got it funded. So here's a field that I was one of the dominant figures in, and yet I hadn't learned enough. I'd never written a grant before, and I didn't know enough about how do you do it right to sell my colleagues to fund me."

Since that early failure, he has perfected his skills and has become one of the most successful grant writers in the country.

Crystal attributes his success to the right combination of brains and resources.

"I find that in laboratories there is a cyclic process – creative waves — that comes about as a combination of what is possible in terms of technology, resources, and, very importantly, the intellectual environment, because a lot comes out of the people you are working with," he explains. "Then, at other times, it's sort of a downtime, and those periods can last for months or years."

To avoid those downtimes, it becomes very important for a researcher to surround himself with those people who are just as bright, if not brighter, and who are also hungry to do the work needed to pursue knowledge.

"It's very, very complex, and it's not just the brightest guys, it's not just the most creative, it's not just the ones who can articulate the best or know the literature the best," he says. "It's a very complex combination of many, many different things that make people successful."

Running a lab is also very different from the path of an individual researcher chasing a single idea. Crystal, like many other successful lab directors, has given up the hard-core daily research grind to focus on the administrative and management chores of his facility.

"I realized that I was better as a leader than I was working at the bench," he says. "It didn't mean I couldn't do it, but I just found I was better at this. So I spend my day most effectively by meeting with people and helping to generate ideas and mold those ideas into practice."

Early in his career, Crystal found that he could contribute more to the academic environment by leading the faculty rather than taking care of patients on a full-time basis. While he does still see some patients, most of his time is spent teaching and leading.

In the lab, he is the CEO and manager who keeps all the parts of this complex organization moving. As the founder of a private company, he has a clear view of how things work in the business world and how important leadership is to ensuring that every member of the organization has the tools, the expertise, and, most of all, the direction to do his job. Much of Crystal's time is occupied in setting policy and directing his researchers, postdoctoral fellows, and other employees. Perhaps the best example of his leadership power comes in the preliminaries to the application for a new grant.

The application represents a new area for his shop, so Crystal confides that "we're developing these new ideas and so I have a group of 15 people who are involved in this individual project."

Much of his effort goes into presenting what his researchers believe should be the focal point of the grant. In essence, this means delineating the ways in which the money is going to be spent to further specific project areas.

"What I'm doing is trying, within the group, to criticize in a positive way those ideas so that we get better ideas," he says. "I try to mold it the best possible way, to help them in generating their part of the grant. That's what I'm most effective at."

Although he hasn't put a lot of thought into the mechanics of what makes up leadership in a research environment, he recognized early that he had what it takes to be effective.

"I had the skills to be able to consolidate ideas and see the fundamental basis of whatever the problem was, whether the problem was how you figure out what scientific thing you're going to work on," he says. "I think people that lead in science are able to take complex ideas and simplify them."

He tells his postdocs and researchers when they're getting ready to make a presentation to just imagine they're presenting their idea to a New York cab driver. If you can make him understand, then the audience will understand as well, because you're able to get past all the scientific jargon to the fundamental heart of the matter.

"And when you're able to do that, then you can achieve true success," says Crystal.

"That's the most fundamental thing about success," he says. "That's what we're all in the business of doing, but it is, of course, more than that."

It's about not just what you do, but what you inspire others to do as well. That's what leadership is all about for a man like Ron Crystal.

Chapter 15

RAYMOND SCHINAZI
FORMULATING THE ELIXIRS OF LIFE

When Emory University in Atlanta announced a record-setting $540 million royalty deal for an anti-HIV drug called Emtriva, it solidified the school's reputation as a major research institution. It also marked a new advance in the fight against one of the modern world's most dreaded diseases.

Yet behind the drug and its promise stands one man in particular, whose creativity and dogged pursuit of an idea, as much as anyone's, made possible this and a string of other advances.

The story of these and other lifesaving drugs is about discovery and the fight to protect an idea. As Professor Raymond F. Schinazi put it: "The problem is finding the true inventors. Probably more people pretend to be inventors than actually invent things. They all come out of the woodwork when something hot is discovered."

Over the past decade, Schinazi has teamed with fellow Emory Professor Dennis C. Liotta to discover such groundbreaking medications as 3TC (lamivudine) and FTC (emtricitabine) to treat the HIV and hepatitis B virus (HBV) infections.

In fact, much of Schinazi's work has taken place during a 20-year partnership with Liotta that has not only produced the key anti-HIV drug used in the majority of AIDS cocktails today, but which has saved countless lives and generated millions of dollars in revenue for the university that serves as their research home.

The chemists' work together resulted in the compound 3TC, which is used in the combination medicines Combivir, Epzicom, and Trizivir to keep HIV-infected individuals from developing full-blown AIDS. 3TC can also be used to treat HBV infections.

They brought to market FTC (emtricitabine), an acronym for its complex chemical name that is marketed under the brand Emtriva – the "Em" stands for Emory and the "tri" for Triangle Pharmaceuticals, a company founded by Schinazi and later bought by Gilead Sciences in order to acquire the FTC needed for the cocktail called Truvada. Truvada is a pill that combines FTC with tenofovir-DF to improve and extend the lives of HIV-infected people throughout the world. The two drugs can be used with other anti-retrovirals as a one-capsule, once-daily medicine for individuals infected with HIV. Other drugs still in clinical trials are targeted to HIV persons who have developed resistance to common anti-retrovirals.

The process has not been easy. Along the way, there have been numerous battles over ownership and discovery issues. Others have tried to stake their claim to the compounds, insisting both in print and in court proceedings that they were the true inventors. As Schinazi and his team know all too well, the world of research and drug development is not for the timid, who are unwilling to stand up and fight for their ideas.

Raymond Schinazi's success at this has come in large part because he is not your stereotypical academic researcher. It's true he does his work within the confines of a university environment, but he is clearly all business. Over the past decade, he has founded six companies to develop a variety of drugs to fight HIV and hepatitis.

That entrepreneurial spirit helps explain how he has managed to build an academic research lab that rivals, if not exceeds, anything to be found in the world of for-profit research. Much of his success has been built upon the hard work of making new discoveries, and then being the first to file patents to protect those discoveries.

"There is no conflict between academic research and protecting ideas," says Schinazi. "If faculty members are well-educated, they should file the patent first so it is disclosed to the university. Once they file, they can talk about it. I have filed patents in one day and the next day I talked about it."

The value of knowing the ins and outs of patent protection were vividly illustrated in the record-setting royalty payment to Emory for Emtriva – the largest lump sum payment for intellectual property to any American university. The academic institution sold a 65 percent share to Gilead Sciences, a California company that now owns the drug, and a 35 percent share to Royalty Pharma, a New York company that specializes in acquiring future pharmaceutical royalties from both academia and industry.

Before the check was ever written, however, the university and its chief researcher were embroiled in a lengthy legal battle over just who owned the drug, and how it could be used. It was a battle that was almost lost – if not for Schinazi's determination and willingness to put his own resources on the line to protect it.

"I'm stubborn and persistent," he explains. "I believed in what I had and we persevered. That's what it's all about."

Some 15 years ago, attorneys filed a patent application for the compounds. This was a case where timing was critical and the passage of a week meant the difference between nothing and vast riches.

A company called BioChem Pharma had earlier filed an application for a similar family of compounds, but omitted the one in FTC, which has fluorine. Realizing their mistake, the firm filed yet another application for a similar compound containing the chemical, but not until seven days after Schinazi and his colleagues had filed the original FTC patent. Schinazi observed "they probably left FTC out on purpose since they thought it would be toxic."

History proved them wrong, however, as FTC is one of the safest anti-retrovirals approved by the U.S. Food and Drug Administration.

Another large pharmaceutical company, Burroughs Wellcome, had acquired the use of FTC and decided to file its own patent application for use of the drug for hepatitis. Emory had already specified that FTC could be used for that disease, making the move a matter of patent infringement.

To make things even more complicated, the other HIV-fighting compound, 3TC, became embroiled in a dispute when GlaxoSmithKline started marketing a rival drug using an identical formulation.

Emory attorneys sued, and a series of fierce legal battles began. GlaxoSmithKline countersued and even named Schinazi personally in the suit, which claimed that he illegally obtained secret information that was used to develop 3TC. The suit was subsequently dropped when their scare tactic proved unsuccessful.

After several years of litigation, the warring parties finally decided to mediate and then settle the dispute. That led to the massive payout for the compounds and millions of dollars for Schinazi, his co-inventors, and the university. With these funds, they could now pursue their ongoing research.

While the timing of the patents stood up in court, the case was by no means assured. At one point, Emory's Board of Trustees didn't want to spend any more money on the court fight and was poised to give up. But Schinazi and Liotta allowed the university to use more than $5 million from royalties received from other technologies they had invented to continue the fight. This money was eventually paid back to them after the school's big payday came through.

The path has been a long and sometimes frustrating one. Schinazi has some experience with not wanting to give up the fight. He is from an Italian-Jewish family who had lived in Egypt for generations, but lost everything they owned when Gamal Abdel Nasser came to power and began confiscating private property and possessions. In the beginning, Schinazi recalls that Emory was less than enthusiastic about spending a few thousand dollars to file a patent for the compound he and his team had developed.

"The university was totally resistant about filing at the time," says Schinazi. "Back in the 1990s, they wanted to find a licensee before they would file a patent. They would not expend the money unless they already had a buyer lined up."

Schinazi kept pushing, however, and finally convinced the recalcitrant academic officials to file. In fact, he still has a memo he received from a senior Emory official with the words "Raymond, stop harassing me about filing the patent!" in bold, italic letters.

"I think perhaps my stubbornness is something genetic," he now says with a laugh. "My father was stubborn. My daughter is stubborn. If we believe in something, we just persevere and keep going and defend what is ours. When people say I am difficult, it is because all I want to do is protect what is mine."

Such was the case with the drugs that he believed held the promise to not just help those afflicted with HIV, but that might also just be able to break the back of an illness whose diagnosis was once nothing short of a death sentence.

The old regime is long gone, of course, and no one remembers just how close the university came to losing the millions of dollars that have made their way into its bank account.

"Universities didn't care about entrepreneurship and patents in those days," Schinazi recalls. "They've learned a lot from this experience over the years."

Indeed, Schinazi has become one of the leading advocates of suggesting just how much a university can contribute – not just to research, but also by making their discoveries into viable, salable products that benefit people around the world. He also had the vision to see the value of combining drugs in the fight against AIDS.

"I understood that combination was the name of the game in those years," he recounts. "It's what you combine it with that's important, that's going to make the difference." Schinazi is a leading expert on antiviral combination chemotherapy and received the first-ever NIH grant given on the topic in 1983. He also published the definitive review on the subject in 1990.

Schinazi got an early start on his research career, publishing his very first paper when just 22. Since then, he has authored more than 400 publications and has won more than 70 U.S. patents.

Most of that work has sprung from the VA Medical Center Laboratory of Biochemical Pharmacology he runs on the Emory campus. It is here in the VA's Research Center on AIDS and HIV that nearly a thousand mostly African-American men and women with the disease are treated, and are enjoying a longer and more symptom-free life thanks largely to the drugs created by Schinazi's team.

Building this research lab, which he maintains is more advanced than anything in private industry, has clearly been a good investment. He has also been able to achieve a high degree of independence, thanks to his unusual success in winning NIH grants coupled with one basic realization.

"I was learning from my boss and mentor, and then I finally saw that I was doing all the work for him, getting the big grants for him," says Schinazi. "He was getting most of the credit for a lot of the work I did. So in 1998, I decided that I had to become independent and set up my own lab at the Atlanta VA."

Many researchers can – and do – remain content in the shadow of others, but not a man with a determined and entrepreneurial mind like Schinazi's. Even though at the time he was making a mere $22,000 a year, even with a Ph.D. and eight years of postdoctoral experience, he decided that he would never again labor under anyone else's shadow. Whatever it took, he would make his own path and follow his own goals. Making money was never his primary goal, but he knew that he could support himself with enough research grants and a clear dedication to his work.

"Probably the most important thing about being successful is to have collaborators who are reliable," Schinazi says. "When they say they're going to do something, they deliver – and you deliver for them as well. And you're going to have something that nobody else has, an asset or a technology that you can do and nobody else can do as well as you can. If you have that, you'll be successful, because everybody will want that technology or that know-how that you developed."

Schinazi's independence is also reflected in the way he runs and staffs his highly productive lab. His dedicated team is led by a man who used to do all the bench work himself, yet still keeps his hand in the ongoing research.

"I've taught them everything I know," says Schinazi, "because that's a part of being a professor at the university. You teach them and you make them responsible and you delegate so you can spend more time educating, thinking, and writing papers."

Schinazi is careful to ensure that he doesn't take credit for everything that passes through the lab. He serves as a mentor and collaborator who has managed the production of a considerable volume of new research announcements.

"The most important thing is to be unselfish, and work with trusted collaborators," he says.

His work with Liotta has always been a 50/50 arrangement, sealed with nothing more than a handshake. That partnership has often been called the Dream Team of research, owing to its success in producing the current slate of powerful new drugs. Mixing Schinazi's ideas with Liotta's grasp of mechanistic organic chemistry has clearly been a winning combination.

"Even to this day, I don't need to formalize anything with him," says Schinazi . "We're partners, and his success is linked to my success and vice versa. I could learn his skills. I could be greedy and go for 100 percent, but what's the point when the university has received $540 million? You've got enough credit for everybody."

Fortunately, Schinazi's success has not made him complacent. While he admits that experience and all the knowledge of science, business, and patents he has acquired has made it easier to get things done, he is still hungry to accomplish more.

"When you're 55 you realize that you're in the second phase of your life and you've got to make everything count," he says. "You're going to spend your time on things that are going to yield important advances, not just for yourself, but for humanity. You want to make sure that what you invent is going to make a difference."

Chapter 16

SCOTT BODEN
ACADEMIC ENTREPRENEUR

Dr. Scott Boden is the first to admit that he wears many hats and has taken on a wide variety of roles since he entered the practice of medicine. As a nationally recognized spine surgeon, researcher, author, and the director of the Emory Orthopaedics & Spine Center in Atlanta, he is a man for all seasons.

While he has demonstrated that it is possible to be both an outstanding clinician and a noted researcher, Boden has also proven that you can be an entrepreneur within an academic environment as well. In fact, he has built the department into a highly successful "one-stop shop" for patients with spinal disorders. His manifested vision was to bring all aspects of diagnosis, treatment, and rehabilitation together in one 95,000-square-foot location that integrates all services into one.

Much of his success has come because Boden is willing to take risks in order to achieve his goals. For example, just getting the Spine Center off the ground was far from a sure thing and required a journey that often presented the risk of failure.

Boden recalls that with the center's new building well under construction, he did a hard hat walk-through to see how things were coming along with the build-out of the five-story facility in a suburban office park. Walking through the bare hallways still covered with construction dust, he made his way up to the fifth-floor surgery area, which was the last to be completed.

"I was up there and it was before they had put up all the walls," says Boden. "So I could look from one end of the building to the other, and for the very first time in the project I actually thought, 'Boy, this is a big thing to bite off.'"

In fact, it was a huge space, and he knew that the center certainly wasn't going to be able to put it all into use right away. Although he had been director of the center's predecessor, the Emory Spine Center, this was truly going to be a quantum leap beyond what had existed before as a relatively small 20,000-square-foot department within the Emory Healthcare System.

"We knew [the surgery center] could bring down the whole thing," Boden admits. "If a couple of key doctors left before we made it here, as the transitions were getting tough, it would create a domino effect."

Boden also knew that the potential success of the operation was worth the risk. It could fail immediately, or it could become one of the Southeast's premier medical facilities. He was willing to bet he could bring it off, and he did. Today, the center is a nationally recognized leader in spinal care and a highly successful enterprise for Emory.

"The Spine Center had been going pretty well since '94 when we set it up, but the economic model in the '90s wasn't going to work in this next decade," says Boden . "We were on a curve that was going to cross and it was going to start to be hard to keep people and maintain the energy we picked up," he says of the decision to build the new facility.

Boden could see the trends and see that a combination clinical and research operation of this nature could only be supported by a large increase in patient visits and procedures performed.

"We pretty much made an awfully big move on sound logic, yet it was still a huge risk," he admits.

The successful operation of the center is just one aspect of this physician's multifaceted career, whose life has been characterized by an ongoing quest for balance and the benefits of knowledge and experience that can be drawn from work in different fields of endeavor. But maintaining that balance isn't easy.

With so many demands on his attention, Boden has become a master of time management. Take, for example, the down hours that plague any business traveler. While sitting in the airport, Boden can be found doing peer reviews of articles for scholarly journals. On a more complex level, when he's in the office, he's developed a keen sense for when to get involved in a situation and when to simply let someone else handle it.

While demanding on both a personal and intellectual level, he also believes that his multiple roles have provided extensive cross benefits because of the knowledge and skills he is able to draw from each widely divergent profession.

He's a better clinician because he also does research. In the course of his work, Boden is able to think about problems and consider the why of each situation. He can evaluate how each procedure can be done better rather than just doing it.

"I think I'm also a better researcher, because as a surgeon I think in a somewhat practical sense, and as a clinician I have the ability to triage lots of different things and try to cull out what are the most important aspects," he explains. "That's something that a full-time scientist doesn't necessarily have to do."

That commitment to efficiency and end results has been a hallmark of Boden's career.

"I try to have a fairly directed and translational approach to research and inventions and ideas," he observes. "So, I'm not going to invent something and find a use for it. I work better in a situation where, here's a problem … and we need a solution, and what's the best solution and how does it fit into a system of solutions?"

He believes that one of his greatest strengths is visualizing problems, situations, and options without the necessity for physically observing them or having to sketch them out in abstract writing.

"I can build complex systems and I can map out in my head an algorithm in a couple of seconds," he says.

For Boden, his greatest inspirations come in the heat of the moment as he converses with others and debates the problem at hand.

"I can say, 'Okay, here's the problem, here's the data, here's the pattern," he says. "We just start talking, standing up, walking around. ... Actually, it's not the people, it's getting me just focusing on something and talking. What happens is, I'm talking as I'm thinking."

His ability to conceptualize problems and see patterns and relationships has led to producing breakthroughs that have stymied others.

"I don't have a photographic memory," he says. "I can't remember where I put something if it's missing. But I can go through the logic string and end up finding it because my brain is wired a certain way. It gets to the same spot."

Whether it's performing a surgical procedure, handling an administrative situation, organizing a research project, or teaching, Boden's driving motivation is to "do it better the next time than the last time no matter how many times I've done it."

A large part of Boden's confidence in himself and his team stems from his philosophy about making mistakes. If he makes the best decision possible using the data available at the time, then the results – even if less than optimum – can't really be considered a mistake.

His interest in the human spine came when he realized that the field represented an unprecedented research opportunity. He realized that bone was the only organ in the body that could actually regenerate itself in a form identical to the original and without the scars produced when skin heals.

"In the 1980s, when I was making career choices, it was coming into an era where there were a lot of spine fusions being done, getting bones to grow together in the spine to either stop them from moving too much or curving or repairing traumatic spines or bypassing degenerative segments," he recalls.

Unfortunately, spine fusion had a relatively low success rate of only about 50 to 60 percent. In addition, while the process often relieved pain, it was a highly traumatic process for the patient that included removing bone from some other part of the body. That additional surgery could cause infection and chronic pain. He realized there was a great opportunity to benefit both patients and the profession by improving and/or optimizing the process.

"The spine is a really tough environment to grow bone," says Boden. "When you fracture a leg bone, 98 percent of the time it heals on its own. So I saw it as a challenge, and I also saw it as an area where many people in the field were focusing on screws and rods and mechanical solutions to get the spine to heal and pretty much ignoring biology because it wasn't really a manly, orthopedic thing to take biology."

He saw the clinical need, and a path to make research have a direct impact on those clinical needs. This path is best illustrated by a new approach to repairing spines.

That unique perspective was the primary motivator behind the development of a genetically engineered alternative to bone morphogenetic protein (BMP). This family of very small proteins is produced by the body naturally and deposits in the bone. When the bone breaks, these signaling proteins are activated and help repair the bone by telling the body to send in the right cells to become bone cells.

While these proteins occur in very small amounts in the bone, Boden's team was able to develop a method for a genetically engineered form of BMP for delivery to a site where bone creation was needed.

"It's about isolating the problem, focusing on it, creating a model system that gives you a distinct advantage to ask the question in a way that's a little different than maybe everybody's been asking it," Boden explains. "We didn't have anything that thousands of labs didn't have in terms of the cells we used, the cultures we used. It's not like we discovered something that allowed us to discover something. We did it with the same tools that everyone else did, but we had a different perspective, because we didn't have a full-time researcher thinking about it."

As a researcher and an administrator, Boden has always exceeded both expectations and sometimes, he says, common sense. His affinity for calculated risk-taking goes all the way back to his high school days.

His father was in the wholesale food business in New York City. It was an occupation that the younger Boden wanted to enter, but his father insisted that he find something with both greater job security and shorter hours.

"It was a tough business," he recalls. "You'd get up at 3:30 in the morning, load up trucks, and then sit in the office, take orders, and [do] accounts receivable. [My father] had maybe 75 employees, but he worked harder than anybody I knew at the time."

The younger Boden began learning the business during vacations and holidays, working in the warehouse or the office taking orders. He quickly saw that one of the frustrating aspects of the business was that he worked in downtown Manhattan in what was basically an apartment building that was converted into a warehouse. With no loading platforms, workmen had to pull every box out of the trucks to the street where they were placed on rollers to be pushed into the warehouse and then back out again for distribution. Since the operation wasn't computerized, more than 2,000 accounts with individual pricing on hundreds of items were kept in a thick loose-leaf notebook.

"So I said, you've got to computerize this thing," he recalls. "My senior year of high school, I helped design the specs for a system and looked at some outside consultants and basically convinced my father to computerize his whole $25 million business."

While going to a computerized system offered many advantages, Boden also found that a number of businesses in the same industry had gone out of business by installing computer systems that couldn't do the job. It was 1981, and in those days the powerful desktop PC equipped with sophisticated software didn't exist. The IBM mini computer was the size of a four-drawer file cabinet. It was equipped with a bulky 10 megabyte disk inserted into one of the machine's slots. It was the pinnacle of modern technology at the time. In addition, there was no software program in existence that could handle warehouse distribution for the food service industry. Boden decided that he would set out to write a program himself.

"I don't know if I fully realized what a big risk it was, but for whatever reason, I convinced my father to trust me," says Boden.

Boden's goal was to create a system that wouldn't force them to change the way the business operated to match a computer system, but instead one that would help them to standardize their operations. In those days computers were new and many companies went out of business trying to accommodate the limitations of these relatively unsophisticated machines.

Boden soon discovered, however, that the consultants he had originally hired to write the program weren't making much progress and probably wouldn't be able to meet the deadline for converting the warehouse operation.

"So I told the guys to let me start typing this in for you," he recalls. "Since I had written the specs for what the program was supposed to do, within about 12 hours of typing, I basically knew how to program in COBOL [an early computer language], so I started writing it."

Within two weeks, all the code was written in time to meet the self-imposed July Fourth weekend deadline, and the business converted all of its accounts receivables and payables, its inventory, and its warehouse, truck router, and order entry to the new computer system.

"My father could have been out of business, but it turned out to be the best thing, because within a year, he moved to New Jersey, got a real warehouse, and got really good people working for him," says Boden.

While he doesn't write computer programs anymore, Boden still has the same can-do attitude and problem-solving approach to the business of medicine. While he encourages risk-taking, he also realizes that with risk must also come a tolerance for making mistakes as well.

"I think ideally you want to have a situation where hopefully you've got more wins than losses," he adds. "And if you do that, then I don't think it's very hard to tolerate some failures and, if anything, you can use them to motivate people to do things better. I'm definitely somebody [who is] motivated by success, but I think some of my greatest motivations come from failures or disappointments."

In addition to encouraging openness and creativity in his staff, Boden sees one of his greatest strengths in serving as an interface for his physicians to the larger corporate structure, while also communicating the corporate message back to them in a way that they understand and still remain positive and motivated.

He makes sure that he is available to staff – to hear both new ideas and complaints as well. Neither, he believes, should have to wait. If he can't be reached in person, he is in constant touch by e-mail, and if he can't produce a complete response, he gives them "at least a word that I'm thinking about it."

"I have a policy that I don't care how stupid it is, if you're thinking of it now, I want you to ask it to me now and not worry about inconveniencing me," he says.

On a more personal level, Boden also sees his varied professional career as a means of keeping fresh and renewed. For him, the key to happiness and self-renewal has been balance and diversity.

"Essentially, what I figure is that there's only so many back-pain patients I can see in my lifetime before I reach my saturation," he says. "On the other hand, if I do about half or 40 percent at the rate of the other people, then I'm probably never going to get too frustrated with that in any given week, because it's just part of the week."

More than anything else, he realizes that many people are doers and just trudge through every day in medicine, but it's essential to align yourself with those who can do more.

"I try and find young medical students or young residents, and try and find that one to five percent of people who will play that role, because we– society– need people who are capable of thinking as opposed to just doing. It's from that combination that much of what becomes innovation flows."

Chapter 17

RAINER STORB
IDEAS FOR A CURE

In the soft light of dawn, Dr. Rainer Storb slips out the door of his house to the dock still enshrouded in fog. Slipping into a sleek single scull racer, he dips the oars smoothly into the chilly water, and the craft glides silently out onto Lake Washington. His morning commute has begun.

For the 70-year-old German-born physician, oncologist, and pioneer in hematopoietic cell transplantation (HCT) research, the scull will carry him across the lake from his Madison Park home to the Seattle campus of the Fred Hutchinson Cancer Research Center. Over the past three decades, he has made this five-mile journey countless times in order to join a team of researchers who are developing some of the most important advances in the treatment of modern society's most dread diseases.

During the 40-minute trip each morning, the steady rhythm of the oars prepares his mind and relaxes his body for the long hours of work that are to follow.

With lights mounted on the bow and stern, he can be seen by the other traffic on the water, but like any commuter, he must be on the lookout for boats that may not be looking for him. A lumbering barge poses the same dangers to life and limb as an 18-wheeler barreling down the interstate. Flipping can be especially dangerous in these icy waters, but he's mastered the art of righting the boat and climbing aboard in less than a minute.

"[The lake] is where I settle down and my mind roams, and it's a very pleasant way to get some ideas," says Storb. "I find that it's a very good balance to mental activity during the day, so I don't have a need for even going on vacation, given that I feel that I'm on vacation as I cross the street to go to the boathouse."

Clearly, Storb loves his work, and out of that devotion he has built a highly successful and extensively recognized research career.

Storb is one of the original founding members of the Fred Hutchinson Cancer Research Center (fondly known as the Hutch), an independent, nonprofit biomedical research institution. It is one of just 39 National Cancer Institute-designated comprehensive cancer centers nationwide.

Storb plunged into this field after coming to the U.S. following a Paris-based residency in basic research. He moved to Seattle to work with Dr. E. Donnall Thomas, winner of the 1990 Nobel Prize for completing the first successful bone marrow transplant, which he achieved by administering a drug that prevented graft-versus-host disease. This work led to overcoming one of the thorniest problems of transplantation, the tendency of implanted tissue to be attacked and rejected by the body into which it is transferred.

Storb knew that Thomas had worked for decades on an innovative treatment for cancers of the blood. In the 1950s, his team showed that dogs could be protected against lethal doses of irradiation by intravenous injection of bone marrow cells. Thomas believed this had potential clinical applications for the treatment of leukemia in humans, and he set out to prove it. Through painstaking laboratory and clinical research, Thomas improved the technique.

In 1963, Storb came to Seattle to work, and in 1968, he become the first director of the Division of Oncology at the University of Washington. U of W and other local institutions provided space for his radical yet promising transplant research. During the next few years, researchers like Storb came from all over the world to work with Thomas on refining the techniques for curing cancer by transplanting human bone marrow after lethal doses of chemotherapy and radiation.

After nearly a decade of work, Thomas and other researchers, including Storb, helped found the Hutch as an independent research institution in 1972.

Throughout those years, Storb was at the center of some of medicine's most exciting breakthroughs. They have included both small victories and large triumphs.

One of the great breakthroughs came in 1969 when, after experimenting for several years on transplantation in animals, "we finally dared apply the protocol that we had developed to a human patient," says Storb. "That is sort of an unforgettable moment, when you can see that the principles you had worked on for so long did apply to the treatment of humans."

Now head of the Transplantation Biology Program at the Hutch, as well as Professor of Oncology at the University of Washington, Boden has worked hard to expand on the work of his mentor. It was here that he developed – in the face of considerable opposition and skepticism – a procedure known as the mini-transplant, which has extended the lifesaving benefits of transplant technology to older patients.

The term "mini-transplant" is something of a misnomer, though, because the only thing small about the treatment is that it uses lower – and less toxic – dosages of chemotherapy and radiation than those given to patients who undergo a standard stem cell transplant. Essentially, it shifts the burden of killing tumor cells to the donor cells.

The technique developed as an alternative to the more conventional procedure that used stem cells as a so-called rescue technique. During that particular process, a patient is exposed to such strong doses that they would normally die as a result.

Only a stem cell transplant from a healthy donor "rescues" them from this fate. Typically, the procedure is unsuitable for the elderly or frail.

Researchers had long known that cancer cells often remain in the body following high-dose chemotherapy and stem cell transplantation. White blood cells from the donor play a critical role in destroying these cancerous cells in many forms of leukemia and multiple myeloma. That led Storb and others to explore the possibility that donor white blood cells could be put to even greater use in fighting these diseases.

Storb speculated that perhaps low doses of radiation and combination chemotherapy could be used to kill only a small number of the cancer cells prior to transplantation. Then the donor cells could be engrafted and allowed to fight the disease by themselves.

Storb's team had been conducting extensive research on animals, when finally, in December 1997, they performed the first procedure on a human patient.

"That was so exciting," says Storb, "because the patient did exactly what we had anticipated, and we can now do these difficult transplants in the outpatient department."

Following the success of the initial procedure, the number of these mini-transplants has grown into the thousands. Yet patients are still at risk for serious and sometimes fatal side effects, such as graft-versus-host disease. But Storb replaced the conventional intense conditioning regimens with optimal post-grafting immunosuppression aimed at controlling both serious graft-versus-host disease and host-versus-graft reactions. His work in this area made Storb one of the nation's foremost experts on this particular condition.

Discoveries such as these keep this researcher moving forward, always seeking new areas to apply principles already learned in other areas.

Explains Storb: "The real thrill comes in finding something that really opens the door to new and interesting approaches – something that really helps the patient population you originally targeted, like the leukemias, lymphomas, and myelomas, but which also all of a sudden opens up the field to eventually help other patients."

These breakthroughs have revolutionized the treatment of some of the most dreaded forms of cancer, and each one has sprung from a mind dedicated to finding answers to seemingly intractable problems. Finding these solutions has always come at the end of hard and patient work.

"I don't think we've ever had a 'Eureka!' moment – maybe small ones, but most of it has been small steps," Storb says of the creative process that leads to discovery.

So, what is Storb's ideal environment for being creative? In a field that demands both great innovation and precise application, the starting point is often something akin to "Chaos, probably," he says.

"We try to keep the environment, on the one hand, structured and disciplined," Storb adds. "On the other hand, when we discuss things, we allow the wildest ideas to surface. We don't really approve them right off the bat, so there is a fair amount of openness and flexibility and willingness to listen to the weirdest things."

Storb understands that the best ideas often arise out of wide-open brainstorming sessions in which no idea is considered too far-out or too unworkable. It is out of these sometimes flights of fancy that the final disciplined protocols are formed as experimentation gets underway.

"That discipline, in turn, comes in when you apply this to human patients," he explains. "They are, of course, the only way to bring something in that is very promising in improving a patient's life and whatever you have written – your protocol – you adhere to almost slavishly. So it's this bouncing back and forth between discipline and almost total chaos that probably allows for creativity."

Brainstorming is, in fact, a hallmark of the various clinical research meetings over which Storb presides. To keep the sessions informal, he even shies away from PowerPoint presentations, but rather recommends that his people use their own words, perhaps scribbling out notes or a formula on the blackboard at the front of the meeting room.

"As soon as you put something onto slides, things become formal," he explains.

As these discussions evolve, Storb often finds himself in the role of intellectual traffic cop. Perhaps there's a point that should be obvious to everyone, but it's being overlooked.

"Then, after about 20 minutes of discussion, you step in and say, 'Listen, have you thought of this?'" he says.

Like other creative thinkers, Storb long ago recognized the intrinsic value of taking risks and being willing to make mistakes. It is out of these so-called errors that genuine insight comes, setting the stage for true breakthroughs.

"My former mentor [Dr. Thomas] gave us a great deal of liberty at least as far as the preclinical research is concerned," says Storb. "On the clinical side, it's a different story, because there you come up with an absolutely formalized research protocol. Once that is in place, there is actually an attempt made at absolute adherence to that protocol."

Yet the path to that final protocol was often fraught with "chaos" as the researchers tried to tap into their innermost creative powers. In addition, the path to discovery came when they learned more from their mistakes than from a successful experiment.

"I find probably 85 percent of the time my preconceived hypotheses are wrong," Storb admits. "The experiment comes out differently, but it eventually leads you into new directions."

The path of discovery never moves along a linear path. Instead, ideas and inspiration come from unexpected directions. New ideas and approaches arise from being forced to think about what went wrong, and those moments can lead you in a different direction.

Over the years, Storb has moved further away from the research bench and now finds himself more in the position of a mentor. When new ideas come to him, he doesn't conduct experiments himself, but instead passes them on to a younger researcher. Yet he hasn't divorced himself entirely from that kind of work. He still does his weekend duties in the animal labs, which he shares with postdocs and staff scientists. He also devotes two and a half months each year doing hard clinical service on the busy marrow and blood stem cell transplantation services.

"It keeps me connected with the translation of my laboratory efforts into clinical practice," Storb says.

"I have discussions with the postdocs and the younger faculty, and I still formulate ideas, except that I hand them off in the end, and then I review the data with them," he explains. "Some of them really aren't in a position to then go onto the next experiment, so I'm attempting to help them accomplish that, and to think – which is something that a lot of people don't do. Then I help them with writing up their summations."

Directing 125 researchers now demands much of his time. Today, at the age of 70, he has evolved into the role of a coach and a manager, although he doesn't like the title of administrator. In fact, he says he has managed to avoid the budgeting and management duties that consume the time of so many research directors.

He also freely admits that he avoids meetings that have nothing to do with research or finding the solutions to problems. He leaves the bureaucratic sessions to others. He realizes that he has greater contributions to make by helping his researchers find solutions, overcome problems, and benefit from the insights of his decades spent pursuing elusive answers.

Being a researcher at the Hutch is a demanding job that isn't for the complacent or those whose data can't stand up to the intense intellectual scrutiny that is an everyday practice there. Those who can't cut it don't last long, and neither do those who are unable to secure grants to support their work. The center doesn't provide salaries, and all researchers – including faculty –must raise their own support.

"It puts the better guys in a position of staying, while the guys who can't write grants and don't have ideas have to leave," says Storb. "If you gain a grant, you gain the confidence that you're one of the people who can finance themselves. So there's a selection process on several fronts."

At the end of a long day, Storb finally leaves the Hutch. By now the sun has set into the Pacific and he makes his way in the darkness back to the dock and his waiting scull. Once more he slips back into the water for the journey home. Another day has ended, and soon another will begin on the long journey of discovery.

Chapter 18

JOSEPH SODROSKI
MANAGER OF DISCOVERY

Read any textbook on HIV research and you will find the work and discoveries of Joseph Sodroski.

As director of the Center for AIDS Research at the Dana-Farber Cancer Institute, Beth Israel Deaconess Medical Center, and Children's Hospital in Boston, he made his first major impact with the discovery of the key HIV regulatory proteins Tat and Rev. With the discovery that these critical molecular signals regulate HIV replication, researchers were given a starting point for all future inquiry in the field.

As governments and doctors have struggled to deal with the worldwide AIDS epidemic, this authority on the molecular biology of retroviruses has made many of the most important findings about how HIV infects cells and causes disease. His work has given both tools and direction to other researchers in the fight against one of the modern world's most deadly and stubborn diseases.

While his path of discovery has led to important new knowledge, it is illustrative of the fact that breakthroughs don't come easily. Results were achieved through diligent work coupled with the foresight to take risks even when there was no clear promise that positive results awaited. Thanks to his innovation in the field, the cure for AIDS is closer than most ever imagined it would be.

"I started by having an interest in cancer and how cells become transformed through the study of viruses – retroviruses in particular," Sodroski says of his entry into the field. "My whole interest in viruses was initially a pathway to understanding pathogenesis. My medical training has always led me to have an interest in how disease occurs, and so viruses were primarily tools to try to understand that pathological process."

In the process of studying these cancer-causing retroviruses, Sodroski and his team began to look at the regulation of those viruses. They soon found that some of the behavior of the cancer-causing viruses could also apply to some of the new viruses that were then being discovered – particularly the immunodeficiency viruses linked to AIDS.

"Ultimately, we began to spend more of our time looking at immunodeficiency viruses because of the major impact they were having on global health," he relates. "Ultimately, most of our work was centered there."

Sodroski admits that his journey into this particular area of research was somewhat circuitous, but underlying it all was a consistent interest in how diseases develop. What he most wanted to understand was the molecular basis for disease.

To follow the sometimes elusive trail of knowledge, Sodroski set rigorous standards for both himself and his researchers.

"You have to learn to approach things objectively," he explains. "It's important to be rigorous and to make sure when you reach conclusions that they're absolutely supported by the data. Then you have to be able to open yourself up to the possibilities and do that without too much bias. You have to ask, 'What are the possible reasons the data could be the way they are?'"

Sodroski believes this is where creativity must manifest itself. The researcher must be able to think of all the possible ways to explain the observations they make and then devise the right means of testing the various possibilities.

"There is also an element of intuition, which is perhaps the most difficult thing to teach people," says Sodroski. "That really comes down to developing some insight into what might be the right answer, so that of the many possibilities that you come up with for explaining the observations, your intuition allows you to focus on a few of those that are most likely and most consistent with your view of nature."

This requires intense preparation by developing a sense of how nature works and how to conduct research effectively. It is perhaps the most important key to ultimately being successful and learning to get to the right answer as quickly as possible.

That emphasis on preparation and creativity has yielded substantial results. Sodroski's laboratory conducted extensive research on the molecular interactions required for HIV to enter human cells. His team was the first to identify the CCR5 co-receptor on target cells, a discovery that changed the way researchers thought about HIV infection. His studies of the major HIV surface proteins – gp120 and gp41 – revealed key aspects of how the virus attaches to cells and how the immune system might recognize the virus.

In addition to investigating the molecular underpinnings of HIV infection, Sodroski helped develop an animal model of the disease. Using the related simian immunodeficiency virus (SIV), he oversaw development of a hybrid organism called SHIV that combined the external components of the human virus with SIV's internal genes and proteins. The resulting virus infects monkeys and has allowed researchers to study HIV-directed pathogenesis and vaccines in animals.

Through continuing animal research, Sodroski and his researchers found that when HIV-1 enters monkey cells, it is stopped by a protein that prevents it from replicating by creating a barrier to its spread into animals.

The finding suggested that a monkey molecule named TRIM5-alpha, which is known to exist in some humans, might be exploited for prevention and therapy.

The researchers believed that it might very well be part of a previously unknown aspect of the immune system that fights viruses and prevents them from harming cells.

Human cells contain a similar TRIM5-alpha protein, but it is less effective than the monkey version in blocking HIV-1 infection. It's possible that the potency of TRIM5-alpha varies among humans due to genetic differences. That theory helps explain why some patients infected with HIV quickly develop AIDS, while others don't even decades after initial infection.

TRIM5-alpha proteins reside in "cytoplasmic bodies" inside HIV-1 target cells. Sodroski was able to present a convincing case for how the virus uncoats and converts its genetic material, RNA, into DNA for replication once it has pierced the cell membrane. In a key step in the process, the inner core of the virus sheds its capsid – a protective coating that encloses its genetic material and replication enzymes – before undergoing reverse transcription.

He and his team showed that TRIM5-alpha recognizes specific viral capsids and disrupts proper uncoating of the capsid. By blocking this step, TRIM5-alpha renders the virus unable to reach the genetic machinery in the host cell's nucleus, and the infection fails.

Researchers might even be able to find ways to increase the effectiveness of the human TRIM5-alpha molecule, or perhaps even use the more potent monkey version as a potential therapy.

During his long career in medical research, Sodroski has changed roles as he has evolved into a manager of a large laboratory and has gotten away from the day-to-day demands of hard-core research.

"I think initially one spends a lot of time learning how nature operates at a firsthand level, so you're not only setting up the experiments and the assays and contributing to their design, but you're making the observations directly," Sodroski says of his early career. "That requires a lot of very careful attention to detail. It requires technical and manual dexterity. It requires good observational skills and concentration on the task at hand, and I think as time goes on, you also develop skills in interpreting the data and thinking about the possibilities and again developing all these creative abilities as well as intuitive abilities."

As he matured, however, he became more removed from the day-to-day experimentation of the laboratory. The manual and technical skills Sodroski worked so hard to develop have become less important as he now leaves the observations to other people and trusts their powers of observation to convey the data to him rather than seeking it out firsthand.

"Increasingly, we need to acquire and develop managerial skills so that we can coordinate the activities of many different individuals, each of whom is looking at specific aspects of the larger question," he explains. "So coordinating those activities and organizing them becomes more important."

These days, putting those observations and conclusions before various audiences, including other scientists, government officials, the media, and the general public, is a much bigger part of his job.

"I've had to learn how to publicize the results and make them understandable to the general scientific reader, as well as the specialists in the field," he says. "Part of that comes along with the need to sell and market your results to study sections and for peer review for funding and things like that. So learning how to make your results interpretable to people and helping them to see how the results and conclusions and advances fit into a larger picture is vital."

Of course, no lab can keep running for long without funding, and Sodroski has developed a reputation as one of the nation's most successful winners of NIH research grants. While developing grant proposals and doing all the time-consuming and detail-oriented work needed to make a convincing case to a study section is essential, it isn't necessarily how he wants to spend most of his time.

"There's a certain necessary use of my time, which means time devoted to obtaining funding and writing grants," he admits. "It's necessary, because we need funding, and to a large extent the entire operation is dependent upon me acquiring that funding. But I'm not sure it's the best use of my time."

Yet Sodroski often asks himself whether these efforts really allow him to do the things he most wants to do with his research work – address critical scientific problems and make progress in finding the answers to key questions about how these elements of nature work. His conclusion is "only a little bit."

"Sometimes grant writing can help you shape your ideas and hone them down a little," he says, "but overall, it really is an exercise in obtaining funding. That's its main purpose and that's why we do it. If there wasn't a need for funding, I don't think we would benefit very much from sitting down and writing detailed grants on what we might do in the next five years."

Thanks in large part to his work, Sodroski's Harvard home base has become part of the newly formed Center for HIV/AIDS Vaccine Immunology (CHAVI), a consortium of universities and academic medical centers established by the National Institute of Allergy and Infectious Diseases (NIAD). The center's goal is to solve major problems in HIV vaccine development and design.

CHAVI will receive more than $300 million in the next seven years in order to address major obstacles to HIV vaccine development and to design, develop, and test novel HIV vaccine candidates. The award transforms HIV research in the United States into a cooperative and collaborative system.

Sodroski will himself fill one of the four senior scientific leadership positions and will be responsible for the center's overall scientific work. These four senior leaders will direct CHAVI research in their own labs and form research partnerships between CHAVI and other academic and industrial labs around the world.

Sodroski knows, though, that these exercises are all part of the drive for knowledge, not just facts for their own sake. He knows that his work is making a difference in finding a cure for a terrible disease that afflicts millions of people across the planet.

Chapter 19

JOANN MANSON
CHAMPIONING WOMEN'S HEALTH

Early in her medical career, JoAnn Manson grew frustrated with trying to fight the end results of chronic diseases that she saw among so many of her patients. She decided that the real answer lay not in trying to fix what was already broken, but instead in giving patients the tools to stay healthy and save their own lives.

Since then, Manson has become one of the nation's foremost champions of preventive medicine, as well as a researcher delving into the nature of diseases that afflict women.

While today, female doctors are commonplace and women are almost always included in research trials, such was not always the case. Manson's entry into the medical field came at a time when the profession was still largely a male-dominated one. Not only were most doctors men, but the emphasis in research was on men's health, with little regard given to gender differences or to the unique maladies that afflict women.

"The medical model was the 70 kilogram male, and almost everything was framed in that context," recalls Manson, who did her pre-med studies at Harvard and entered Case Western Reserve Medical School in 1975. "In most medical schools at that time, there was little discussion of reproductive issues, birth control pills, hormone therapy, breast or ovarian cancer. Even diseases that are more common in women than men, such as osteoporosis and autoimmune diseases, received limited attention."

When her mother died from ovarian cancer, Manson made a decision that would influence not only her own life, but the progress of medicine as well. She concluded that the best way to change the benign neglect that characterized women's healthcare was to go into research. Healthcare for women could only be improved by a greater understanding of the etiology of diseases and gender differences and their impact on health.

Her specialty throughout medical school, residency, and fellowship had been geared to becoming a clinical endocrinologist and her training had focused on internal medicine. But like many other clinicians in the field, she grew increasingly discouraged by the advanced states of disease that she saw in the diabetic patients that made up the bulk of her practice. Many suffered from cardiovascular disease, stroke, or other vascular disorders. Advanced eye disease and visual loss were common, as was kidney disease, nerve damage, and other complications of the disease.

"I became increasingly interested in the prevention of diabetes, especially type 2 diabetes, which makes up 90 to 95 percent of the cases," she says. "Even from my earliest clinical experience, it seemed to me to be highly preventable."

Manson realized that obesity and lack of exercise coupled with dietary factors were playing a major role in causing the disease, and that lifestyle modification could be a powerful factor in its prevention.

Those realizations led her to detour from what had been a traditional path of training in internal medicine and endocrinology to a decision that she would add to this advanced training with study in epidemiology, biostatistics, and public health.

In pursuing medicine from a public health vantage point, she could make a more substantial impact on the lives of a much greater number of people. She decided to go back to graduate school to flesh out her background and training, and in the process earned a doctorate in epidemiology from the Harvard School of Public Health.

That training led to a National Research Service Award training grant and then an Andrew W. Mellon Fellowship, which enabled her to conduct epidemiology research at Harvard Medical School. Her work in public health led eventually to her appointment as Chief of the Division of Preventive Medicine at Brigham and Women's Hospital, the first woman to hold that post. A board-certified internist and endocrinologist, she also became a full professor of medicine at Harvard Medical School. In 2003, she became the first incumbent of the Elizabeth F. Brigham professorship in women's health, an endowed chair at Harvard Medical School.

Over the past two decades, Manson has been in the vanguard of a number of groundbreaking advancements in the much neglected areas of prevention and women's health. From the vantage point of her current success, it's perhaps hard to imagine that some discouraged her passionate interest in the field. Others told her it might be difficult to get funding for the studies she was interested in doing. Early in her career, there wasn't that much interest in clinical trials involving women or studying how different interventions might affect their health.

Yet medicine and the views of its practitioners and researchers were even then beginning to show signs of change. As Manson was pushing into the field, there was also a growing realization that a greater emphasis on remedying the gender-based research gap was needed.

The National Institutes of Health began mandating more funding for women's research and requiring that researchers include women as participants in research studies.

At the same time, epidemiologic research that once focused nearly exclusively on infectious disease had begun to change. It was moving toward the prevention of chronic diseases through a greater understanding of risk factors and determinants.

Manson was in the right place at the right time to become a leader in the movement.

Over the years, she has focused her research labors on acquiring a greater understanding of the role that factors such as lifestyle, diet, and hormone replacement therapy play in the development of cardiovascular disease. Her curiosity was aroused because so little was known about these factors – particularly the use of hormone therapy.

"I was really amazed that there was a medication that was so widely used – 20 million American women were taking it – and there had never been a long-term clinical trial to evaluate the relative benefits and risks," Manson observes.

She was in a position to help find the answer to these questions when she became a principal investigator of several grants from the National Institutes of Health. Her charge was to look at the impact that various interventions might have on women's health.

One of the most important of these interventions is the Women's Health Initiative – the largest study of women's health ever undertaken in this country. A group of more than 164,000 women enrolled in the study; 27,000 participated in the hormone trials and nearly 50,000 were asked either to adhere to a diet of no more than 20 percent of calories from fat daily or to continue their usual diet. Manson now had the opportunity to look at the long-term benefits and risks of hormone therapy, as well as of dietary intervention, in a large-scale trial.

Many experts had long believed that estrogen therapy lowered the risk of heart disease in women. Yet the Women's Health Initiative found an increased risk for heart disease and stroke, while secondary prevention trials also suggested an increased risk of cardiovascular events or, at best, no benefit at all. It was a startling revelation.

"With hormone therapy, timing is everything," says Manson. "When you start seems to be a very critical factor that hasn't received enough attention. In observational studies, 80 percent of women started taking hormone therapy within a couple of years of menopause onset."

They tended to begin in their early 50s or late 40s as they developed the hot flashes and other symptoms associated with menopause. In the Women's Health Initiative, however, the average age was 63, and the meantime since menopause was 12 to 13 years. In the secondary prevention trials, the meantime since menopause was even greater, at 16 to 17 years.

"These are entirely different populations, with very minimal overlap in terms of age and time since menopause," explains Manson. "And a current theory is that estrogen may be good for the coronary arteries if started early and bad if started late, because the effects depend on the underlying stage of atherosclerosis. If you have advanced plaque, then hormone therapy is detrimental, because it increases the risk of clotting and can lead to an increased risk of plaque rupture."

The WHI was instrumental in clarifying the dangers of hormone therapy when started many years past menopause.

This work cast the therapy in a new light and gave the medical profession a better understanding of this widely used but little understood treatment.

Another significant research role Manson has undertaken has been as a co-investigator on the long-running Nurses' Health Study – so named because registered nurses are the study's participants. It assesses the role of dietary and lifestyle factors in the prevention of heart disease, stroke, breast cancer, diabetes, and other illnesses among 120,000 women originally aged 30 to 55 and followed for 30 years. Manson serves as the principal investigator for the cardiovascular and diabetes components, where she has concentrated not only on lifestyle factors, but also on genetic and biochemical predictors of both heart disease and diabetes such as inflammatory markers like C-reactive protein.

"We've already found that in addition to fasting insulin and fasting proinsulin, there are many chemical messengers produced by endocrine organs or by the fat cells themselves that are strong predictors of the risk of developing type 2 diabetes even years in the future," she says.

Manson also started the Women's Antioxidant/Folate Cardiovascular Study to look into the benefits of using vitamins E and C, beta carotene, and B-complex vitamins such as folic acid, B6, and B12. The goal was to discover whether they might help in preventing cardiovascular events in high-risk women with the disease or those with multiple risk factors.

She has also investigated the role aspirin plays in the prevention of cardiovascular disease in women and the effects of different micronutrients and supplements such as vitamins E and C and beta carotene.

"We've done randomized trials involving all of those antioxidant vitamins and more recently folic acid to see the effects on the prevention of cardiovascular disease," says Manson.

Another vital aspect of her work in preventive medicine came with the realization of the important role of physical activity in inhibiting chronic disease.

"One of the most surprising findings that we've seen consistently in our epidemiological studies is that even moderate-intensity exercise such as brisk walking – 30 minutes per day – is associated with about a 40 percent reduction in the risk of heart disease, stroke, type 2 diabetes, osteoporotic fracture, and even a reduction of 20 to 30 percent in breast cancer and colon cancer," she remarks. "So here is something that is as close to a magic bullet for good health as we have in modern medicine, and it's something simple that nearly everyone can do."

The realization of its value for the general population and the fact that you didn't need a prescription also led Manson to expand her already prodigious writing beyond scholarly journals to the popular press. She was deeply disturbed that an estimated 75 percent of the population is getting less than the recommended amount of exercise. This has contributed to the epidemics of obesity and type 2 diabetes, while the prevalence of hypertension is "just off the chart," she says. "People have trouble getting started and maintaining a regular exercise program. So it became my mission to get some guidelines out to the public to help create a realistic exercise program that could be worked into a very busy schedule, especially for women."

That led to the writing and publication of *The 30-Minute Fitness Solution: A Four-Step Plan for Women of All Ages* with coauthor Patricia Amend. Published by Harvard University Press, it has become a highly popular and accessible guide for thousands who want to reap the proven benefits of exercise.

While Manson's primary focus is that of a researcher, she is also actively involved in clinical practice as well. Although currently on leave from her practice following the birth of her third child, she has maintained a practice in internal medicine and endocrinology. Most of her patients are women with health problems specific to their gender. While all these roles make for a demanding schedule, including family responsibilities, she believes that the activities enhance each other.

Seeing patients helps her stay current with the latest developments in her specialty, as well as maintaining her original career goals of clinical practice. Work as chief of a hospital division also calls for attention to administrative duties and teaching and mentoring as well.

Yet for all the juggling she must do, and the understanding that there are some things she simply can't do because of lack of time, she still finds great joy in her work and what she has been able to accomplish over the last 20 years of her career. Along with her scientific accomplishments, she has helped to clear a path for women in medicine, while also making medicine better for those women who need its care.

Even as she has helped other women achieve a similar career goal, she also is grateful to those who came before her. In particular, she says that her early choice to study medicine came about because of a female chemistry teacher at her high school, who first showed her that the sciences were open to women as well.

"She believed that women tended to steer away from science and often that was due to not receiving much encouragement during middle school and high school," says Manson. "She gave me positive feedback about my abilities in science, and that was one of the factors leading to my long-term interest in medicine." She also credits her family for nurturing this early interest.

Thanks to that early encouragement, women everywhere have benefited from this dedicated physician and researcher who has helped transform the study and treatment of women's health.

Section IV

ONE PATH TO CREATIVITY
IN HEALTHCARE
THE MEDICAL DEVICE
INDUSTRY

Chapter 20
THE LANDSCAPE OF INVENTING

This section is first and foremost about the invention, patenting, and marketing of medical devices. But it is also much more than that. It is an exploration of how creativity and the creative process can be used to generate tangible manifestations of ideas that solve problems and in turn provide great satisfaction and great rewards to their creators. In the previous chapters of this book, we've explored the essence of creativity and how it can be used to better both the lives of physicians and the field in which they work.

Here I offer a more in-depth road map of one particular target of creativity in action – the medical device industry. It will serve as a guide on how to nurture this process within yourself and how to make it a vital part of your everyday life. In these chapters, and in the profiles of the industry's great inventors that follow, you'll discover what it takes to be successful in the competitive and complex world of commercial innovation.

While the focus here is on the creation of medical devices, the same principles and tools of creativity could be applied to any other field – whether it's publishing a novel, managing a research team, or launching an innovative practice model.

I choose to focus on the medical device business because it is one of the fastest growing areas of healthcare. It offers tremendous opportunities for personal fulfillment and significant financial rewards for those who choose the creative path of invention. Today's companies are seeking ideas for groundbreaking inventions like the stent, as well as modifications on existing medical tools and devices.

Dr. Julio Palmaz, the primary inventor of the Palmaz-Schatz coronary stent, launched a new era in the treatment of coronary disease. Today, more than one million stents are used annually throughout the world. As a result of the invention, his name has become virtually synonymous with this lifesaving procedure, and he has reaped tremendous financial rewards in the process.

Many people have ideas, but they have no concept of how to turn their inspiration into a workable, sellable product. I was in that same category as a young resident working in a major urban hospital. I had a great idea for a device that had tremendous potential, but I didn't know how to go about getting it manufactured or even how to develop a working prototype.

After learning the intricacies of patent law, venture capital, market research, and negotiating with medical device companies, I realized that many were on the same path I had walked, they too without a road map. That realization gave birth to this examination of the invention process. Recognizing that there was no reliable guide to follow, I decided to do something about it. Had I had the pages that follow, my own experience would have been much easier.

After the difficulties, roadblocks, and learning curves I encountered, I wanted to develop a practical, easy-to-follow blueprint for success regarding the process of creativity and inventing. While there are numerous books on patents and marketing, there are few, if any, that combine those hard facts with the soft skills of developing the mind of an inventor.

Limitless Opportunities

For those who believe they have the ideas and the creative drive to make their ideas a reality, this exploration of the medical device industry represents one path back to independence and control of your professional life. Through the process of inventing, patenting, and marketing your ideas, you can establish not only new areas of interest and vitality for your life, but also new streams of income that aren't dependent on your coming in every day, seeing patients, and always playing the role of technician. Whether you have a brilliant idea or would like to invest in the ideas of engineers or other health professionals, the medical device industry offers unparalleled opportunities.

The development and marketing of medical devices is one of the fastest growing sections of the $1.4 trillion U.S. healthcare industry. Today, medical technology spending has reached $221 billion – fully 15 percent of all healthcare spending. More than $170 billion is spent on medical devices bought for hospitals, while another $49 billion flows from the pockets of Americans for retail medical devices. Increases in spending in this area will come in an easy-to-predict manner consistent with growth in the population and in direct correlation to the number of Americans in the prime healthcare consumption years. There are already more than 44 million citizens over the age of 60, and that number is expected to rise to nearly 60 million by 2013. Between the ages of 60 and 70, the average senior citizen consumes more healthcare services and resources than he did during the first six decades of life combined. By age 85, the average patient is accounting for more than $16,000 per year in medical-related spending, ranging from artificial hips to bone grafts to laser surgery.[1]

In my own practice, I've seen a tidal wave of baby boomers demanding the latest and best treatments available. Many of them are increasingly willing to pay for this care from their own pockets, regardless of whether or not they're covered by insurance.

This tendency is in sharp contrast to the last generation of aging Americans who were often unwilling to pay for any treatment that wasn't covered by insurance or Medicare.

The baby boom generation — anyone born between 1946 and 1964 — is now well into middle age and rapidly approaching retirement. Yet, unlike their parents, they don't see old age as a time of inevitable decline and are not shy about demanding medical fixes that can keep them active.

"You see these guys in their fifties who are still out on the basketball court even after they've had a knee replacement," observes Tom Brooks, a venture capitalist who specializes in the development of medical devices. "They want to continue being active long after their fathers would have accepted a sedentary lifestyle."

Demand for medical devices by this population will only increase as they get older.

I share these numbers and observations with you to demonstrate just how dynamic and profitable this market has become. And the number of these devices is truly legion – 90,000 of them have been approved by the FDA according to the most recent figures. Niches range from implantable pacemakers to imaging devices to laser tooth-cutting tools. Most of these devices are being developed and brought to market by large corporations who control their patents. While physicians use these devices in treating patients, they often have little to do with creating them and are cast in the role of buyers and users rather than as owners who profit from their sale.

This represents an area of great potential for doctors. Inventing a medical device represents a golden opportunity to develop a profitable and exciting complement to your career. This burgeoning market can and should benefit from the input of those who can serve as both inventors of devices and consultants to the companies that ultimately sell them.

My own plunge into invention put new spice into my life and practice. Through this process, I found more energy and motivation to continue using my skills to help patients. It became a way to contribute to research even though I didn't consider myself a researcher.

In fact, as the figures I will share with you reveal, there is far more financial potential in making medical devices than there is in any of the other activities that physicians are prone to get into, from buying a restaurant or bar to day trading. Medical devices offer the advantages of relatively little competition and a high margin of return on successful products. Best of all, the invention of medical devices keeps you within your area of knowledge and away from matters where you may have little or no expertise.

As you explore this market, you'll start to acquire the skills and knowledge needed to determine whether or not your device is unique and whether you should seek patent protection for it. I'll take you through the entire process, from filing a provisional patent to finding a patent attorney. I'll show you what you need to

know about the FDA's regulatory process, as well as the optimum means to develop and sell your device so that you can realize the maximum return on your investment.

Strategy for Exit

This book will prepare you to find your own exit strategy once you've developed a device. Many of you have read about the IPOs and various other means for
realizing a product's financial potential. While these are the means that many
investors use, for the inventor of a medical device, there are really only two methods. You will sell your idea to a large company for a flat fee, royalties, or a combination of the two. That's the route I chose, and most likely it will work for you,
too. But it's not the only way. The less common, but often much more lucrative
and ultimately satisfying, path is finding someone who can take your idea and run
with it.

Phil Romano was a wealthy restaurateur who had just sold his successful
Fuddruckers chain. He was looking for an investment for his newfound cash when
he was introduced to Dr. Julio Palmaz who was developing the idea of the heart
stent. Without him, the young physician might never have realized his dream of a
device that eventually revolutionized the treatment of heart disease.

The truth is, most doctors and healthcare professionals are in no position to
start their own company but could team up with someone with the expertise and
capability to do so. In these pages, I'll also show you how to find the right entrepreneur or venture fund that can help turn your device into a successful, moneymaking product.

In writing this book, I realized that many inventors want and need to know
the processes and pitfalls I navigated through to accomplish the ultimate sale of my
device to a large company. I also came to see that many of you have ideas, but
you're so unsure about what to do with them that you often end up doing the
worst possible thing – nothing. Then, perhaps, years later you see your idea on the
market, making someone else millions, and you say, "Hey, I thought of that!" As
the great inventor Dr. Thomas Fogarty noted: "Inspiration without application is
truly useless."

Like many others, if I had realized just how much I didn't know and how
much I needed to learn, I might have never even started. Yet, naive and filled with
passion, I plunged in headfirst, and before I was done, I gained a level of knowledge and self-confidence that made possible many other ventures, such as opening
my own solo practice in an area where few had successfully been able to do so.

Although I never went to business school, I gained more knowledge about the
business process than many with advanced business degrees. In fact, countless

MBA graduates told me they had never written a business plan or done market research or pitched an idea to a venture capitalist. I learned to do all those things, and in the process, earned my own "MBA" from the well-known "University of Real Life."

You can do the same thing without taking any courses at the local university. As my old friend and Wharton business school graduate Ken Hoffman told me, "One of the primary benefits of getting an MBA is increasing your Rolodex."

As a physician, you already have the contacts, and your M.D. degree conveys a level of prestige that, coupled with a good elevator pitch, will get you a hearing at any medical device company.

REFERENCES

1.   Health Care Industry Market Update, October 10, 2002 (Centers for Medicare and Medicaid Services.)

Chapter 21

ADDED VALUE
HOW TO GET THE MOST OUT OF YOUR INVENTION

Venture capitalists, angel investors, and others who invest in the growth of new businesses are often a strange lot. On the one hand, they are risk-takers who will put large amounts of their own cash into unproven ideas, hoping to hit a home run. On the other hand, they are hard-nosed businesspeople who want all the facts. They are willing to take risks, but they're usually highly calculated ones.

They don't throw their money away. They see possibilities where many others do not, but they always keep their feet planted firmly on the ground.

Understanding what a potential benefactor is looking for in the process of converting your idea into a business is essential to getting the most out of it. You want to see your device become a viable product that can in turn make a contribution to society – helping or curing patients, perhaps saving lives, and making the world a better place to live. You also want to get the best price for your product, and in order to do that you must add value.

Many inventors have been paid what seems like large sums of money for their ideas, but the question I always ask is, What could they have done to turn that payment into an even larger payoff?

Restaurateur Phil Romano invested $250,000 in a company that developed the heart stent with Palmaz and Schatz. At the time, their device needed additional research and animal testing. If they had been further along in the process, Romano might have been willing to invest even more or taken a smaller percentage.

No device emerges perfect and complete. There is always a trial-and-error process that transforms it into something better. To the extent that you are able to make these improvements not just to the device, but to the idea and its salability as well, then you can reap greater rewards.

In this chapter, I want to explore some of the main areas that you should consider before you seek out your investor or business partner. Implementing ideas from each of these areas will increase your invention's value and allow you to more easily attract and persuade investors to part with their capital. Here I will hit the highlights, with more in-depth explorations in chapters to come.

Write It Down

One of the most important– and one of the most neglected — things you can do as an inventor is to keep good records of your activities and contacts. Get a notebook – one of those lined, hardcover notebooks from an office supply store will do – and begin keeping a log of all your activities related to the device. This record will be invaluable when you begin the patent process, and especially so if you ever run into any problems with others trying to steal your idea.

Immediately after conceiving of the heart stent, Palmaz put his ideas in a report to his university faculty chairman. Later, this dated report would become proof of when he actually invented the stent that he used in the face of challenges by others who claimed they had thought of it first.

You also need to keep track of the events that make up the inventing process. As you talk to others to solicit criticisms or endorsements, keep a detailed record of these communications. Write down the name of the individuals you talked to and what you told them about it. Be diligent. The written record you're developing is an important part of the whole inventing process. It will help to keep you on track and inspire you as you move along.

OPI: Other People's Intellect

While I was developing my own medical device, one of the most important decisions I made was to seek out the advice and counsel of people I knew and trusted. Calling on friends and experts with backgrounds in law, medicine, finance, and business, I established an advisory board to help keep me on track. Just as smart entrepreneurs often make use of OPM (other people's money) for investments, I reasoned that OPI (other people's intellect) was just as valuable.

My own experiences have proven that it is vital to surround yourself with experts in order to get their opinions on the issues you're facing. Is that offer from the medical device company the best you can get, or should you hold out for more? Your advisors can help you formulate an answer to that question and a host of others. Certainly not everything you hear will be right for you, but even when you're given conflicting appraisals of a situation, informed suggestions will lead you to think in new ways. You'll have the option of considering perspectives that you might not otherwise have encountered. You'll also profit from wisdom gained through their mistakes, not yours.

It's Confidential

Along with excellent record keeping, you should attempt to get everyone to sign a Confidentiality and Nondisclosure Agreement (NDA). This simple letter ensures that the people with whom you share your information won't turn around and use it elsewhere. Most people won't, of course, but this document is insurance against the possibility of theft.

While many, if not most, medical device companies and venture capitalists won't sign such documents, it's still worthwhile to present it to them and ask for a signature. By doing so, you display a level of seriousness that says emphatically that they shouldn't even consider spreading your ideas to unauthorized persons, even in casual conversation.

In the Appendix, you'll find a sample NDA that you can copy and edit to your own specifications. Make sure you have your NDA (and all other legal documents for that matter) checked by an attorney to ensure that it meets the requirements of your particular state.

You Own It

Perhaps the single most important part of the process is obtaining a patent. In Chapter 22, I lay out the procedure for obtaining first a provisional patent and then the big one – a conventional patent – that gives you complete and unassailable rights to your idea.

A patent is a temporary legal right that is granted to you, the inventor, by the federal government to ensure that others can't begin manufacturing and selling your device. You can obtain a provisional one just by sending in your application and paying a small fee.

Once you obtain the provisional from the United States Patent and Trademark Office (USPTO), you can begin stamping every document with the words "Patent Pending." In fact, you should immediately obtain a stamp, which you can get from most office supply stores, that allows you to apply those two words in large red letters to every document that relates to your device. A provisional patent offers an inexpensive means to preserve your rights.

The first step in securing a patent is to conduct a patent search of the extensive database of the USPTO website to make sure no one has already thought of your idea. The easiest way to do this is to hire a patent attorney to conduct a professional search. Since that can be expensive, you may not want to invest that kind of money in an unproven device. In the chapter on patents, I lay out a simple search procedure that you can do yourself. It's not easy, but it's cheaper than hiring someone to do it for you. Whether it's worth your time to do so or not is a decision you need to make based on your own set of circumstances.

Develop a Prototype

Another factor to consider is developing a prototype of your device. Most of the inventors that you'll read about in this book developed simple models in their basements using basic materials obtained from an electronics or hardware store.

If your device is complex and highly technical, you may be forced to hire a company that specializes in building prototypes. Usually, you won't attempt to create a workable model until you've received some funding to pay for this sometimes expensive endeavor.

Research to Validate Your Device

One of your most obvious tasks will be testing and research to validate that your device actually works. Because what seems like a good idea in theory can quickly prove unworkable when it's put to the test in a lab setting. These tests can also point to where improvements are needed. As other inventors have noted, nothing works perfectly the first time – or possibly even the hundredth time.

This testing, which you should carefully document in your logbook, will serve as part of the documentation that you use in selling your invention or obtaining funding for larger-scale research.

Endorsements: It's a Great Idea

While you may be convinced that your new invention or idea is an incredible advancement, the true test is often whether or not you can convince others of that fact.

At a particularly discouraging time in the development of my own alignment device, my work was energized when I received written praise and endorsement from a prominent member of the academic medical community. In person and in writing, he told me that my device would be a "godsend" to the residents he taught. That heady praise motivated me and convinced others that it was an idea worth pursuing.

I also sought out endorsements from other doctors who practiced the same kind of medicine that I was going to practice and who might use the device if it were available. I recorded these testimonials using my video camera or got them to write endorsement letters to me.

So, one of your first tasks will be approaching other members of your field, demonstrating your idea, and getting their feedback. This process will not only give you something tangible that you can show to investors and potential buyers, but it may also give you powerful ideas for improving your invention.

Don't be discouraged if everyone doesn't leap at the opportunity to offer an endorsement. As I've said earlier, you must approach this process with an internal fortitude that can withstand the inevitable rejections.

Look first to your own colleagues, friends, and associates, but don't be afraid to approach others you respect but may not know personally. The endorsement I got from a Vanderbilt University professor came through a referral by another doctor I had approached.

Where's the Plan?

A business plan outlining the market that you see for your device and its financial potential is a must. In this document, your goal is to outline your prospective customers' problem that needs to be solved or, in some cases, pain that needs to be relieved. Then present your device and how it will address these needs, and discuss how many potential customers there might be for the device and what the competition is like. Writing this plan is something you can do yourself, although you may want to hire a consultant to help.

I drafted a business plan on my own with the help of some business friends, and it proved to be – to put it mildly – a highly educational process. In fact, by the time I was done, I knew more about writing these kinds of documents than a great many business school graduates.

A business plan will help you in drafting your patent application, and it will also serve as an essential tool in obtaining financing from outside sources. In fact, it's probably going to be one of the first things that a venture capitalist wants to look at before he writes you a check.

FDA Regulations

At some point, the federal government, in the form of the Food and Drug Administration or some other agency, will get into the act. In order for your device to be commercialized, it must pass through a number of regulatory hurdles.

In Chapter 23, I explore the changing environment of the FDA's increasingly complex regulation of medical devices, along with the less onerous requirements in Europe. While you need to know the terms and how the process works for different classes of devices, this is definitely an area you shouldn't venture into alone. By the time you reach the point where you need the government's approval, you will have lawyers and experts by your side to handle the process.

Along the way, you can figure out where your device fits into the regulatory scheme. Is it an improvement to an existing device that doesn't require an extensive review process, or is it something totally new that pushes it into a different realm of regulation?

By focusing on each of these areas, you can greatly enhance the value of your new invention. You will not only make it better as you work toward perfection, but you will build a stronger argument for both acceptance and funding from those who can help make your bright idea a profitable reality.

Chapter 22

PROTECTING AND PATENTING YOUR DEVICE

One of the most important parts of the inventing process really has nothing to do with inventing or creativity or inspiration, or anything remotely like that. It's all about how you protect your creation once you've invented it; it's the dry stuff of lawyers and accountants and those fine-print types.

If you're the creative kind – and if you're reading this book up to now, you are – you may be put off by the patent process. First off, it seems like a lot of work, and if you have to hire an attorney who specializes in patent law, you know it's going to be costly.

Yet patenting your invention is extremely important for a number of reasons. Your invention, after all, is your property. You birthed it through inspiration and hard work, and you deserve to benefit from your labor when companies, venture capitalists, and others with loads of money in their pockets come calling. The worst thing is to take your invention out into the marketplace only to find that someone else invented the same thing but got patent protection before you did. Or worse, that they stole your idea. It's rather like coming home one day to find a stranger sitting in front of your TV, eating the food in your fridge. It's unfair, but if you don't have title to the property and he does, then you have little recourse.

It's crucial to protect your idea so that when you, or someone you choose, is ready to develop its commercial potential, there's no question as to ownership. Today, fully 65 percent of most major corporations' assets are tied up in intellectual property (IP). These companies employ armies of lawyers to protect their IP rights from infringement by competitors. For many, IP is an important source of income for their bottom line, which includes royalties and sales of rights.

Corporations large and small know all too well that a well-protected patent can create significant revenue streams either for you or for someone else. Many companies have launched a product they thought was their own only to find that someone else held the patent. Then they were faced with either turning back or paying up to the true owner.

Jerome Lemelson is a name well-known in corporate boardrooms and law offices across the nation. Not only is he considered "the most prolific inventor of all time," but he possessed a remarkable talent for evaluating technology to determine trends and then filing patents that took into account new developments in products.

The holder of more than 550 patents, he conceived of automated manufacturing systems and bar code readers, automatic teller machines and cordless phones, cassette players and camcorders, fax machines and personal computers, even crying baby dolls. He won his first patent in 1953 for the propeller beanie.[1]

Although he never actually took any of these products to market, many companies paid him for the rights to do so. Auto manufacturers, for example, had to recognize that he was the inventor of intermittent wiper blades – a common feature on virtually all cars and trucks – when he sued them for infringement.

Lemelson stands as an example that if you want to avoid paying someone else for the rights to a device you thought you invented, then a strong patent is a vital course of action.

Let me add that while patent protection is important – and that's why I've made it an integral part of the inventing process – many inventors have a tendency to become overly paranoid about the possibility of someone lifting their ideas and running with them. As I found with my own device, few people, if any, are going to understand your idea or see its true potential. It all comes back to the passion side of inventing. Your deep feelings and motivation to develop your idea give you the ability to see where it might go and the problems it can solve. Other people won't necessarily share your emotional connection, so the notion that they will steal it is remote.

Yet as I pointed out in an earlier chapter, you must protect your ideas by getting anyone with whom you share them to sign a Nondisclosure Agreement. You also must follow the steps involved in obtaining first a provisional patent and finally, the actual patent. In the pages that follow, I'll show you why and, more importantly, how – step by step – to do so.

In simplest terms, a patent is a temporary legal right that is granted to you, the inventor, by the government to ensure that others can't begin manufacturing and selling your device. While patent rights don't last forever, the patenting process does give you the opportunity to profit from your work without fear of others stealing it.

Even though I say "without fear," others may still try. If you have an innovative and potentially lucrative invention, that danger always exists. But if you follow these steps, you will have a firm and probably unassailable legal basis to ensure that they can't get away with it if they do try. That's important for both you and the economic health of our nation. The whole purpose of patents is to encourage and reward innovation through the profit motive, while at the same time creating a permanent record of the invention itself.

The first step in securing a patent is conducting a patent search to make sure that no one has already patented your idea. Unfortunately, a patent search won't uncover whether someone has already thought of the idea unless they themselves have filed an application to patent it.

The easiest way to conduct a patent search is to hire a patent attorney. However, that can be expensive. If you're a novice inventor, you probably don't want to invest that kind of money in an unproven device.

Thanks to the Internet, you can access the full text of all patent applications filed since 1976 on the United States Patent and Trademark Office database by logging onto their website, www.uspto.gov, and going to the patent section. The site also contains images of every patent from 1790 to 1976, but you can't do keyword searches through these older documents. If your technology goes back further, you'll have to look through each image just as if you were thumbing through printed documents.

The USPTO site offers a seven step search strategy, which can be found at www.uspto.gov/go/ptdl/step7.htm.

Using this process, you have a good shot at determining whether anyone else has already beaten you to the punch by filing for protection.

Once you have determined through a patent search that no one else has already thought of your idea, the next step is to file for a provisional patent.

A provisional patent application is something of a misnomer. It really isn't a patent application, because no patent can be issued from it. It is never actually reviewed on its own merits by the good bureaucrats at the USPTO. It must be followed by a formal application within one year of its submission.

A provisional patent is simply a convenient means of filing a complete disclosure of your invention and establishing a record of the date of its conception without the high cost of drafting a formal application. The filing fee is quite low, usually about one fourth that of a formal application.

You can even file additional provisionals to add improvements to your invention for up to a year, at which point you must file a formal application in order to maintain the date you established as your point of invention. Chances are, after you've seen your attorney file the first one, you can do it yourself.

So if the provisional doesn't get you an actual patent, what is the point of filing one? The answer, obviously, is that it's a cheap, simple means of getting your invention on record.

"The provisional application in the U.S. is simply a bookmark," says Ryan Schneider, a patent attorney with the law firm of Troutman Sanders LLP. "It is basically a rough draft that can serve as the basis of what will eventually be a conventional application. Many erroneously think that a provisional application is nothing more than just writing down your ideas on a napkin and sending it into the patent office."

Experts point out that the provisional application really should contain many of the same elements as a business plan, and that you should approach it with the same seriousness that you would the blueprint for getting a company off the ground.

"A good provisional application sets forth the problems the inventor sees out there, why this is going to answer those problems, where this is going to go economically, how it will benefit the world," says Schneider. "A good provisional application has the same elements as a conventional application, just a lot less formal, and satisfies the same legal requirements as a conventional application."

While the patent office doesn't lay out any hard and fast rules as to the number of pages or even number of sections, if you want to have a successful patent experience, there are certain general elements that need to be in your application. Each application, just like each invention, is unique in itself.

The central virtue of a provisional patent is that it allows you to say "patent pending" and to stamp those two important words on the Nondisclosure Agreements you make everyone sign. It also sets forth a moment in time when you developed a new idea, and from that moment forward, you own the rights to that creation.

Yet in order for the provisional patent to be effective, it must satisfy the same basic elements as your forthcoming conventional patent application. Otherwise, you may lose the effective date that you set up when the patent examiners look at the two documents and conclude that they aren't talking about the same thing.

As I mentioned earlier, this is where a good attorney comes in handy. A professional, skilled in patent filing, will know much more about the process and how to draft the proper documents. In addition, he will have a much greater understanding of what is patentable than you, the actual inventor, will.

It is probably worthwhile, if you can afford it, to have a patent attorney draft your provisional application. But it is absolutely essential that you go to a skilled professional to draft your formal application. Too much is at stake for you to attempt to be your own lawyer.

Making it Formal

Whether you take the plunge yourself or hire someone to do the job, you should know the elements of the formal application. Because the more you know, the more you'll be able to help your attorney – and perhaps save a few billable hours.

A good formal patent application will contain the following elements:
1.   A disclosure that contains a complete description of the invention.
2.   An argument on why the invention is patentable.
3.   Legal definitions of the invention and the areas of technology that you want to control.

The disclosure and the argument are grouped into the specifications, which may include the following elements:
1.   An abstract, or clear, concise description of the invention.

2. Drawings of the invention.
3. Reference to any prior applications, such as a provisional patent.
4. A statement of the technology that is affected by the invention.
5. A statement of the need for the invention or the problems it will solve.
6. A condensed summary of what the invention is and how it works.
7. A written description of each of the drawings contained in the application.
8. A description of how the invention might be manufactured and marketed under the ideal circumstances.

Now you have a good overview of the patent process and its importance to you and your invention.

Your Patent Search Strategy

There are numerous methods for doing a patent search, and there are plenty of professionals who will be happy to do one for you – for a sometimes hefty fee starting at around $750. While such professionals have access to databases unavailable to the general public and are experienced in focusing on proper search essentials, if you're just beginning your inventing career you probably don't have – or don't want to invest – the funds needed to retain a professional for this task. Yet even if you take on the job yourself, you must complete a thorough search to ensure that you have the basis for continuing the patent application process. Otherwise, the time you do invest will be wasted.

Here is a simple method for conducting your own patent search using the USPTO website at www.uspto.gov.

1. Begin by looking at the classification definitions in the site's Index to the U.S. Patent Classification. Determine all the classes into which your invention may fall.
2. Look at the titles of patents listed to narrow your class list.
3. Get a list of all patents in those classes. You'll have to search a list of all patent numbers granted from 1790 to the present and all published applications from 2001 to the present for every class and subclass to be searched.
4. Check for recent additions to the list of patents filed. These newcomers can be found in the Patent Official Gazette issued each week.
5. Read the abstract of each patent, and cross off those that don't relate to your invention. Set aside plenty of time for this job, because it will likely take hours. In the end, though, it will be worth it.

REFERENCES

1. Jerome Lemelson Biography, Lemelson Foundation (Accessed October 2, 2005 at http://www.lemelson.org/about/bio_jerry.php)

Chapter 23

THE FDA AND THE REGULATORY PROCESS

One of the most complex, confusing, and often expensive aspects of inventing a medical device is encountered while running the gauntlet known as the U.S. regulatory approval process. The Food and Drug Administration, or FDA for short, is charged with, among other things, ensuring that medical devices sold in this country meet certain standards for safety and effectiveness.

This is certainly a laudatory and vital goal, but as technology has produced increasingly intricate and invasive devices, the process itself has grown more complicated as well. Getting a device to market can be a lengthy process, particularly if your device is truly unique. You may, for example, be called upon to produce extensive reports on clinical trials to prove effectiveness and safety. In the meantime, the clock is ticking away, and your device isn't yet on the market, where it might just be helping to save lives.

When you begin this process, you might consider retaining a number of experts to represent you, including lawyers skilled in the intricate policies and political nuances of the FDA, along with a host of quality control experts, engineers, statisticians, contract research organizations, and other experts depending on the complexity and type of the regulatory submission required for your product. If this sounds like an overwhelming task, that's because it is, and is getting more so every day. It also helps explain why most medical devices are produced by large corporations endowed with the resources to meet these challenges.

Over the past decade, the FDA has changed its procedures, alternately tightening and loosening its standards. When the AIDS epidemic was at its height, the agency put potentially lifesaving drugs on a fast track. But in light of the drug scandals of recent years and in the face of mounting criticism from both Congress and the public, it has tightened procedures. It's safe to say that what is required of manufacturers in this area is truly a moving target.

Here, I want to give you a basic overview of this process. It is by no means an exhaustive one, but it will give you a general idea of what you're going to face as you offer up your device to the regulatory approval process. We'll also take a look at the second biggest potential market for your device, the European Union, where things are done a bit differently.

Know Your Class

There are three basic classifications (I, II, and III) for approximately 1,700 different generic types of devices assigned to 16 medical specialties known as panels. Each of these generic types of devices is placed in one of these three regulatory classes based on the level of control necessary to assure the safety and effectiveness of the device. Class I represents the lowest risk to the public, while Class II devices have moderate risks, and those in Class III have either the highest risk or there is simply no other device like it on the market.

While each class carries with it different requirements, all of them are subject to certain general rules that prohibit adulteration or misbranding of the product, such as false or misleading labeling. In addition, all devices must meet the demands of a regulated quality control system.

As for pre-market requirements, in general, a device must be cleared by the FDA through the pre-market notification (the so-called 510(k) notice) process or approved by the FDA through the pre-market approval (PMA) process before being legally marketed in the United States, unless it is expressly exempt from those requirements. As you move up the chain, the standards are higher and the amount of work needed to clear the hurdles increases tremendously.

The purpose of the 510(k) notification process, which is the most common way to obtain market clearance for a device, is to demonstrate to the FDA that your product is "substantially equivalent" in intended use and technological characteristics to another FDA-cleared product. If there are any differences in technological characteristics, you must show that these differences do not raise any new issues of safety or effectiveness as compared to the already cleared device. Some people refer to this as a me-too process. Some Class I and most Class II devices require a 510(k) notice.

In order to determine your device's classification, as well as whether any exemptions may exist, you can go to Part 800 of the Code of Federal Regulations and to the FDA's website atwww.accessdata.fda.gov/scripts/cdrh/cfdocs/cfPCD/classification.cfm and search for the device type and classification number, if one exists for your device. The FDA maintains a very detailed site that will answer many of your questions and help you through the process of deciding which classification your device fits into. A good place to start is www.fda.gov/cdrh/devadvice/313.html.

However, according to Ted Wilson, a partner in the medical device group of Hogan & Hartson LLP, "some devices are not classified by the FDA, and the sponsor must develop a convincing argument that its product should be regulated as a Class I or Class II device to avoid the more stringent regulatory pathway for most Class III devices."

Class III devices represent the hardest nut to crack when it comes to regulation. They are the ones that sustain or support life and any failure is life threatening.

Not all Class III devices require an approved PMA application in order to be marketed. Devices that are equivalent to those already legally marketed before May 28, 1976, may be approved through the 510(k) process unless the FDA already requires submission of PMA data for that type of device. Some examples of exempt devices are implantable pacemaker pulse generators or silicone gel breast implants.

To make matters even more complicated, there are some devices that have been on the market for a long time in Class III, but the FDA has never required a PMA for them. If your device is "substantially equivalent" to one of these types, then you may be able to escape PMA as well. If your device is not substantially equivalent, either because your intended use is significantly different from the predicate device or your technology raises different questions of safety and efficacy, then the FDA is likely to say you are not substantially equivalent (NSE), and then they will require a PMA for that product.

"There are certain regulatory hurdles that are particularly challenging for a Class III medical device," says Wilson. "Most people, particularly inventors who want to get to the market quickly or who don't have a lot of money to spend on the PMA approval process, want to try to get their device classified into Class I or Class II."

If you have to go the PMA route, it will be costly in terms of time, dollar outlays, and the sheer amount of data and information, including clinical and non-clinical data that you will need to generate. It also typically takes much longer to obtain PMA approval than 510(k) clearance.

"In addition, the rules for when an FDA application is required for a device modification are more stringent for PMA-approved devices than for 510(k)-cleared devices," says Wilson.

After reading the above description of the regulatory process, you may be quite confused about how to proceed. The truth is that there are several gray areas where outcomes can be quite uncertain. If your device is simple and much like others already on the market, and its use is not substantially different, then approval can be relatively simple. If, on the other hand, you've ventured into a new area, then it is vital that you get the right advice.

Law firms such as Hogan & Hartson handle numerous applications and often appear before FDA reviewers and advisory boards. There are also companies that can help you with the drafting of 510(k) applications. An attorney can do it for you as well, but these firms tend to be much less expensive – if your application is relatively simple and uncomplicated.

If you're a first time inventor, my recommendation is to always seek out the best help you can afford.

Selling Offshore

Another fact to consider is that while the U.S. is by far the biggest market, there are substantial markets in other countries as well. The nations of the European Union offer the second biggest area for selling your device.

The EU has its own regulatory and approval process, but it tends to be simpler and easier to navigate than the one in the U.S.

"One of the nice things about the European system is that the EU has actually outsourced their regulatory oversight to private companies that are responsible for enforcing conformance with the ISO standards," says John Guzowski, who serves as the vice president for finance at a medical device company that markets its products in Europe. "Things that typically require clinical trials in the U.S. don't necessarily require clinical trials in Europe. The regulations and device classifications to obtain a CE mark [mandatory marking indicating conformity with European health and safety requirements] seem to weight the potential injury to a patient in the event of a product failure versus the benefit to the population if the product functions properly."

As you have probably discerned from reading just this brief discussion of the process, regulatory approval of medical devices is a complicated and very demanding undertaking. It is certainly not for the faint of heart and the unprepared. When you get to this point in your own inventing, I hope that you will use this information to ask the right questions of the right experts who can help make your appearance before this agency successful.

Chapter 24

STRATEGIES FOR YOUR EXIT

Third-round venture capital funding, 10b5-1, 8K, 10Q, put option, strike price, acid-test ratio, after-tax profit margin, unsystematic risk, EDGAR, EBITDA, mezzanine financing…

Recognize all those terms? If you're like most inventors, some may sound vaguely familiar, while others might as well be a foreign language. Yet all of this jargon is familiar to businessmen who run companies, and if you decide to create a company to produce your invention – perhaps with the intent of eventually going public – they'll have to become an integral part of your vocabulary as well.

If you've spent any time reading books about starting a company and building a business, you've undoubtedly come across many of these terms. Tons of paper and millions of words have been devoted to telling you how to start, build, and eventually sell a company.

The business gurus will tell you that even before you start a business, you need an exit strategy. That is, you need to know what you're going to do with your invention when it becomes a commercial reality. Many inventors get caught up in the idea that they must start their own company, and then worry about either selling it to someone else or eventually taking it public in the form of an initial public offering (IPO).

How businesses work, how inventions are commercialized, and all of the various terms that apply to this process are important to know and understand. When you comprehend this language, you can speak more intelligently to the people who can help you make your device a success.

The Only Exit Strategy You'll Ever Need

I'm now going to tell you something that you and many others may consider heresy. The idea of starting your own company and taking it to an IPO is unrealistic, to say the least. It isn't for you, and most likely it isn't going to happen. Now at this point you're going to say, "But I know lots of inventors who have started their own companies."

That's probably true, and some of them may even be physicians, like Dr. David Ku, the founder of SaluMedica and a leader in tissue regeneration, but they are the exception and not the rule. There are really only two exit strategies for inventors in the medical device field. In this chapter, I'll explain them to you and help you determine the one that's right for you. But before we begin, let me explain why the traditional idea of starting a company probably isn't for you.

Inventors tend to fall into two broad categories. The first one is the researcher who works as part of a team in a large corporation. He does his work for the company, and the corporation handles the process of commercialization, patenting, and so forth.

The second kind – and I'm betting you fall into this category – is the inventor who works in a medical practice, a hospital, or some other organization such as an engineering firm. His practice, job, or other business is his primary occupation and inventing is basically a sideline or hobby. I belong to this category myself.

If you're a part-time inventor, like me, you're faced with two problems. The first is limited time, since you have to concentrate on making a living, and the second – and this is really the most important – you have limited business experience, contacts, and expertise. For you, trying to start a company could very well be a prescription for disaster.

An inventor with a start-up company – even one with a product that is clearly superior to those already on the market – faces tremendous barriers in getting his product into a market. While we live in a nation founded on the theory of capitalism and free enterprise, there are often forces at work that you may not anticipate or even understand.

Take, for example, the case of Thomas Shaw and his retractable syringe. In medicine, one of the greatest occupational hazards facing doctors and nurses is the accidental needle prick. They occur far more often than we like to admit, and they can sometimes have deadly results.

Shaw devised a syringe with a needle that snaps back into the barrel after the drug has been dispensed. This engineer was an idealist who believed his invention was clearly superior and a giant advance in safety that needed to be on the market. Yet he soon found himself barred at every turn from selling his invention to hospitals.

He was turned away, sadly, because most hospitals were locked into contracts that required them to buy their supplies from giant consortiums. Doctors and nurses who learned about the device wanted to buy it. Their hospitals told them no. It didn't matter how much better it was than the conventional device.

Shaw and his company, Retractable Technologies, eventually sued the giant consortiums and syringe makers for antitrust violations, including restraint of trade. After a six-year battle, the companies settled by paying him a $150 million settlement, which he is using to manufacture his invention. He hopes that the forces of competition and superior design will win out. So far, however, most hospitals still aren't buying because of their exclusive contracts.

Know Yourself

The secret to being a successful inventor is to be aware of both your strengths and weaknesses. In the earlier chapter, Understand Yourself and Find Your Strength, I talked about the different personality types and how you can realize more success by playing to your strengths rather than your weaknesses.

As an independent inventor, you just may not have the time to do all the things that are required, such as building a prototype, writing a successful patent application, or marketing your device to a large company, much less raising venture capital, hiring managers, or negotiating the FDA's regulatory process.

In an earlier chapter, I related my story of working with companies and ultimately selling my idea to Medtronic. After spending countless hours working on the device, I came to the realization that doing these necessary tasks yourself can be a gross misuse of valuable time. If you're in practice, then you must concentrate on doing what you do best. Time is money, as the cliché goes, and you must focus on the highest value activity that you can carry out every minute of every day. In Chapter 5, titled Time and Value, I took you through the process of determining the value of your time and making the best use of it.

In most cases, this means getting experts to perform the jobs at which they excel and you do not. It makes little sense to attempt to write a patent application by yourself when someone else can do it better, faster, and sometimes cheaper. There is a long and sorry history of poorly executed applications that failed not because the idea was bad, but because the presentation was poor.

The same is true of many aspects of marketing. Although I succeeded in making a convincing presentation to company officials, many inventors don't feel comfortable cold-calling people they don't know and then making presentations to individuals who may not understand the concept. Here again, you must be brutally honest and completely realistic not just about the potential of your device, but about your own skills and abilities.

Passion for Your Idea

One thing you must understand clearly is that if you want to be successful in this business, you need to realize that you are not only the inventor of your idea, but the chief marketer as well. Nobody knows it as well as you do and nobody is going to have as much passion. You have to be able to communicate the basic facts to anyone you come in contact with.

Guy Kawasaki, the noted entrepreneur and founder of Garage Technology Ventures, an early-stage venture capital firm located in Silicon Valley, says that anyone looking for investors must have an "elevator pitch" ready at all times. Basically, this is a quick and concise explanation of your idea that can be presented during the few minutes it takes the elevator door to close and open again a few floors later.

You can develop your pitch by practicing it on friends and family members. It will prove to be extremely valuable, not only for you, but for those who invest in your product. After all, nobody knows it better or has more passion for it than you.

"An idea, first and foremost, must have an underlying compelling need," says Christopher Chavez, president and CEO of ANS Medical, a major developer of neuromodulation products. "You must be able to demonstrate that you're solving a problem that needs to be solved, that there is a real reason to innovate."

Physicians are very good at finding clinical problems that cry out for a better procedure or device. Yet the problem to be solved must be big enough to interest a medical device company or investor.

"There must not only be a major clinical need, but there must be a substantial number of patients," says Chavez, explaining his company's approach to evaluating ideas. "In addition, it must not just be a 'me too' idea. In other words, you may find a different way to treat a problem, but inevitably it's got to be better than the current gold standard in order to make investing in it worthwhile."

In order to determine whether you can meet the criteria of companies like ANS, you must have a solid appreciation for your device and its potential and you must also understand the market and business needs of the company you're pitching. It takes a lot of time and effort – perhaps more than you're really willing or able to invest.

While device companies such as ANS are willing to consider and take on specific technologies from inventors, many venture capital funds are only looking for companies with seasoned management and a solid track record of nurturing devices to success. These funds invest the capital of numerous investors and are looking for a specific return and a precise timeline for achieving liquidity.

"For the first-time inventor [who is trying to start a company], I would say he has no business doing what he's doing," declares Dr. T. Forcht "Teo" Dagi, president of Cordova Technologies, LLC and a managing partner at Atlanta-based Cordova Technology Partners. "The first thing he needs to do is get professional help, because the likelihood that he's going to succeed and be able to amass the capital required to take a company into the market is as close to zero as it can possibly be."

Dagi can tick off a litany of reasons why the lone inventor faces near insurmountable odds. They range from the difficulty of securing a defendable patent in the face of adversaries who are more than willing to outspend you in court to the need to understand the market, the structure of a company and its boards, the regulatory process, the technical aspects of manufacturing and quality control, not to mention the intricacies of venture funding. Just as Thomas Shaw discovered with his retractable syringe, it takes more than a superior product to crack open a market.

"Most inventors fail because they simply don't have the sophistication, much less the money, to get this done," Dagi adds. "On average, to take a medical device technology to market is a matter of tens of millions of dollars. That's not something most people can support on their own. Some can, but most can't."

The Best Exit

At this point, you may be asking, "Just what are my options then? Should I give up?" The answer is, not at all. Let me explain what I consider to be the only true exit strategy for the vast majority of inventors. It is time tested, and many inventors have used it successfully. You must find a partner, an entrepreneur or a venture capitalist who is willing to take your device and your idea and run with it.

In the profiles of several of the inventors in the next section, one of the central elements of their success was finding a partner who could help them develop their ideas into a viable business product. The quality that these partners bring to the equation isn't typically technical expertise, but rather it's their drive, entrepreneurial skill, and an understanding of business realities.

Richard Schatz found an exit strategy for himself and Julio Palmaz thanks in large part to his ability to network with all the right people. He met Phil Romano at a formal dinner party and, using a napkin, sketched out the idea of the heart stent. As a wealthy restaurateur, Romano had no prior scientific training or medical device experience, but he immediately saw the idea's potential.

It was a chance meeting, and many great connections are made this way. But like everything else, the more you work at it, the more likely you are to find your own partner or benefactor.

Another example is David Muir. He was a quadriplegic with Duchenne muscular dystrophy when he invented a valve that enabled patients with tracheotomies to speak. His device became commercially available to hundreds of thousands in his same situation after he met Patricia Passy, the wife of a noted University of California pulmonologist, who saw the possibilities of the device. Although not a wealthy investor like Romano, she was consumed by the passion of this young man and of his idea's potential. Together they founded a company that developed and marketed the Passy-Muir speaking valve, which helped to enshrine Muir's name in history.

Start Me Up

Perhaps your idea – and your faith in it – is so big that you want to create your own company. If that's the case, then your work has just begun.

Angel financing is a first step, but you'll also need to move forward through various venture capitalist (VC) rounds. At each step, the stakes get higher, along with the money available. The demands also rise, particularly with VCs who are investing other people's money. They must have a clear idea of when they will get a return and how much. Once you get to this stage, you're really in the big leagues.

While it may be nice to dream about being the CEO of a company, the reality is often quite different. Few start-ups succeed, and even those that do often go through tumultuous times and frequent changes of leadership and personnel. That path is probably not for you. Those who want to form their own company with little business experience and only a great idea may be confusing an exit strategy for their device with their own desire to escape their current job situation. This confusion can be a recipe for disaster.

You must realize that your job is being an inventor, not an entrepreneur or CEO of a business. As such, you have to realize both the potential and limitations of both yourself and your device.

Many inventors have approached venture funds and been offered a deal for their device that seemed shockingly low. The fund agrees to form a company, conduct necessary testing, seek out additional rounds of funding, and take the device to market. You, the inventor, will get, say, 10 percent of the possible revenues from the company. "Now wait a minute," you say. "If I form my own company, then I'll get 100 percent of the take. Why should I give all that up? Despite what everyone says, why shouldn't I at least give it a try?"

Yes, it's true that if you do it yourself and retain ownership and control of the invention, you could realize a much bigger payday down the road. It's possible. Sometimes it happens. Not very often, but it does every now and then.

What you have to decide is whether the risk is worth it to you. As Dagi pointed out, the amount of knowledge you need to acquire and the hurdles you must overcome are numerous.

"If an inventor tries to start his own company, then he has maybe a five percent chance of success," says Gerard van Hamel Platerink, a principal with Atlanta-based Accuitive Medical Ventures. "If he goes with an experienced venture fund, those odds improve to maybe 50 percent."

Accuitive is a "one-stop shop" that provides venture funding coupled with an incubator for new companies built around devices. They do reach out to inventors with new technologies because they fill the gap of business and operational experience left by most venture funds like Dagi's Cordova Ventures.

By coming in early and taking on the burden of developing the product, doing necessary testing, and really applying a sound business model to the process, Accuitive is often able to create a product that is salable in the market and attractive to larger VC funds. It is this experience that the inventor is able to capitalize on, thus raising the odds for success.

Companies can also help inventors to see the real market potential of a device. You may invest large sums of money into securing a patent, developing a prototype, and even setting up a company only to find that it doesn't really have a market.

"Somebody may invest $20,000 to $30,000 and they think they've done something really fantastic," says Chavez. "Yet there may be 10 or 15 reasons not to go forward with it that they aren't aware of."

He advises inventors to develop relationships with one or more companies or funds that can help them determine the true marketability of an idea.

Making the Right Decision

For many inventors, deciding on how to get your device to market and with whom you should sign a deal can be a difficult decision. Many VCs have seen inventors walk away from deals, convinced they could raise their own funding and do it themselves. Then, a year or two later, they come back seeking the same deal, but by then technology has passed them by, and the fund is usually no longer interested.

Even when they accept a deal, some inventors have left money on the table because they didn't want to give up such a large share of the company. Then a few months or a year later, the company has burned through its bank account and goes down for want of a little more capital.

"If the money is there, take it," advises John Guzowski, vice president of finance at a medical device company. "Those companies ultimately went out of business because they didn't have that extra million or two dollars. They didn't want to give away that extra share of the company, and in the end lost everything."

What is the best use of your time and resources? Medical doctors in particular often find it difficult to concede that they can't do something. After all, we are a can-do, success-oriented, problem-solving bunch. Our egos tell us we can, even when the facts tell us it's unlikely.

Whatever you decide, make sure you move forward clear-eyed and ready to do what's best for yourself and your invention. Many inventors may approach venture funds or angel investors with suspicion, wondering if they're going to steal their idea. That distrust can surface when a fund refuses to sign a Nondisclosure Agreement as a prelude to looking at your idea. While I suggest getting these signed whenever possible, the fact that a company refuses to do so doesn't necessarily mean they're out to get you. On the other hand, some companies will sign a Nondisclosure Agreement if it is drawn narrowly enough and the discussions don't venture beyond the limits set forth in the document.

Companies such as Accuitive look at many similar ideas over a period of time, and they can't really be bound by an agreement that could prevent them from looking at other technology. The VC world is a small one and reputation is everything. So it's unlikely that they will take advantage of you. To do so would quickly dry up the flow of ideas, as inventors found them to be untrustworthy. In addition, they know that successful inventors tend to produce multiple ideas over a period of time. One good invention usually leads to another, and it is in the companies' best interest to build long-term relationships, so don't be overly concerned in this area.

As we discussed in the chapter on added value, there are other steps you can take to protect your idea, such as filing a provisional patent application, keeping a log of contacts, and putting your ideas down on paper in the form of a description with drawings.

Look closely at the deals you're offered, and make a judgment about whether it's the best one you can get. Don't be swayed by your ego or the idea that your next door neighbor used to run a small company and he might help you. You must base your decision solely on the numbers and reality.

Chapter 25

ANGELS AND VENTURE CAPITALISTS
MONEY FOR YOUR IDEAS

Phil Romano didn't look like your typical venture capitalist. When he arrived at the University of Texas Health Science Center in San Antonio to visit Dr. Julio Palmaz for the first time, he attracted quite a few stares. While he was wearing the requisite Italian suit, he hadn't bothered to put on socks. To complete the unconventional look, his long hair was pulled back in a ponytail.

Yet for Palmaz, the inventor of the heart stent, Romano was truly an angel bearing gifts. The young physician and his partner, Dr. Richard Schatz, needed funds if they were going to continue their work on this new approach to dealing with the ravages of heart disease.

Before he was done, Romano had invested $250,000 for a 30 percent share in a three-way venture, which was enough to continue research and development. By the time the device was sold to Johnson & Johnson, the total investment, from all sources, topped more than $100 million.

This is a story that nearly every would-be inventor hopes will be his own. Since virtually no one has the personal funds to take a medical device all the way from conception to market, you're going to need some help along the way.

Romano, a restaurateur who owned eating establishments around the country, was looking for a place to invest the millions he had gotten from the sale of his Fuddruckers hamburger chain. Richard Schatz was in the right place at the right time to make the pitch that piqued his interest.

Romano was the angel investor they desperately needed. In the course of your own inventing career, you will have to seek out similar sources of funding. Asking others for money is perhaps the last thing you might want to do, but it is almost always a necessity if you want to see your idea on the market.

Friends, Family, Angels, and Venture Capitalists

Many entrepreneurial inventors will begin using their own personal resources, such as savings, credit cards, and lines of credit, to foot pre-launch expenses and initial seed investments for their companies. For those who lack available liquidity, borrowing against 401(k) funds, retirement accounts, and home equity is not uncommon. Obviously, betting the farm, so to speak, on an untried product takes a good bit of courage or foolhardiness. Only the individual can say how much of his life savings he can prudently invest – and be willing to lose. Much depends on your immediate cash needs, short-to immediate-term goals, and where in the life cycle you find yourself.

A more sensible course – and one followed by nearly every successful investor – is to use OPM (other people's money) whenever possible. There are many different types and sources of this kind of funding, but they can usually be placed in one of three categories. The first of these is friends and family. Then there are angel investors such as Phil Romano, who support small and early-stage companies. And finally, there are venture capitalists, who typically invest other people's money in later funding rounds for selected projects as part of a "venture fund." As you might guess, these last two breeds, while similar, are often very different in their approach to investing in new inventions.

Soliciting investments from friends and family is often the first place you want to start when you are putting together funds for a start-up. By some estimates, 90 percent of all start-ups receive this kind of funding, which is more plentiful than you might think. In 2003, for example, one survey found that so-called nonprofessional investors contributed approximately $108 billion to new companies – far more than the $18.4 billion shelled out by VCs.

The people who surround you and to whom you are related may not understand technology, but they know you. The money your mother chips in is going to be an investment in you, not the company.

"There's significant advantage to friends and family, because you don't have all the onerous terms and the valuations can be very reasonable," says John Guzowski, who has been a participant in numerous start-up ventures. "You don't have to deal with any agendas, and basically these people are betting on you – the jockey – to ride the company to success."

While this type of funding is often easy to get, it carries its own special risks. First, unless you're related to a millionaire, the amounts tend to be small compared to those available from a VC fund – ranging from a few thousand dollars to less than $500,000. Most investors receive simple common stock in return for cash, or a loan arrangement is made that repays the amount with interest at a later date. Secondly, since start-up ventures have a high rate of failure, there's a significant likelihood that investors will lose their initial outlay, much less realize a profit. It's easier to lose a stranger's money than it is your brother's, who you'll still have to face at holiday get-togethers.

Yet the upside will outweigh the risks in many cases. Along with fewer strings attached, this money may be a necessary prelude to getting either angel or VC funding. A few hundred grand can facilitate the development work needed to get your device to the point where those with deeper pockets are willing to even look at it.

In this situation, you must proceed with extreme caution and realize that you are responsible for the money of people who you care about and who trust you. As in every aspect of business, ventures like this are filled with cautionary tales.

Take, for example, the story of my friend Dennis, who lives in San Francisco and was involved in several of the Internet ventures that sprang up during the city's tech boom in the late '90s. A seasoned investor, he's someone who understands the inner workings of both business finance and venture funding and someone I frequently called on for advice about my own business and professional dealings.

A couple of years ago, Dennis joined up with a group of tech veterans to launch a new start-up. With VC funding scarce, he approached his family and circle of friends about investing in a company that had a strong chance of making it. His mother and uncle both withdrew money from their savings accounts and IRAs after hearing convincing talks about the prospects for the company. So did several other friends. He even approached me, but at the time all my capital was tied up in getting my medical practice up and running.

The entire group raised quite a bit of money, and Dennis was a central partner with a 25 percent share. That's when things began to go awry – not with the company or its products, but with the group of partners who owned it. His two partners turned against him and he soon found himself being pushed out of the venture altogether.

The company issued more shares and diluted his holdings from 25 percent down to just two percent. He was blindsided, and so were the people he had brought into the deal. In the process, he learned a painful lesson.

"Regardless of your strong relationships and trust in your business partners, not only should you hire a corporate attorney to draw up the documents that represent the corporation, but you should have separate personal representation so that you understand how these documents affect you," he now says.

It was too late for Dennis when he realized that his own interests had not been protected. By starting a company with two men he thought were his friends, he allowed himself to be distracted from provisions in the terms of the corporate documents that let them take over.

"Had I spent a few hundred dollars and had my personal attorney review the documents, I'd have been in a very different position when everything went south," he says.

While Dennis still believes in using friends and family for the right deals, he'll approach things much differently next time. He never again wants to be put in the position of explaining to his mom that her son won't be running the company after all.

On Wings of Gold

As the name implies, angel investors often appear out of nowhere to bestow largess on worthy inventors. Often, they are a source of funding when no other is available. Along with VCs, they make up two primary sources of funding for new companies and start-up ventures, but they differ significantly in what they can provide you.

Because angels are investing their own money, while the VC is charged with investing the money of others, several factors come into play. For example, an angel will typically give you more value for a stake in your company than will a VC. They also tend to be somewhat less risk-averse than VCs and more willing to invest in new and innovative devices.

Angel investors will come into the deal with a desired timeline and exit strategy in mind, but because it's their own money, they have much greater flexibility. A VC, on the other hand, has a much more rigid schedule for the desired "liquidity event" that will return money to the investors – often pension funds – he represents.

Angels are often much more willing to get involved in the inner workings of a company and often bring a wealth of business and operations experience to the table. On the other hand, you won't find a VC anywhere near the day-to-day operations of the company unless he's occupying a board seat.

Finding an angel investor is somewhat like getting a date. You can wait by the phone for a call, or you can go to places where prospects are likely to be found. Being in the right places, along with looking presentable and being able to make witty conversation, greatly increases your chances of finding the right person, whether you're seeking an investor or romance.

Made up mostly of retired executives or wealthy professionals, with the occasional young entrepreneur rich from a successful IPO thrown in for good measure, the angel community is becoming more organized. In recent years, some have organized investment groups with websites and sometimes even paid staff. These groups have come together to form a trade organization called the Angel Capital Association, which holds an annual convention and presents educational programs designed to help angels make better investing decisions.

Of course, the search for your angel begins with personal preparation. As I detailed in the chapter on added value, there are a number of actions you can take that will make your idea more appealing and potentially more lucrative for an investor. A finely tuned business plan, coupled with "patent pending" stamped on each document, endorsements, and the other features that improve the salability of your device, enables you to make a powerful case. And don't forget one final thing: Decide how much money you want. The final figure is always negotiable, but you must have a good starting point. If you can't name a figure, your angel may not take you seriously.

Make sure you've done those things first, and then set out to find the angel of your dreams.

Of course, money is one thing all investment angels have in common, but how they acquired it can vary widely. Some angels are highly successful business-people like Phil Romano, while others are independently wealthy individuals or professionals such as doctors or lawyers, or even investment clubs and other types of organizations. Their interests vary widely as well, but you can be sure they are also calculated risk-takers. Otherwise, they wouldn't be handing out money to develop unproven ideas like yours.

An angel may be someone you know, or you may find him through someone you've met. Ask your attorney, business advisor, or other professionals for any leads they can provide. You can find them in your own city by contacting investment clubs, business organizations and affiliations, or perhaps even a local economic development agency. Many major cities have organizations that bring together angels and investment opportunities. A simple Internet search will return numer-ous sites that can put you in touch with angel investors you can approach for financing.

It's also helpful to read your local and regional business journals. They will contain up-to-date news on recent deals and give you a sense of economic condi-tions and where the money is going.

If and when you do find an angel, he will interview you and ask lots of prob-ing questions about your idea and its potential. You'll have to be able to answer them with in-depth knowledge and passion. Wealthy people didn't get that way by throwing away money on harebrained ideas, despite appearances when all that cash was tossed around on the dot-com fiasco of the late '90s. Many of them will be investing as much in you as they are in your idea. If they don't see both compe-tence and enthusiasm, they likely won't have a good feeling about you and proba-bly won't write the check.

"I invested because the idea was good, and they were able to explain it in lay-man's terms using pictures and studies," recalls Phil Romano.

His attorneys, accountants, and other advisors told him it was a crazy idea and didn't make good investment sense. While he understood their reasoning, like so many other canny investors, he also knew that sometimes you have to let your instincts pick up where the numbers leave off.

He liked the idea, but even more than that, he liked Palmaz and Schatz and was convinced of its value by their passion. Besides, if it turned out the device was a bust, because research and development costs were then still tax-deductible, he could recover part of his investment.

Angels like Romano may also want to see how much of your own money you've put into the project. So prior to approaching an angel, you should at least consider friends and family as funding sources. As I have noted before, asking people you know for money can be one of the hardest jobs you'll ever undertake, but having a pot of ready cash that can be combined with money from an angel will give you a stronger bargaining position.

At the same time, you also need to make sure you feel comfortable with the potential investor. If you're putting together funding to develop your device to a point where it will be of interest to a potential buyer, decide how much you're willing to give up for the funding. Obviously, your angel will want a return on his money.

If you're seeking someone to help develop your idea and then sell it to a larger company, then you want someone who has experience, or access to experience, in negotiating deals of that nature.

Perseverance is all-important in your search. If your first attempt at finding an investor isn't successful, don't give up. There are lots of angel investors out there and you can always approach another one. If you choose an investor who has a prior history of financing inventions such as yours, your chances of getting the financing are greatly increased.

Capital Ideas

Angels are good for the early rounds of investing in the development of a new product. However, if your product is a true platform technology, larger amounts of venture funding and greater expertise may also be needed.

In that case, you will need to seek out venture capitalists to make larger investments. This funding most often comes in the form of a series of "rounds." After the initial investments, the company must meet specified "milestones" in order to receive the next infusion of cash. The idea is that these rounds will ultimately lead to a liquidity event, such as a sale to a larger company or an IPO.

VCs operate under strict investment criteria that shape where they make placements, as well as the return they expect. With them, it's often strictly a numbers game. They aren't moved by anything other than the projected return on investment.

As a result, they are more likely to be looking for a device or product that is well-developed and proven and that offers the opportunity for a sure return. As a result, VCs are often less likely to invest in truly new, innovative, and, of course, unproven ideas. A study by two venture capitalists published in the technology magazine *IEEE Spectrum* found that heavy investments from venture funds typically produced little innovation. They looked at 1,303 high-tech IPOs for a 10-year period ending in 2002 and sorted out the ones that were VC funded and the ones that weren't. The level of innovation during that time period actually dropped, even as VC funding rose dramatically. I suspect that a look at VC funding in the medical device industry might produce very similar results.

It's easy to understand then that whereas angels often jump into extremely early stage ideas, VCs are more cautious. After all, it's not their own money that they're spending, so there are more people to answer to if things go awry. Therefore, you stand a better chance of securing VC funding if your device has been developed and you have given it as much "value added" as possible.

Along with money, VCs also bring connections and relationships for an exit strategy – something that most angels don't possess.

"In fact, venture capitalists are the experts of the exit strategies," says Guzowski. "They have the relationships with either the investment banking firms to help you go public or, in many cases, have relationships with potential acquirers. Often they may have been previous clients, so they can put together a deal very easily."

It's important to understand the needs of the VC when you're thinking about raising money for your idea. This is a point that can be difficult for many inventors who have great passion and enthusiasm for their device and an unshakable belief in their own abilities.

The VCs will look at each deal through the microscope of their individual firm's policies and guidelines, as well as current market conditions. They're going to be swayed not by emotion, but by market size and return on investment. It's also unlikely that they are going to share your vision of how important this particular device will become. After all, they don't get paid for having visions.

"Most of the sources of capital are institutional, and most of them are not interested in individual technology, but in portfolios of technologies," says Teo Dagi of Cordova Technology Partners. "The reason is that the understanding that any given technology is likely to fail precludes them from intelligently investing in one portfolio or one technology. They want to invest in a basket of technologies."

Dagi brings a unique perspective to the world of venture capital. A Harvard-educated neurosurgeon, he was deeply involved in research when he had his own particular epiphany about the way medical research is funded.

He had just accepted a position at a major research university where he saw a deep commitment to the development of technology. Yet no sooner had he arrived, than he saw that commitment wither and die.

"I saw it fail, not for any nefarious reason, but only because the priorities within the university and the priorities within healthcare funding had changed," he recalls. "I decided that [technology funding] was something that I wanted to learn how to do."

So he added an MBA to his already impressive list of credentials and began to explore the idea of how to fund medical technologies, how to bring them to market, and how to fund a capital portfolio.

As a participant in the venture capital arena, Dagi has seen firsthand how priorities are shaped and decisions are made.

"People who are sophisticated investors will not invest in a technology," he says. "They will invest in management. So what you're really doing is investing in a few companies. That's a different situation than investing in a few technologies."

With individual technologies, it becomes difficult to gauge just how well a particular device may do in the market. There are too many variables, including doctor acceptance, reimbursement, and the vagaries of patent law and competitive pressure. Better to put their money on a team that knows how to make technology work. Then if one product fails, they have the ability to move on to something new without the whole enterprise going down because of a single device.

That explains why venture funds have very specific points along the timeline of invention development in which they want to invest.

"Typically, venture funds only want to come in at the point where they see something has been done with the IP that's proven the principle, such as studies on animals or a prototype," says Gerard van Hamel Platerink, ofAccuitive Medical Ventures. "They want to come in here with a pretty clean product that looks likely to turn into something they can put money into and then exit within a specified time period."

An inventor will spend three or more years evolving the idea, securing the patents, and developing the IP to the point where he actually has a substantial device to show to potential investors.

"It's real, and it can turn into something that's worth marketing as an actual product," says Van Hamel Platerink.

It is only at this point that most VCs are willing to put in money for getting the product off the ground. Getting the idea to this point is often the most difficult period for the inventor. He may not be able to find funding because he doesn't have the right connections in the investor market, or he may not have the expertise to develop a working prototype. Out of virtually thousands of ideas, only a handful make it to the stage where they can even be considered by VCs.

Accuitive is one of only a few venture funds that also support an incubator where young ideas and companies can be nurtured before going out into the marketplace on their own. It fills the gap between conception of an idea and worthwhile product by providing an environment in which the idea can become a market-worthy reality.

It is the sort of company that appeals to physicians and other professionals who don't have the time to leave their practice or their job but who want to see their idea developed. An inventor can license his patent or IP to the company, which then uses in-house talent to execute patent development and handle regulatory issues, along with management to carry it forward to the point where a typical venture fund is willing to bite.

An inventor can show up with an idea "scrawled on a napkin," and if that scrawl has the look of something that can be protected and developed into market-worthy IP, then the company is likely to take it on. By taking this route, the inventor is spared the time and expense of filing for a patent, developing a prototype, and seeking funding.

While Accuitive is willing to look at an idea that is far less developed, they apply the same criteria to determine worth as other VCs do. Value is driven by the market size that a device can potentially serve. If the market isn't big enough, then there isn't enough value to the VC. Each fund has a predetermined market size that they're seeking. For example, they may only look at deals that promise a potential market of $100 million or more in sales. They will determine an average selling price (ASP) for each device and multiply that by the potential number of procedures. If your product is geared toward a market that's smaller than their cutoff, then typically they'll have no interest, no matter how innovative.

"It's more of an art than a science," admits Van Hamel Platerink. "You're talking about products that aren't going to have revenues for six to eight years. So there's a lot of forecasting involved, but, generally speaking, we take a market-first approach. Rather than chase technologies and try to fit them into markets, which is a very common way of doing things, we look at big unmet market needs and determine what existing technology or IP will serve that market."

In addition to market size, an important consideration is whether or not the new product is a real improvement over existing products. In many areas of medicine, the existing "gold standard" treatment is low and begs for improvement.

"The spine is a good example," says Van Hamel Platerink. "There is a bunch of stuff going on there where you have 450,000 [spinal] fusions a year, and it's a pretty basic way of trying to treat a disk that's not right. These are the areas where, because we've invented enough devices in our time, we can sit in a room and come up with creative ways of treatment that will fit a certain market."

Is It Right for You?

Many inventors may be relieved to know that they don't necessarily have to do all the dirty work needed to get their device to market. Others may be aghast when they learn that by not doing it themselves, the payoff is only a fraction of the potential they might realize if they took it all the way on their own. This realization is often particularly hard to swallow for physicians who often believe there is nothing they can't do themselves.

"The trick is to work with physician inventors who understand that they don't have the commercial experience necessary to turn some IP into something that can be fundable by a VC," says Van Hamel Platerink. "These are people who've gone through all that training and who are very smart people. So it's not unusual that they think they can do everything themselves."

In general, inventors don't usually have the business skills and market savvy to pull off the creation of their own company, despite having a next door neighbor who used to run a company in a past life and some relatives willing to ante up their life savings. Some do acquire the skills and some even become successful. You must ask yourself, however, whether you want to go to that length, abandon your practice, and devote yourself to working gruelingly long weeks for an uncertain payoff. Better to let the experts take over and spend your time inventing more devices that you can sell.

One of the biggest hurdles the solitary inventor faces is not what he knows, but what he doesn't know. The typical medical device company must bring together many arcane areas of expertise to work together. No one individual possesses all the skills needed to carry such a project forward.

"If you're holding it all yourself, unless you have tremendous financial resources, you're not going to have the ability to surround yourself with the experts that you need," observes John Guzowski. "So it does most often take some form of outside capital to acquire those experts. You have to recognize that you will need engineers to do your research and development, regulatory experts, clinical experts, and business operations people."

Surrounding yourself with all the experts you will need to run an effective medical device company requires tremendous amounts of capital. In fact, one area in particular illustrates the problems that the inventor faces in going it alone.

At a 17-person start-up company I visited recently, three of them are charged with doing nothing other than handling regulatory and quality control issues. The FDA requires that every medical device has its own quality assurance system. You can't simply walk out to your garage and throw some parts together and hope that you can get it through regulatory approval. You must develop a precise and well-defined system of processes, testing, and controls that ensures that the device works the way it is supposed to and meets all requirements for safety. Experts are trained and credentialed in setting up systems like this that meet FDA requirements.

The further you try to take your invention, the less your chances of realizing that big payday. Finding your own Phil Romano is perhaps the best discovery that any inventor can make. You'll be much happier in the long run and probably a great deal wealthier too.

Chapter 26

TECHNOLOGY TRANSFER
FROM UNIVERSITY TO MARKET

In the not-so-distant past, universities shared newly acquired knowledge with society through teaching and publishing scholarly papers. Now they've become a prime source of new ideas, scientific advancements, and great discoveries. While academic researchers sometimes become entrepreneurs building companies around these discoveries, most often they are the prime source of many of the new drugs and medical devices that corporate America needs.

In just the past decade, turning academic research into marketable products has grown from just $200 million to a more than $1.3 billion industry. Academic institutions with well-funded research efforts have now realized that discoveries by their faculty may have moneymaking potential when patented and then licensed to a company ready to turn that knowledge into a product. Some discoveries may even be big enough to justify forming a company to develop and market the resulting products. To develop that market, a number of universities have developed their own incubators, where infant companies can be nurtured into hopefully strong and viable enterprises.

With so many academic institutions facing rising costs and declining support, commercial licensing of research seems an obvious means to help bridge the budget gap. Yet the road to commercialization can be strewn with obstacles and unexpected pitfalls for the faculty member, the university, and sometimes the company seeking to license a new discovery for commercial development.

The Perils of Academia

Traditionally, many faculty members have conducted research without consideration of whether or not they had the right to use any of the technologies that were part of their efforts. At least some were covered by patents held by parties other than the university itself and raised the prospect of infringement.

Before tech transfer became such a pressing issue in academia, many researchers believed they were protected from infringement claims by the "experimental use" exception.

John W. Holcomb, a partner at Knobbe Martens Olson & Bear LLP, a law firm specializing in patent, copyright, trademark, and trade secret matters, writes that, "The university or nonprofit alleges that it is not liable to the patent owner, even though the university or nonprofit is practicing the invention claimed in the patent, because its use is merely 'experimental' or for purely research purposes. In other words, the university or nonprofit argues that its practice of the patented invention is not intended for commercial exploitation so it should not have to pay the patent owner any damages or royalties."

That defense was largely rendered useless by a federal appeals court decision that found the institution was acting as a business in a case involving its laser research lab. Legal authorities agree that this decision raised considerable risk for academic institutions that conduct research without benefit of patent clearance and any third parties that might then license that technology.

For the independent inventor such as myself, one of the prime issues that comes up in developing technology in a university environment is how the university protects its proprietary interests in that technology. While a resident at a major university, I was appalled to learn that my employer might own the device I had developed and that I would be limited to a 30 percent share of the profits at best.

Fortunately, this restrictive and unrealistic policy didn't apply to me because I had never signed a contract – although it did apply to my professors and attending physicians – and I was able to move forward without seeing my hard-won gains gobbled up by the institution.

Yet these policies are a fact of life for many inventors who work at universities, and they must be carefully considered.

Dr. Todd Sherer, director of the Technology Transfer Office at Emory University notes, "The point that deals with the money is always the most contentious part. We're also mandated under federal law to share some portion of the revenues with inventors as well. It's very different from the corporate world, where you might get a promotion, but that's it. You don't share in the royalties down the road."

Indeed, for the few academic investigators who have defied all the odds and have developed a new blockbuster AIDS drug, the rewards have been great. But these entrepreneurial individuals are the exception.

Most researchers who come up with ideas face a daunting task. The pressure within the university is to do research and publish it. Those who do these two things successfully are rewarded by their faculty peers with tenure and promotions. Bringing a new device to market or founding a start-up, on the other hand, won't get you tenure, and in the eyes of your peers, may even hurt your chances of success within the ivory tower.

To make matters worse, the ability to patent an original concept can be greatly diminished if a researcher has published a paper or presented a poster at a conference revealing the idea to the world. At that point it may be in the public domain and can't be protected for commercialization.

While the corporate world typically doesn't reward successful researchers with anything more than a bonus or gold watch, the academic researcher can count on getting a little more of the profits for his idea.

At Emory, for example, the university has developed a formula that seeks to equitably share any royalties or profits with the inventors, while also allowing the school, the department, and its attendant lab to recoup expenses and share in the largess.

According to Sherer, "A simple rule of thumb is that there tends to be three parties: the inventors, the department or lab or school, and the central administration. They tend to get one third of the revenues each."

At Emory, the first $25,000 of revenue derived from royalties and sales of an idea goes entirely to the inventors. The university takes anything above $25,000 but less than $4 million and recovers patent expenses off the top.

"And then we distribute 33 percent of that split equally among all the inventors," Sherer explains.

An additional 33 percent goes to the department to split with the individual lab that developed the research. An additional 10 percent is parceled out to the individual department (such as the School of Medicine), and the final .24 percent is the general university's share.

Net revenues above $4 million are broken down with 25 percent going to the inventors, 33 percent to the department and lab, and 17 percent earmarked for the school. The final 25 percent ends up in the treasury of the university itself.

According to Sherer, Emory is in the middle of the pack when it comes to generosity to inventors, but the formula tends to be pretty consistent throughout the academic world.

Patent Factories

Across town from Emory, the Georgia Institute of Technology produced a state-leading $370 million in research in 2003 and filed 60 patent applications, says George Harker, the director of its Office of Technology Licensing. While it can take three to seven years to navigate the U.S. Patent Office approval process, his school typically wins approval on 30 to 40 of its patent applications within one year.

This major engineering university is among a number of institutions across the country that have set up technology transfer offices to market patents and licenses for commercialization of technology spawned by research. Patents can be secured to protect everything from a groundbreaking new cancer drug to an improvement in an industrial process.

These offices frequently work directly with faculty to help them understand what is new and marketable and what isn't. Just like major corporations, they also retain ownership of what is patented and share a smaller portion of the gain with faculty. There is often little negotiation involved, as colleges and universities have written polices that specify what share a faculty inventor can expect to receive.

Sometimes it isn't much if the university isn't very good at finding buyers and negotiating with big companies. Dr. Richard Schmidt, whose story I present in the next chapter, gained little from two patents he developed while in the employ of major universities. Despite his brilliant innovation, he has little to show for it.

His story is a cautionary tale for any faculty inventor who wants to stay in an academic environment while he does his work. Certainly, for many professors whose primary passion is teaching and research and who don't want to be bothered with the intricacies of patents and commercialization, it may be the best way to go. Many are happy with the deals they get.

Tech transfer may be particularly true to institutions where there has been little commercialization in the past. At these institutions, the biggest obstacle is just getting the faculty to think in business terms.

"There was a lot of education to do," says Michael Gabridge, who serves as director of the Office of Technology Transfer and Economic Development at the Medical College of Georgia (MCG). "We let faculty know what patents were all about and what to do and what not to do along these lines."

Gabridge's office has grown along with the research program at MCG, which until five years ago was producing little in the way of marketable discoveries. The truth is that faculty members frequently have little or no experience – and sometimes interest – in developing a business around their research projects.

At Georgia Tech, the tech transfer operation has streamlined the process of bringing forth new patents by providing faculty with an invention disclosure form with which they can provide basic information about themselves, their discovery, and the markets for it.

George Harker receives about 200 to 300 of these forms each year. Before filing a patent application, the office's expert staff must determine that the invention is marketable enough to at least earn back the $12,000 to $20,000 required to file an application.

Typically, only a handful of submissions make it through the process. Those that do may eventually earn the inventor a few thousand to a few hundred thousand dollars in royalties.

To earn those fees, however, universities must find companies willing to purchase licenses or invest in the technology.

"We send out periodic mailings and copies of our [patent] catalog to companies that we feel might have an interest in acquiring our technology," says Michael Gabridge, who recently added a full-time marketing specialist to his staff. "At the same time, we're reactive because we get inquiries – sometimes almost cold calls – from people with a technology shopping list asking, 'What do you have in this area?'"

Faculty are sometimes the best source of marketing ideas by providing leads of interested companies and also by spreading the word about a particular technology at meetings and conventions.

While the potential for hitting it big with a new market-disrupting drug to fight cancer is exciting for both university officials and faculty alike, the pitfalls on the road to riches are many.

Even after patenting the discoveries, universities must still not only find customers, but must successfully negotiate a deal that fairly compensates everyone. Most universities have developed policies that set schedules of payments that can include royalties, equity in the company, and milestone fees to be paid along the FDA regulatory process.

While this process often suits the typical faculty member quite well, it may not be such a good deal for the more entrepreneurial minded. The university, like the large company research department, owns the work of the faculty member who is little more than an employee. While deals from university to university may vary considerably, they seldom give the inventor the full value of his discovery.

Rules of Research

To avoid the conflicts of interest that could arise between academic research and business, many universities set strict guidelines about how much time faculty can devote to an outside company. At state universities like Georgia Tech and the Medical College of Georgia, a faculty member can't take more than a 25 percent equity share in a company. They are usually prohibited from holding an executive position that takes too much time away from their faculty duties.

Yet academic institutions tend to be supportive of those who want to turn their research into a start-up that could provide direct economic value to the state.

"We like to promote start-ups because they tend to stay close to home," says George Harker. "We also like to license the technology to Georgia-based companies that produce jobs in the state."

Medical device companies are often on the lookout for new discoveries produced by universities and are frequently found looking through discovery catalogs published by the institution or consulting with tech transfer officials. While many a faculty member may not realize the market value of their device, you can be sure these companies do.

Section V

INVENTORS IN-DEPTH

Chapter 27

DAVID KU
PHYSICIAN, INVENTOR, ENTREPRENEUR

In this age of increasing specialization, it's rare for any one individual to move successfully from one area of skill and endeavor to another. Those who succeed tend to be not only very smart, but very flexible.

Dr. David Ku, who has been a practicing surgeon, a university professor and researcher holding multiple degrees, and a successful founder of several start-up companies, is one of those people.

Today, he combines all these interests as president and CEO of SaluMedica, a company he founded in 1998 after developing the biomaterial known as Salubria, which is used in orthopedic implants.

The story of his entrepreneurial ventures grew out of his dedication to learning, research, and healing patients.

"I did research," says Ku about his early career in academia. "I did clinical work, and then I tried to marry the two and then go back and forth between them."

He earned a master's and PhD in aerospace engineering from the Georgia Institute of Technology while simultaneously completing work for a doctorate at Emory University School of Medicine. Later, while on staff at the University of Chicago, he plunged into the hectic and often grueling life of an academic clinician. While it was an experience that gave him considerable satisfaction, he soon realized that it was also consuming him.

"I loved being a surgeon," he says. "I loved taking care of patients and seeing them get better, but I also loved research and I wanted to be able to potentially impact thousands, or perhaps millions, of people."

He also realized that he was spending so much time in medicine that it left him with very little time and energy for his family. Faced with that disturbing reality, he decided that he didn't want to become the prototypical academic surgeon with a wife who felt lonely and neglected and children who barely knew him.

Ku was confronted with a choice. Did he want to continue along the path of being a practicing clinician or should he opt for research and more time for his family and other interests? For him, the answer was obvious. He chose research, and was able to combine his unique training in medicine with a doctorate in fluid mechanics.

"I felt that I could contribute more that way than if I stayed in clinical medicine," he recalls. "I knew I was a good doctor, but I also knew there were 10 other good doctors who could take care of my patients."

While there are many skillful and talented clinicians, few could bring his knowledge and background to the research arena. It was there that he believed he could make a unique contribution that would help far more people than if he were to spend a lifetime in the operating room. Through the avenue of research, he saw the opportunity to make breakthroughs that could have immediate and beneficial applications in society.

"The practical things we work on do not win people Nobel Prizes," says Ku.

Instead of doing work that only ends up in publications sitting on university library shelves, he was determined to create products that had value in the marketplace and could make a patient's life better.

Ku moved south from Chicago to Atlanta, where he took a faculty position with the Georgia Institute of Technology. There, he began developing and filing patents on the first versions of a biomaterial that could be used in orthopedic implants.

While much has been written about technology transfer from universities to major corporations, in reality, few of the big players are interested in taking on an early-stage product. While they might be happy to pay you a premium for a well-developed device that can immediately begin contributing to the bottom line, they probably aren't willing to assume the financial risk associated with the development of a new medical device.

" [Large companies] are not really going to bring it in-house until it has been fully developed, and then they want it to be incubated with a traditional start-up model for a while," says Ku.

Handing the product off to a smaller company or venture fund proved to be difficult as well. The truth is that many of the marketing people who make decisions at these companies have a difficult time understanding how fast a technology can be developed, and then how well the market of physicians and other healthcare providers will accept it.

"They're not talking to doctors every day," he explains. "I was going to meetings and social functions where I could try out a bunch of ideas on doctors and see whether they made sense or not. I got an idea of where the marketplace really was going to be."

He realized that if he wanted to get his device to market, the surest route might be to do it himself. While many inventors believe they can pull off the difficult and time-consuming job of starting a company, few have either the skills or the connection to funds and resources to do so. Ku was a rare individual who combined both considerable scientific knowledge and research skills with an entrepreneurial spirit and an in-depth knowledge of the market.

In the course of his research, he had developed a biomaterial that could be used as an implant in orthopedic procedures, such as replacement cartilage for arthritic joints. With millions of American baby boomers fighting the effects of aging and determined to maintain their active lifestyles like no generation before them, finding a solution for this problem could uncover a potentially lucrative and rapidly expanding market.

"So we ended up developing it ourselves," says Ku. "We get to keep the intellectual property because we developed it in-house. We don't have to share it with someone who will sell it for money."

With proof of concept in hand, Ku set out to find investments from his many contacts. His passion for the idea quickly convinced a variety of angel investors that he was onto something. He found private placements, eschewing institutional investors who would demand excessive ownership in the company for their financial commitments. Soon he had the funds he needed to get his new company off the ground.

He also set about assembling a team that could take the company, located in a trendy renovated warehouse in downtown Atlanta, in the direction he envisioned.

"In a company, everyone is working toward a product and there is no individual glory, and so we're able to put together people with a complementary set of talents," he says. "One person doesn't need to know everything, because you have someone handling the regulatory issues, another (person) the manufacturing processes, and another development. That team fits together and you can put really excellent people together to strive within their individual niches."

Ku has learned a great deal on his path to entrepreneurship. From finding the right investors and the most competent managers to negotiating the regulatory process, he's tackled everything in the business arena. His experiences have helped him, of course, but Ku also puts them to work teaching other would-be entrepreneurs through a university course.

Aimed at engineers and other technology generators, the course covers the basics of accounting, reading balance sheets, the difference between the top and bottom lines, how to negotiate in the business arena, and other facts of company life. Beyond these business basics, he is able to offer intimate and up-to-date knowledge that can't be found in any textbook.

He is able to tell them, for example, which venture funds are currently making placements and what kinds of companies and products the funds are looking for.

"I bring that to them because I'm expecting our class graduates to turn around and think about starting a company within 6 to 12 months, and so they need this kind of timely knowledge," says Ku.

Indeed, those seeking to find their way along this seldom trod path could find no better guide than David Ku.

Chapter 28

DAVID MUIR
PATIENT/INVENTOR

Perseverance in the face of adversity is often a central factor in the success of any inventor. Finding within yourself the fortitude to keep going when everything around you says to give up is a quality that each of us must develop to one degree or another.

Success is also in finding the resources to bring your invention to reality. Often, that resource is a person who can take your idea and move it forward.

David Muir was a young man in despair when he made the transition from a patient with a debilitating condition to a revolutionary inventor whose work has bettered the lives of hundreds of thousands of people. The story of the inventor of the Passy-Muir speaking valve is a testament to ingenuity and determination in the face of overwhelming physical disability.

It is also a classic example of how the fires of creativity can be stoked by adversity. Great advances are seldom achieved when we're comfortable and everything seems right with the world.

A quadriplegic with Duchenne muscular dystrophy, this young man's life is one of the most inspiring in the annals of inventing.

It begins in 1984, when Muir was a young college student finishing what had been a tough semester and was busy preparing for another one. Confined to a wheelchair, he did much of his work using a voice-activated computer. For most people, this might seem like a virtual hell on earth, but filled with optimism and drive, Muir worked diligently to transcend his disability. He felt lucky to have loving parents who supported him in his quest to live a normal life.

He didn't realize that life was about to become far more difficult than he had ever imagined.

David Muir was tired. No matter how early he went to bed, he couldn't seem to get enough rest. He'd continually wake up weary and drained, and wished he could get just a little more sleep before heading off to class. Final exams had been exhausting, and the start of a new academic session was dragging him down rather than energizing him as usual.

He was still in bed one February morning when his mom, June Muir, decided not to wake him. She had seen how tired he was and decided that a few extra hours of sleep might be what he needed. As she closed the door to his room, however, she felt a twinge of uneasiness. Something just didn't seem right. She had never seen her son so exhausted, but she knew he had been working awfully hard lately. Maybe he was just pushing himself too much.

She headed out to the kitchen and spoke briefly with David's grandmother, asking her to watch David while she went shopping with her mother.

Just as she was about to leave, a nagging feeling welled up inside her. She suddenly knew that she needed to check on her son and she quickly turned and made her way back to David's room.

At his bedside, she looked down at him and gasped in horror. His frail body had taken on a bluish tint, and his breaths were shallow. "David, are you all right?" she asked insistently. When he failed to respond, she reached over and pressed the MedicAlert button on David's nightstand.

Less than 10 minutes later, paramedics were in David's room working on him. He had suffered respiratory arrest, which had been coming on for weeks. The early signs were the exhaustion he had felt and not recognized. The medics pushed a breathing tube down his throat and rushed him to the local emergency room.

Two days later, David woke up in a hospital room overflowing with brightly colored balloons and fresh flowers. At his side sat his parents, and other relatives and friends filled the small space. At first he was happy to see them, but he couldn't figure out why he was in this unfamiliar place.

Then he noticed that his mouth felt incredibly dry. He opened his mouth to ask for something to drink, but no words came out. His throat and nose were sore. At first he marveled at his lack of ability to form words, but it wasn't long before a sense of dread settled over him. This isn't right, he thought.

He soon learned that he had been intubated and placed on a ventilator, resulting in his loss of speech. In the days that followed, David realized just how important the ability to talk was in communicating even his simplest needs.

He wondered, "How am I going to get them to understand what I want?" The medical staff and his family had to ask yes or no questions, and David answered by blinking his eyes. They told him that the intubation was normal for his condition and that they would gradually wean him off of the ventilator. Therefore, David accepted this new situation and thought that after dealing with and overcoming his other physical disabilities, this one couldn't last for long.

Recovery did not come quickly, however. Doctors soon decided that he needed a tracheotomy because of his inability to be weaned from the ventilator and a declining ability to breathe properly. The procedure is usually reserved for those who need long-term support with a breathing machine. David didn't like the idea at all.

At first he resisted the procedure, even as doctors barraged him with horror stories about how he would not be able to speak again or even eat without the trach. Finally, his surgeon told him, "Let's make a deal. If you don't like it, I'll take it out."

David agreed. So the surgery was performed and David received a tracheotomy tube. His breathing cycles continued to be assisted by a ventilator. To further complicate matters, the trach tube being used was cuffed by a small balloon forming a seal. No air could come out of his mouth, and as a result, he was unable to speak.

Two weeks passed before he was finally allowed to go home, with a portable ventilator attached to his wheelchair.

By this time, David was becoming very good at using an alphabet board to communicate. But he still wanted to talk! The medical staff recommended a variation of the trach tube called a Communitrache. It was designed to provide a continuous airflow to the vocal chords, thus allowing speech.

The Communitrache, rather than provide a solution, created another problem. The constant airflow caused David's throat to dry out and subsequently it became very sore.

The incision in his throat and the assistance of the portable ventilator helped David to breathe a little easier, but he was still unable to speak. Because he was quadriplegic, he couldn't raise his hands to finger occlude the opening of the trach tube to redirect the air over his vocal chords to speak. This still made him dependent on others, which he hated. It was inconvenient and frustrating. To make matters worse, he was unable to wean himself from the ventilator.

David's optimism and belief in his own ability to overcome any problem swiftly began to erode. His body had betrayed him, and on top of his other physical limitations, he lacked the ability to speak. Medical authorities told him that the condition was typical and that he just needed to get used to it.

As his situation became clear, David sank to the lowest depths of his young life. Depression took over, and he lost interest in family, school, and even eating. Anger welled up inside him as he thought about ending a life that suddenly seemed quite bleak and unfair.

But he never quite lost the spark that had driven him to overcome confinement to a wheelchair. There had to be a way for him to conquer this new problem, as he had done so many times before.

For the next three months, he pondered his challenge and searched for a way around his disability. Then one night, in one of those moments of insight so common to inventors, the seeds of an idea came to him.

"He was lying in his bed one night, watching his ventilator, and looking at all the different parts," recalls June. "Then, he said, 'If I can make myself a one-way valve, then I can be just like anyone else.'"

David had noticed a one-way valve in his ventilator circuit that was designed to allow an extra breath to be taken between inspiration and exhalation. He reasoned that if he took this valve and adapted it to fit the hub of the inner cannula of his trach tube, it could allow him to breathe through the trach, forcing the air up over his vocal chords and through his nasal passages. He would be able to speak.

When he presented the idea to his mom, she was horrified at the thought of tampering with the ventilator. What if it didn't work and he was unable to breath? David convinced her and added that if it didn't work, then he no longer wanted to go on living. In fact, he asked her to promise that she would help him to end his life. She agreed, knowing just how determined and serious her son could be.

When his father arrived home, David told him that he needed two parts from the ventilator. Using extra parts, the elder Muir connected them with Crazy Glue to form the first prototype. Then he inserted it into his son's trach as instructed. Both parents held their breath, until suddenly their son began to speak. The makeshift device worked better than any of them had expected.

"See, I told you it would work," David said to his parents.

Excited by his discovery, David explained the idea to a psychologist he was seeing, who was able to connect him with Dr. Victor Passy at the University of California at Irvine. When the young man arrived at the office to discuss his idea, the doctor was surprised to find that David was a patient and not an engineer or physician.

He showed the doctor his valve and told him of his overwhelming desire to help other trach patients. Impressed by both his idea and his desire to help others, Dr. Passy went home that night and talked about the invention with his wife, Patricia.

Although she wasn't particularly business savvy and didn't even have a college degree at that time, Patricia immediately saw possibilities for the valve. Her research told her that more than 2 million tracheotomies are performed each year on a wide variety of patients. Many of them would be candidates for this new kind of valve.

Despite her inexperience, Patricia joined forces with David to start their own corporation. She also approached a venture capitalist she knew and asked him to loan them the seed money needed to get the project rolling.

With renewed enthusiasm, David told her that he not only wanted to get the valve manufactured and marketed, but he also wanted to be involved in the entire process.

Working together, they developed a successful prototype for what would become known as the Passy-Muir speaking valve. Regular appearances at medical conventions and articles in journals spread the word about the effectiveness of the device. David became a celebrated regular at events, discussing the advantages of the device with physicians and professionals from various disciplines. At work at the office, he even took phone orders for the device and did the invoicing using his voice-activated computer.

Still, his health was frail, and after a few months, David entered the hospital. The first day he was there, Patricia got a call from her young partner.

"I need something to do," he said insistently.

She told him that he was in the hospital and he couldn't very well take orders from his sickbed. But he kept asking for some task to perform that would keep the company rolling.

"Well, we have all these brochures that need to be mailed out," she said finally.

He told her to bring them to him and he would work on stuffing the envelopes, pasting on mailing labels, and getting them ready for the post office. She arrived at the hospital with two large sacks and dragged them down the hall to David's room. Every step of the way, she was followed by the curious stares of patients and hospital personnel.

The next morning, she got another call. David was on the other end saying, "I'm finished. Bring me something else to do."

"You're kidding?" she said in disbelief.

Arriving at the hospital, she stared in amazement at the thousands of envelopes all neatly stuffed with the new brochure and a mailing label applied to each.

David told her that he had enlisted the aid of other patients and nurses on his hall to get the work done. His boundless enthusiasm had motivated them to help in the cause.

Later, David's father was transferred to a new job in a new city, and David had to leave the company he and Patricia had started. He sold his shares to their investment partner, but even though he was no longer involved in the day-to-day work of the firm, he continued to keep in touch. When reporters called with questions about the valve, Patricia referred them to David. He was interviewed frequently and even appeared on TV touting the device and telling his story.

Faced with a problem that had left so many others defeated, David Muir rose to new heights of invention and discovery. In the process, he helped thousands to regain their voices.

Unfortunately, David passed away in 1990 at the age of 28. He lived much longer than most other patients with his condition, which usually claims its victims in their late teens. He lived long enough to see his invention become a part of routine medical care for patients with MD. His mother, June, believes that he lived as long as he did because he came to this life to carry out a mission of giving voice and hope to patients in his condition.

"I sometimes think that David was put here to create the valve that would help so many others, and that's a hard thing to say because of how it affected me," says June. "Because I loved this kid so much and to see him go through all of this pain, mental and physical, was very hard. Just like how so many other people are put here for other reasons, I think that was his reason and I think he accomplished it well, and he was a good example for all of us. He said, 'You know, I don't want people to forget that I lived,' and I think he accomplished that completely."

At David's funeral, Patricia Passy spoke of her involvement with David in building the company. She discovered that there was even more to David than she had realized. Many of his friends were totally unaware that he had been an entre-preneur who had been written about in major newspapers and magazines. He never bragged about his accomplishments. From his friends, she learned that he was a poet. And although confined to a wheelchair, he loved sailing small motor-ized boats.

His mother remembers that even as a child he had an insatiable curiosity.

"He wanted to know everything about everything from the time he was a small boy," she explains. "When he was about 4 or 5, he comes in and says, 'Mama, where do babies come from?' So I give him the little nursery school ver-sion about how the stork brings 'em. And he looked at me for a moment and says, 'I refuse to accept that answer.' So from that point on, I knew I was in trouble. He just had this curiosity about life, and it was important to him to live every day like it was his last, because he didn't know if it was going to be his last. And that taught me to live every day like it was going to be my last."

David Muir's impact reached far beyond his circle of devoted family and friends. Just as he wanted, he will be remembered as someone who changed the world and made life better for some of society's most challenged citizens

Chapter 29

DEAN KAMEN
THE CELEBRITY OF INVENTION

Dean Kamen doesn't really believe in those legendary "Aha!" moments. The ones, he says, when an inventor "shouts 'Eureka!' as he goes running down the street naked." Yet even he admits that one of his greatest inspirations came to him in the shower in a moment of illumination that he still doesn't quite understand.

The multimillionaire inventor and entrepreneur has grown both rich and famous from a slew of groundbreaking inventions, ranging from sophisticated insulin pumps for diabetics to the innovative Segway human propulsion device featured in TV shows like Frasier. Many of these inventions stem from Kamen's ideas of what should exist, not necessarily what venture capitalists believe will meet established market projections.

One of his greatest inspirations came from just such an observation that began, of all places, at the mall. This casual outing sparked a revelation that would change his thinking completely.

"Sometimes you can spend years on a project, and sometimes over the course of 10 minutes you are incited to throw away what you had been doing for years and start with a new approach," he says.

For a number of years, Kamen had been working on improvements to the conventional wheelchair. The device hadn't changed much at all in the last two centuries and was still "really a crummy, inadequate solution for a very strong medical need."

Yet Kamen and his team were getting nowhere on the task of improving the mobility that it provided for those who could not walk on their own two legs. They first tried attaching tracks to create something like a little bulldozer, and then gave it multiple articulating limbs like a spider. The goal was to create a kind of "all terrain vehicle" to allow people to climb stairs, get over curbs, and do so many of the things that were simple for most people but nearly impossible for the wheelchair-bound.

After spending a considerable amount of time and money and realizing that none of the obvious solutions were working, the project faded into the background. Not quite gone and forgotten, but at a standstill in the face of tremendous technical hurdles.

A Moment of Inspiration

Leaving his Manchester, New Hampshire, office late one evening, Kamen drove to a nearby shopping mall, intending to pick up some parts at Radio Shack for a project he was working on and, in general, to take a break from the work that consumed most of his days and nights.

As he hopped out of his car and headed toward the entrance of the mall, a soft rain began to fall. In the eerie light cast by the overhead lamps, he saw ahead of him a young man with well-muscled arms and a husky build, seated low in a wheelchair.

Kamen paused as he watched the guy shoot across the parking lot and up to a low curb. There he stopped and tried to force the chair up over the lip of concrete. Despite his considerable upper-body strength, he was unable to move forward. He was stuck, with no ramps to provide him access.

With the assistance of a couple of other shoppers, he helped the man onto the sidewalk and into the mall. With the man's "thank you" resounding in his ears, Kamen walked on, thinking, "This is really absurd. I can do pirouettes off my roof from a six-foot helipad. Men can walk on the moon. We can build submarines and spaceships. Yet this guy can't get off a flat parking lot onto a flat sidewalk a few inches higher."

The thoughts faded as Kamen went from one store to the next, checking off the items on his list. As he passed another store, he glanced in, and there was the same guy in his wheelchair, in front of a shelf stretching up as far as he could for an item just out of reach.

A half-hour later, Kamen headed toward the mall exit with shopping bags under his arms. It had been a long day, and he decided an ice cream would be just what he needed. As the teenager behind the counter handed him the cone, he started to turn, but bumped into something that almost sent him spilling forward. Catching himself, he looked down. It was the wheelchair guy – at 39 inches high, just below his eye level.

After exchanging apologies, he headed out to his car. He fretted over the problems this young man faced, certain that there had to be something that could remedy the shortcomings of the conventional wheelchair.

By the time he arrived home and went to bed, however, he had forgotten about the incident, and when he stepped into the shower the next morning, he was already focused on his schedule for the day. The images of the guy in the wheelchair were long gone. Yet as he stepped out onto the polished granite floor to reach for a towel, his feet met a thin film of moisture. He lurched forward, and his heels slid like tires hydroplaning on a rain-slick street. He swung his arms back, trying to regain his balance. In a split second, he was sliding across the room and into the opposite wall, remaining upright the whole time.

As he stood there pressed against the wall he thought, "The problem is solved. People stand up. People balance. People do something that's bizarrely illogical, and certainly not an obvious way to be safe and stable."

Crawling actually makes more sense, he thought to himself, because then you didn't have to worry about falling. Nonetheless, man stands tall on two small, narrow platforms. It was at that moment that Kamen realized that all his efforts to make a better wheelchair had failed to meet the central human needs. The low-riding chair was statically stable, but human beings, on the other hand, are dynamically stable in everything we do. With a high center of gravity, we are constantly correcting our balance in order to remain stable and upright.

Kamen and his team had been concentrating on mobility, which was really the easiest thing to restore. Instead, stability was the main problem that needed their attention.

"If we were a sack of potatoes, then a wheelbarrow would be a good way to get around," says Kamen. "But if you're a human being, it isn't about mobility. It's about dignity. It's about access. It's about being able to do what all of your colleagues do. It's because we built our whole world for people who have high centers of gravity and who are dynamically stabilized."

Stairs, for example, are nothing more than very short sets of platforms, each a foot or so wide and all in a row. Walking up them isn't a perpendicular movement, but one in which the walker is always moving vertically, something a big machine with a big base – like a wheelchair– can't do.

After his inspirational shower, Kamen hurriedly dried off, threw on his clothes, and raced to his office at DEKA Research & Development Corporation. Once there, he called in the team that had been working on the wheelchair and began excitedly telling them of his experience and his realization that they were trying to solve the wrong problem.

"Forget about mobility," he exclaimed. "Let's just figure out how to build a dynamically stabilized machine that has the same footprint as a human being. It should have two feet, because we have two feet sideways, so we don't need to get lateral stability."

Kamen knew there was enough gyro technology on the shelves that it could provide stability even better than the mechanisms of the human inner ear. Powerful microcomputers could process data faster than the human brain and send signals to motors that could constantly make corrections when an object pitched forwards or backwards.

The result of his shower revelation was the technology that became the INDEPENDENCE IBOT Mobility System. This radically different robotic wheelchair allows its rider to sit higher – at eye level with people walking– and its six wheels can easily go up and down stairs and even traverse sandy or rocky terrain. This breakthrough device, which is being marketed by Independence Technology, a division of Johnson & Johnson, gives a completely new meaning to mobility for the wheelchair-bound.

Dropout Inventor

Kamen has created his inventions and made his fortune by not just defying the conventional wisdom, but by utterly ignoring it. A poor student, he barely managed to graduate from high school, much to the chagrin of his parents. He attended college, but didn't graduate. Nonetheless, his mom and dad always provided the moral support he needed to keep going.

"I can't say that they were happy about my unwillingness to deal with the convention of school," he admits. "But in the end, they supported me. If I wanted to go out and do something different, although they were concerned and worried, they supported me, and that's a big deal."

It wasn't that Kamen lacked a thirst for knowledge. On the contrary, he wanted to know things that everyone else didn't.

"If I found out that the answer was in the back of the book, then I wasn't interested in the question," he reveals. After all, if the answers could be found so easily, why not start reading from the back, he wondered. Merely repeating what was already known and well-established simply didn't appeal to him.

"Why would you go and watch a football game if, before it started, someone told you who was going to win?" he asks. "If there's no excitement, mystery, and everything is a foregone conclusion, what's the point?"

On the other hand, when a subject caught Kamen's fancy, he would begin devouring everything he could find on the topic. He preferred questions that no one knew the answer to, because they were the fun ones. "Neither the teachers nor the other students had the advantage over me," he says, "because I knew that nobody had gotten to the back of that book. It hadn't been written."

Kamen's father was an artist, but the son didn't seem to inherit his father's talent. In fact, he says, "I can't draw a straight line even with an edge." Yet the elder Kamen recognized a different kind of creativity in his son.

"As I got older, my father said, 'In some ways you are like me,'" Kamen recalls. "He said, 'You go out and create things that weren't there before. You just use the tools of engineering, while I use a brush.'"

Kamen's nonconformist approach to learning helps explain his approach to inventing as well. Plainly, he is uninterested in making incremental improvements to commonplace devices. He doesn't want to simply invent; he wants to innovate. He wants to create things because they ought to exist to make people's lives better.

Although he has become a wealthy businessman who hobnobs with the likes of George W. Bush and a host of other celebrities, venture capitalists, and high-powered executives, he still retains the soul of an idealist. He has an unshakable faith in the power of technology to solve man's ills – or at least make them manageable.

Early Inventing

Many of Kamen's early achievements stemmed from personal experience. With both his parents and his brother suffering from diabetes, he had a personal stake in dealing with the problems faced by people with this particular disease.

While attending college in the '70s, his brother – a good student who had made it to medical school – complained that there were no reliable ways to give steady doses of drugs to patients. So Kamen invented the first portable infusion pump, which was capable of delivering drugs like insulin to patients who had previously required around-the-clock monitoring. The AutoSyringe freed them from confinement to a hospital.

He also devised a phonebook-sized dialysis machine at a time when dialysis machines were the size of dishwashers and were only available to patients at centralized medical facilities. Called HomeChoice, the device gives patients with chronic renal failure the freedom to travel without being forced to stay close to a dialysis center.

Another of his inventions is the Hydroflex irrigation pump, for use in common medical procedures, such as laparoscopy. This device removed the need for separate, dedicated irrigation pumps and allows physicians to use only one system during procedures.

While medicine was his early focus, and continues to take up most of his company's research and development time, Kamen has focused his attention on even bigger problems, which demand even grander solutions. He believes science and technology can solve widespread problems such as pollution, lack of electricity, and contaminated water supplies in less developed nations, and he's been willing to put his money and his company's research expertise where his mouth is.

DEKA is busily engaged in developing a non-polluting engine that Kamen is convinced can run water purifiers to cleanse contaminated water with UV lasers, generate power for electricity, and even allow access to the Internet. Called the Stirling engine, it is based on a concept first published in the early 1800s, and is currently being funded by Kamen's own money.

His best-known invention, however, is perhaps nothing less than a frontal attack on conventional thinking about people and transportation. The Segway human transporter was an immediate sensation when first released, and quickly appeared at airports and on urban streets. In addition to guest roles on TV shows, the device was also seen at auto races, where Michelin, the company that makes the solid, non-inflatable tires for both the Segway and IBOT, uses it in the pit areas.

The Segway uses the same self-balancing gyro technology as the IBOT to keep riders perpetually balanced and upright on its two oversize tires. The hope is that this new kind of vehicle will give the more than 3.2 billion people who live in cities an alternative to the big, clunky, polluting automobile.

Pop Star

Clearly, Dean Kamen loves taking on big technological problems, but one of his most daunting challenges has nothing to do with technology at all. He wants to turn scientists and engineers into pop culture icons and give young people a different kind of role model. Considering that few teenagers today can name even one scientist, and that most count professional athletes and pop singers as their top role models, creating a nation of science and technology fans is going to take quite a bit of persuading.

Kamen believes that, for all its shortcomings, the American educational system is not to blame for young people's lack of interest in science. Trying to change the school system is not nearly as important as changing the cultural prejudice that assigns unwarranted glamour and importance to athletes and entertainers.

"We celebrate two profoundly disturbing propositions – entertainment and sports," he says. "I see the mayor of Boston is closing down the streets because [the New England Patriots] are coming back to town [after winning the Super Bowl]. It's just a game. A game that most of us gave up when we started doing more important things."

Yet these same athletes are held up as role models to be emulated by today's youth, even though few have any prospect of ever joining the pro ranks.

"There are a lot more lottery winners than players in the NBA," Kamen asserts. "Kids show up at school with a passion to get in the band, be on the football team, or become a cheerleader. Our whole culture idealizes people from the world of entertainment, and every celebrity kids see is from the world of Hollywood. Let's create an institution that will give kids some self-confidence, and if they put the same kind of energy and passion into learning how to solve real problems, there will be many more career opportunities for them."

To encourage kids – particularly young girls and minorities – to become engineers and scientists, Kamen founded FIRST (For Inspiration and Recognition of Science and Technology). This nonprofit organization sponsors a national competition that matches high school students with engineers from local companies. For the event, the kids are given a standard kit of parts and are challenged to build a working robot in six weeks. The robots are then pitted against each other on a playing field, with the best robot eventually winning the top prize.

Kamen wants to create a world in which knowledge and technical achievement are valued. To do that, attitudes have to change. While Super Bowl winners get parades, scientists who cure diseases might get a headline inside the newspaper.

"If we as a society don't value what they're doing," Kamen says, "they can't open up the heads of these kids and pour in something that nobody wants to have." With 65,000 people attending the annual FIRST event, Kamen is beginning to change minds about the role that technology should play in society. Just as he has never accepted conventional wisdom about anything, whether it's a better wheelchair or a new mode of transportation, he's convinced that things don't have to stay the way they are. Technology can change society, and engineers can be as famous as pro quarterbacks and scantily clad pop stars.

Chapter 30

RICHARD SCHMIDT
A CAUTIONARY TALE

Dr. Richard Schmidt thought he had it made. His life revolved around a prestigious academic position and a research program involving a device he invented that was yielding unexpectedly good results. His patients adored him and the FDA had granted approval for a ground breaking new invention.

Then everything fell apart. His research was closed down by a suddenly hostile University department head, and he found himself forced out and back in private practice. What happened to turn so sour the story of such a promising inventor? It is a tale of what can go wrong in the world of academic research and of woes that can't be solved by brilliance of mind.

Dr. Schmidt's story begins with an emerging trend in research. Beginning in the 1960s, medical science made tremendous strides in the development of neural prosthetics for use in hearing, seizure control, control of spinal pain management, and even pacemakers. With the successful control of the heart, scientists began branching out into devices that could control other areas of the nervous system.

The University of California at San Francisco became a center of research regarding the problems related to bladder control and voiding dysfunctions. As a young urologist, Schmidt became involved in finding a means for controlling the bladder through stimulation of the pelvic nerve.

"I started off down that pathway with the idea of developing a pacemaker for paraplegics to control their bladders," he says.

While the idea worked well, his research ran into a common problem in the commercialization of medical devices. With only about 10,000 paraplegics in the entire country, no venture fund was interested in paying for the development of such a device.

"There was no market interest, no companies that would come in and fund that kind of thing," he admits.

Yet the principle had far broader application than anyone had originally thought. Schmidt discovered that the device would also prevent incontinence when he was able to block the seizure of the sphincter in a test animal. If the idea worked for paraplegics, it might also work for the large number of people – mostly women – who suffer from some form of voiding dysfunction, including the more than 40 percent of the American population currently over the age of 65.

"Like many things, if your mind is open to ideas or to situations and the information is there, you'll recognize it," says Schmidt. "That's the key to a lot of inventing."

As the project progressed, these alternative uses would prove to be decisive in attracting commercial support for the device.

"When the NIH [National Institutes of Health] finally said we'd done enough lab work and that we had to try it in humans, the only companies that expressed interest were those that saw that they could market it [for incontinence]," says Schmidt.

It was at this point that things began to go awry. Many companies view university research labs as one of the prime sources of new ideas for medical device companies. With much of the work already done, there is less risk to the companies, who can often pick up licensing deals from inexperienced academics for far less than they might otherwise have to pay. The world of big corporations can be ruthless, and companies are often quite willing to take advantage of the inexperienced and unwary in academia.

"I was a young faculty member and had no control over the whole process of patenting and negotiations," says Schmidt. "The chairman above me was excluding me from some certain key dialogue situations, and I just didn't have any input in it. So, 10 years later, you find that they screwed it up."

Schmidt learned the hard way that the patent and all aspects of intellectual property generated by his device were controlled by the University of California. In an academic setting, most work done by faculty researchers is wholly owned by the university, just as major corporations own and control all IP created by their employees.

Medical device giant Medtronic eventually walked away with the rights to the device, which is now marketed as the Medtronic InterStim System for Urinary Control.

After spending five years working to gain FDA approval, Schmidt learned just how poorly the University had negotiated the deal. On the day that approval was secured, the company informed the University of California that they were no longer going to recognize any licensing fees because of previously published work.

"So they walked out of the deal," he says. "And now there are more than 10,000 of these implants across the country and they've never paid us anything in the way of royalty."

Schmidt's unhappy experiences with technology transfer in an academic setting began in California, but they didn't end there. Disenchanted with the situation in San Francisco, he decided it was time to seek a better situation and an employer who was more supportive of his research efforts.

With an outstanding reputation in urology and an important device on its way through the regulatory process, Schmidt was heavily recruited by the University of Colorado's Health Sciences Center. In fact, the fast-growing upstart university facility offered him $200,000 a year in salary and bonuses to come east to seek his fortune. They promised a tenured position as soon as one became available.

Everything looked good as he packed his bags, bid farewell to the Bay Area, and moved to the Rocky Mountain State. He began teaching and doing research, including a project to gain FDA approval for the InterStim device. His work demonstrated that the device, which sent electrical impulses through wires placed under the skin to nerve centers at the base of the spine, provided significant pain reduction and bladder control in 3 to 4 out of every 10 patients who used it.

Between 1993 and 1999, more than 170 patients enrolled in the study and eventually, the FDA granted its stamp of approval to the device as a safe and effective treatment for various forms of pelvic pain and voiding dysfunctions. During this time, Schmidt also won a patent related to an innovative use of botox (a purified form of botulism toxin) in nerve-blocking treatments to control certain conditions marked by involuntary muscle contractions.

On the surface, everything seemed to be going extremely well. Yet, unwittingly, Schmidt had joined an institution that many thought was ruled more by politics, power plays, and personal vendettas than academic quality.

Today, he no longer works there, having been terminated for various – and many contend unsubstantiated – charges of impropriety and incompetence. His program has been shut down and patients left to fend for themselves without follow-up care. With his career in ruin and an intense desire to clear his name, Schmidt is now locked in a court fight with the University of Colorado officials who fired him. The battle has even spilled over in the public media, and members of the state legislature have gotten involved.

The big losers have been not just Schmidt and the other personnel caught up in the fight, but the reputation of what is now widely regarded as a troubled institution. Among other problems has been the embarrassing shutdown by the FDA of hundreds of reportedly inadequately monitored clinical trials, as well as a federal investigation into improper Medicaid and Medicare billing. A number of researchers have left over the years, claiming a hostile working environment.

Schmidt contends that his career came to an end because he crossed swords with the former head of the surgery department he served under and not because of any academic failings on his part. This contention is supported by others, including the university's own tenure committee, which found the department head's review to be fundamentally flawed if not plain wrong.

The original committee – composed entirely of faculty under the surgery department head – accused Schmidt of conducting unconventional research. They said he was "uncooperative" because he denounced as immoral the performing of surgery techniques that yielded poor patient outcomes. As a surgeon, he agreed with the age-old adage that doctors should "first, do no harm."

At the same time, as the department's head was seeking his dismissal, the university hospital was running ads proclaiming that Schmidt and five other doctors were named to The Best Doctors in America 1999.

Many of Schmidt's patients besieged the university with complaints following his dismissal, but to no avail. A number claimed that they were left with the implants still in their bodies, but with no medical care to keep them running properly.

Schmidt's accuser and the engineer of his dismissal, the head of the surgery department at Colorado, has left his job as well. Following an arrest for solicitation of prostitution, he tendered his resignation.

Schmidt remains unvindicated and in private practice. He's trying to rebuild his life and overcome the many missteps that brought such a promising career crashing down.

He's working with a company to develop a computerized diagnostic program for incontinence. He's older and wiser and a good bit more perceptive about university research.

"I trusted people above me and believed that they were acting in my best interest, but they weren't," he says. "They were acting in their own interest, and that's an unknown."

Success in the world of invention seldom comes simply from brilliance and a great idea. Richard Schmidt certainly had both of those factors in his favor. Yet he found himself in situations in which it seemed almost as if the stars were aligned against him. It is a cautionary tale of how even the best and the brightest can fall victim to the ignorance, greed, and ego of others.

Chapter 31

MIR IMRAN
HOLISTIC INVENTOR

There can be found few greater examples of the role of creativity in inventing than in the life and work of an immigrant American named Mir Imran.

Entrepreneurship came early in his life. As a young boy in his native India, he started his own small-scale business building toys for his classmates. To meet demand, he set up an assembly line in his bedroom, putting each tiny part together in a manner that would have been familiar to even the auto manufacturers of faraway Detroit.

While other boys were playing with their toys, Imran often began by taking them apart to see how they actually worked. In fact, when his mother noticed what he was doing, she began giving him two toys – one to play with and another to disassemble. By encouraging his innate curiosity, his parents were providing the external conditions that would help his highly creative nature flourish. It was an upbringing that would serve him well in his career as one of America's leading inventors of medical devices.

"I was always interested in building things and selling them," says Imran. "I don't know if it was a genetic mutation or not. In my family there were no businesspeople."

Although Imran's father was a physician, the family was far from prosperous, as India didn't reward its professionals very well. Their lives were comfortable by local standards, but Imran realized early on that the path to the life he wanted to live wasn't to be found there. As time went on and he learned more and more, he found his surroundings increasingly confining.

He discovered what would become a great passion for technology when he was introduced to electronics. Between a few night classes and studies on his own, he began building small AM radios in matchboxes and selling them.

"It was deeply ingrained in me to combine science and technology," he acknowledges.

That dedication would make him one of America's most prolific inventors and entrepreneurs. From the time he was a senior at Rutgers University until today, a period of only 25 years, he has founded 18 companies. Each enterprise is built around an innovative device arising from his more than 200 patents in a variety of industries that have solved intractable problems and, in many cases, saved the lives of countless patients with chronic diseases.

Imran's greatest contributions – and his greatest love – have come in the area of medical devices, where he has brought a holistic and humane approach to finding solutions to some of the most vexing medical challenges.

He possesses the ability to see the relationship between diverse fields of knowledge and to find solutions that combine basic medicine with groundbreaking technological solutions.

Imran's entrepreneurial ambitions led him to leave India while still a high school student of 17. He knew that if he was to be a success, it would have to be in America. He began writing to colleges and collecting information about the programs they offered without telling his parents of his crystallizing plans.

"Once I had everything lined up, I went and asked them for some funding," he says.

His parents were shocked when he told them of his intentions, but they too realized that his future lay elsewhere. Despite modest financial means and restrictions placed by the Indian government on currency exchange, the elder Dr. Imran acquired $4,000 on the black market and gave his son cash to fund his trip and a start in the new land.

Imran arrived in New Jersey, where he attended Rutgers University while living out of a small room that he recalls as "little more than a closet." He earned a bachelor's degree in electrical engineering in just two and a half years. At the same time, he completed all of the course work for a degree in mechanical engineering, but lacking the funds, he was unable to acquire the second degree. He also attained a master's degree in bioengineering before enrolling in Rutgers' medical school.

His years at college in a new and strange country were often trying. Money was always short, and he had little time for the parties and social life that occupied so many of his fellow students. He knew all too well that he had left behind the relative comfort of his home and family for an uncertain future. Yet he persevered, never complaining and always moving forward.

In fact, he sometimes devoted as much as 18 hours a day to his studies, research, and business. "Being an entrepreneur really requires that kind of focus," he says. "Being an inventor requires that kind of focus."

Acquiring knowledge and being better prepared than anyone else was his purpose in life.

"I had a real single-minded focus on knowledge and acquiring as much education as I could," he explains. "I was always interested in applying it to solve real-world problems and commercialize them. I was actually never focused on finding a job, and my education was always more for gaining knowledge than for getting a diploma that would lead to a job."

This inquisitive and open-minded approach to learning gave him an advantage over many of his peers. He never saw a boundary between disciplines or areas of knowledge.

"I became as good at thermodynamics and heat transfer as I was at electric fields and electronic circuits," he says. "For me, it was all one continuum of knowledge and I never really recognized the boundaries."

He also displayed an ability to take intellectual risks, acquired through self-confidence coupled with highly developed scientific and technological abilities. If Imran didn't know the answer, he knew where to look in order to find it.

While an undergraduate, he founded the first of what would become a long line of companies. Unlike most of his start-ups that followed, he decided to get into the security systems business. He hit upon the idea when a friend told him that his home had been burglarized and so he wanted to install an alarm system.

Even in those days, security monitoring systems were costly, so Imran volunteered to put his engineering studies to work and build a custom system. He assembled a unit using the newly emerging system of microprocessors, and when it was done, he realized there might be a market for his new creation.

With the help of a friend, who became a partner in the business, Imran set up operation in the friend's basement. He did all the manufacturing, assembly, and testing himself. That first year, the fledgling company made $30,000 in revenue – a substantial amount of money for a young college student.

"Unfortunately, it was not a scalable business," he admits. "I had not figured out how to market the product. It was all word of mouth, and you couldn't grow nationally with the resources that I had."

His first effort at running a company proved to be far from a runaway success. While he made a small profit, it never took off the way he hoped. Yet out of this experience, he realized his own shortcomings. He lacked both the capital and business experience needed to make a new company a success.

"I realized that financial resources are essential for commercial success," he says. "Very rarely can you build a business using just savings and credit cards."

Imran is philosophical about the downside of risk-taking. With every success comes one or more failures, but even within a setback lies the seeds of future success.

"I never see any failure as a complete failure or any success as a complete success," he admits. "In any success there are many little failures, and in every failure there are many small successes."

Another seminal event in Imran's life occurred one day at Rutgers. Walking down the corridor of a lecture hall between classes, he paused to look at an unruly mass of papers pinned to a bulletin board. There, amidst the handwritten note cards and official documents, was a notice asking for help at a school for children with cerebral palsy.

"They were seeking some engineering help for developing communication tools for the children," he recalls. "In those days, technological applications in those areas were very limited."

Scribbling down the contact information, he decided to go over and talk to the school's administrators. Over the course of the summer, he developed a number of devices and fabricated them as communication aides for the handicapped children.

"It proved to be such a positive experience, I decided that I was going to devote the bulk of my career to life sciences," he says. "That was the turning point that pushed me toward going to medical school."

Imran approached each challenge with a self-confidence born of intense preparation. One of the biggest risks he took was early in his career when he was still in school. He was hired to work on the development of a new medical device called an implantable defibrillator that held the promise of preventing sudden cardiac death.

He joined a small team that included Steven Heilman and Al Langer, who were attempting to work out the design of the promising device.

"They had been trying to find somebody to lead the development of the defibrillator," he recalls. "They went to the pacemaker companies, and the pacemaker engineers who had a background in implantables looked at it and said it couldn't be done. They said, 'I don't want to put myself into this high-risk project.'"

In order to proceed, the team needed someone who wasn't afraid to venture into this unknown realm, so they sought out Imran through the recommendation of a medical school professor. They needed someone who could solve a large number of complex technical problems in the design of the device's electronics. Imran had already developed a reputation for tackling technological problems that others avoided while in medical school. Heilman and Langer realized that Imran was their man.

Although he took on the project without hesitation, he was still well aware of just how much was at stake.

"This was a device that a person's life was dependent upon," he says. "I spent many sleepless nights making sure I was doing the right thing."

At that point in time, the young scientist wasn't exaggerating the risk. The first version of the device was limited in its ability to detect irregularities in the heart's function.

The vital ingredient that Imran brought to the table was the classic ability to think in innovative and creative ways.

"I was thinking three or four steps ahead and anticipating problems we might encounter and addressing them upfront rather than doing it in a linear fashion, step by step," he says. "We were moving in quantum leaps, and every six to nine months we had a new model of the defibrillator."

His work on the defibrillator was just the beginning of a long and distinguished career that includes the development of such highly publicized devices as the EEG monitoring sensor array that former Senator John Glenn was shown wearing in the Time magazine story about his last space mission. The array became the first product for Physiometrix, just one of the many companies Imran has founded, and has become a standard diagnostic tool used in neurophysiology.

He also created InCube, Inc., a Silicon Valley incubator for medical and internet companies. Using this model, Imran has founded several medical and high-tech start-ups.

His interests have been as wide ranging as have his inspirations for new devices and ventures.

A close friend underwent a colostomy and Imran was forced to watch as she fought infections and other shortcomings relating to the admittedly crude treatment for the condition. Others might look at a situation like that and say simply, "That's too bad." Instead, Imran began to ponder a new and innovative treatment that might spare others the pain and suffering that eventually claimed his friend's life.

Inspired, he began conceptualizing an artificial rectum that could provide a prosthetic replacement for a colon removed in surgery. Soon he had a company going to develop his concept into a workable medical device.

While visiting his wife's obstetrician, Imran was intrigued by the doctor's use of an ultrasound machine for imaging. He told the doctor he wanted to get one for his own use.

"Do you know how much these machines cost?" asked the physician.

One machine costs upward of $200,000, he told him. Unperturbed, Imran decided that he should be able to build his own machine for much less. In the process, he created a machine that not only was a quarter of the cost, but one that was also able to do scans at a much faster rate.

Imran's success stems from an innate ability to combine inventing and problem-solving skills with a courageous approach to business. While he takes a loving and nurturing approach to each company and device, he keeps a keen eye on its progress. If he determines that the device has no future, he is quick to end it before too much time, effort, and resources have been wasted.

He believes that the true entrepreneurial inventor is neither wholly present at birth nor entirely created through experience. Rather he is a person who can forge ahead on a mixture of faith and solid facts and not be daunted by the details he doesn't yet know.

"The most important quality in an inventor is the ability to take risks," he says. "It's more the psychological state of your mind than scientific skills. You see a lot of professors who are doing basic research, but they're not taking real risks intellectually, and they're not putting themselves out there where they might fail."

While the academic arena is populated with many skilled and often brilliant people, they tend to be averse to risk-taking. The idea that you can only publish a paper on a particular subject once you're sure of the result is a strategy that would create failure in the business world.

"A lot of smart people have great ideas, but few ever follow through with them," he says. "The fear of failure is what holds people back. What separates an inventor and entrepreneur from the academic researchers is their ability to take risks and to fail at something and not be devastated by it."

While many inventors have achieved their more original work while young, Imran has been one of those rare individuals who has continued to create highly innovative ideas in a variety of disciplines years after his first big success.

Imran's highly productive record of inventing has been aided by an approach to looking at problems that he has come to call "need finding." It centers on looking first at the clinical need and how patients are actually seen by the physician.

"A lot of engineers don't have that medical or clinical vision," he says. "They rely on physicians. And a lot of physicians don't know what the engineering capabilities are – what can and cannot be done."

With a unique combination of skills in electronics, mechanical engineering, and medical science, Imran is able to ask, "How is this device going to be used clinically? How does the physician who is managing the patient see the disease, and how does he correlate that to the device therapy?"

His success can be owed to his fascination and study of what makes people creative and how to foster that impulse in himself. He realized long ago that creative ideas arise from both the conscious and subconscious mind.

Through lucid dreaming, for example, he has found a way to free his mind to find new ideas without the distractions and sensory overload that usually comes during waking hours.

"It is a state of mind in which you are at your most creative, because it is creativity without distractions," he says.

This approach has yielded more than 200 patents for innovative devices and processes. In 1990, he invented a basket catheter that obtains multiple ECG signals simultaneously from various areas of the heart. This invention became the initial product of Cardiac Pathways, and is now widely used by cardiac electrophysiologists.

In 1992, he developed a low-pressure balloon and aspirator system for use in catheter-based interventions. It was the first device to articulate the concept of distal protection during high-risk interventions. Imran's device is now the primary innovation for PercuSurge, a company that is currently completing human clinical trials on the device.

Despite all this success, however, Imran confesses that he is still largely unmotivated by the wealth that his products have generated for him and the many investors in his companies.

"[Money] has always been just a byproduct of my work," he says. "You have to make sure the business is going to be viable and that you're addressing a large market. That you're well-positioned from a competitive standpoint and that the business will make money. Otherwise, you won't attract investors. So if you do the right things, you'll make money."

Chapter 32

PAUL YOCK
TEACHER AND INVENTOR

When he looks back, Dr. Paul Yock realizes that, for him, the path to invention was being in the right place at the right time in order to find the solution to a frustrating problem.

Yock was a fellow in angioplasty in the early days of the revolutionary procedure, which combats heart disease by inserting a balloon catheter into a coronary artery clogged with plaque. The catheter is inserted through an artery in the groin or arm, and carefully moved up the aorta using a long metal guide wire, where it is dilated in order to open up the blocked vessel.

Working with renowned surgeon Dr. John Simpson, Yock assisted with the standard, over-the-wire system procedure. Standing at the end of the operating table, his job was to maintain the correct position for a 10-foot-long guide wire as the lead surgeon snaked the device up a delicate path through the arteries.

"It was actually a little bit tricky, especially as you were just learning the technique, to keep the guide wire in the right position," he recalls. "The guy at the front of the table – the senior guy – was driving the catheter and moving it back and forth."

As the assistant, Yock had to respond to the moves of the primary operator, which was sometimes difficult to do in the absence of considerable experience. Some might argue that making the right moves required a certain amount of psychic ability.

"The problem was, it was always your fault if something went wrong. It was a no-win situation. If the guide wire lost position, that was big trouble."

As a young physician just learning the ropes, Yock was cast in the unenviable position of dealing with a problem that his superiors either didn't perceive or perhaps had forgotten even existed.

"The senior physicians didn't really perceive it as a problem area," says Yock, "because they had graduated beyond thinking about it."

Like so many doctors on a learning curve before him, Yock saw all too clearly the difficulties presented by a device that was less than perfect. He lost the guide wire position and suffered not only the embarrassment of his mistake, but the resultant prolonging of the procedure as well. Other assisting surgeons encountered the same problem, and for some patients, that meant tragic consequences.

While Yock never had that one, particular "Aha!" moment so many inventors talk about, he came to the gradual realization that there had to be a better way of designing the device in order to overcome the problem of the lost guide wire position.

"There was a cluster of things I was thinking about at the same time that brewed together," he says. "I was also thinking about how limited angiography was for looking inside of vessels, and I was starting to percolate the idea of intravascular ultrasound, and because of that, I was thinking of ways of delivering catheters."

He reasoned that if they used intravascular ultrasound, it was essentially going to mean inserting yet another catheter. In intravascular ultrasound, which is performed along with cardiac catheterization, a miniature sound probe on the tip of a catheter is threaded through the coronary arteries. Using high-frequency sound waves, it produces detailed images of the interior walls of the arteries.

Yock began making prototypes using simple tools. He did thousands of drawings as his thinking about the relationship between the guiding catheter, the guide wire, and the balloon catheter developed. He took existing wire balloon catheters and began modifying them to shorten the wires.

As he worked with the existing tools of the trade, he continued laboring to modify the devices into something that would be better for doctor and patient alike. Like so many inventors before him, he was driven by dissatisfaction with the process he was then trying to master.

"I think that big inventions typically come to younger people, who are in some stage of their training or early development of a procedure," says Yock. "There is a frustration that you haven't mastered the technique, and you see the bad outcomes and you feel personally responsible for them, and one response to that is to make the procedure better."

While many surgeons are able to overcome their frustrations with tools and techniques, the younger practitioners are often the ones who clearly see the shortcomings. Yock experienced firsthand that the emerging field of interventional cardiology was producing sometimes less than sterling results. For this budding physician, who had switched from noninvasive cardiology to a daunting new field of medicine, there were times when he felt that he might have made a mistake. He wondered long and hard about whether he should abandon what he was doing and return to his original career. But as he began to work on his new devices, he was inspired to throw himself wholeheartedly into interventional cardiology. He started observing more and more cardiac procedures to learn as much as he possibly could about the techniques and equipment. As he watched how other surgeons handled catheters, he formulated ideas about a new device to deliver them. He studied ultrasound engineering and the physics behind these devices.

He was encouraged in his work by Simpson, who had himself invented the over-the-wire balloon angioplasty catheter, which led to the founding of Advanced

Cardiovascular Systems (ACS) in 1978. In 1984, Simpson developed the concept of directional atherectomy (the removal of atheromas from the coronary artery) and founded Devices for Vascular Intervention (DVI), and other companies as well.

Yock acknowledges that he was fortunate to work in an environment that welcomed innovation. It also helped him see early on the commercial potential of the device he invented that evolved into the Rapid Exchange balloon angioplasty system, now the most widely used angioplasty system in the world.

"[Simpson] made inventing seem possible and encouraged all of us in the program to help with his developments."

Simpson not only mentored him in the process of his invention, but also pointed Yock toward his own patent attorney. He was able to license the Rapid Exchange angioplasty system to ACS, a division of the giant medical device maker Guidant Corporation.

This early encouragement and success made it all the easier for Yock to handle critics when they arose, as he presented the device to ACS for consideration. He was invited to do a demonstration for the company's president and board of advisors.

Standing in front of the group following his presentation, which included a prototype and animal studies, Yock asked for questions. A well-known cardiologist at the other end of the table raised his hand and asked dryly, "Why in the world would you want to do this?"

Although startled by this response, Yock calmly repeated his arguments. In the end, he was successful, and the company recognized the logic of using a device that allowed one doctor to perform the procedure in a manner that was both faster and safer than the earlier two-man version.

The Rapid Exchange system was the first of many devices that have sprung from Paul Yock's fertile imagination. This early success also inspired him to develop a Doppler-guided hypodermic needle system called The Smart Needle and PD (Percutaneous Doppler) Access System. This device allows physicians to locate difficult-to-find veins by allowing the user to hear arterial or venous flow and direct the needle to first-stick access.

But Yock's flair for inventing has not been limited to the lab. He shares his talents with students at Stanford University, where he holds the post of Martha Meier Welland Professor of Medicine.

It is in this academic setting that he has created an environment in which he, himself, is not only more creative, but he has also been able to build structures that encourage innovation and advancement in others as well.

He founded Stanford's Program in Biodesign, a group of nearly 200 faculty members from various departments who promote the development of new health technologies through research and education.

"I'm sitting in a place that's basically a university prototyping facility, and I have a glass box for an office," he says. "They call it a Yock in the box."

In fact, the entire building in which he works is made up of glass walls and flexible workspaces. Meeting rooms have whiteboard walls and are located next to prototyping shops. The facility serves as the focal point for an initiative that is seeking to bridge the gaps between medicine, engineering, and other scientific disciplines.

At the heart of the process is creating a place where "collisions" can take place between researchers. As Yock explains it, "It's really important for the creative process to have your mind jogged loose by bumping into people who think about different things, have different expertise, and different backgrounds. Collisions are really important fuel for thinking about new ideas, even when they're slightly painful. When you come across someone who knows so much more about an area than you do, it pokes at you a bit and makes you break out of the way you've been thinking."

From Yock's point of view, the more collisions that take place between researchers of varying backgrounds and disciplines, the more synergy can be created and the more new ideas will emerge that transcend the niche thinking of each.

As an accomplished inventor, Yock has seen firsthand how discomfort fuels the inventing process. The young cardiologist learning how to handle a guide wire experienced intense anxiety and was forced to be more creative.

In fact, he often finds that he is motivated to enter that creative space, so familiar to inventors, when he is faced with intense and unappealing workloads.

"I found myself being most creative when I just had a huge amount of stuff going on. I was trying to write papers, something that was difficult for me, and my mind wanted to take a vacation from it. So I would give my mind permission to wander and invent."

Even though he has gained his greatest fame for the medical devices he has developed, Yock sees the best use of his time in following a seemingly quite different track. He is first and foremost a teacher, and his greatest passion is giving other would-be inventors the time and the place to break new ground and conceive new ideas.

"I strongly believe that with a few exceptions, Mir Imran for example, the really big platform ideas come from young minds," he says. "My best contribution at this point is to really try to enable a new generation of folks who can have the lucky experiences that I did."

Chapter 33

HEILMAN, LANGER, MIROWSKI, AND MOWER
SHOCK TO THE HEART

Alois Langer could feel the tightness in the pit of his stomach as he entered the brightly lit operating room. Although clad in mask and sterile gown like the figures around him, he felt oddly out of place. He wasn't a surgeon, after all, but rather an electrical engineer, who wouldn't normally be expected to see the inside of a place like this unless it was looking up from a gurney.

Yet here he was at Johns Hopkins, one of the world's most famous medical centers, carrying a small sterile package about the size of a deck of cards. In it was a device he had spent almost a decade helping to develop.

On the table, surrounded by doctors and nurses, was a middle-aged woman who had experienced repeated episodes of sudden cardiac death in a swimming pool. Inside the package Langer held was a new device, an implantable defibrillator that was designed to shock her heart and correct otherwise fatal abnormal heart rhythms.

As the operation proceeded, everything seemed to be going well. A nurse came over and Langer opened the package. The nurse picked up the new defibrillator and was returning to the operating table when the device suddenly slipped from her grasp and went crashing to the floor. For a moment, there was total silence.

Fortunately, however, that potentially disastrous slip did not spell the end of the operation.

"We had two [defibrillators] because we thought, 'Well, what if someone dropped it?'" recalls Langer. He laughs now about that moment in 1980, although nobody thought it was especially funny back then. "So we brought two and the second is the one that went in."

They had painstakingly built and tested two units, because, says Langer, "We always had this fear that someone would drop it or it wouldn't work after sterilization or something like that."

Their insurance of having a backup device handy also reflected just how cautious Langer and his team were about this radical new approach to dealing with ventricular fibrillation.

Langer was part of a team that accomplished one of the great feats of medical device invention. Over a period of almost a decade, he joined a group of inventors that consisted of Drs. Steven Heilman, Michel Mirowski, and Morton "Morty" Mower.

Finding a way to prevent fatal abnormal heart rhythms had become both a passion and an obsession for Dr. Mirowski, a talented and determined cardiologist. He was a Polish Jew who fled the advancing German army during World War II. Moving to Russia from Warsaw, he was the only member of his family to escape the Nazi death camps. Following the war, he attended medical school in France, before moving to the U.S. After a stint in pediatric cardiology at Johns Hopkins, he decided to "seek his fortune" in Israel, where he set up practice.

Even though he was a doctor who specialized in treating bad hearts, he still wasn't quite prepared when his colleague and then chief of cardiology, Professor Harry Heller, suffered an attack of malignant ventricular arrhythmia. Mirowski knew, perhaps instinctively, that it was only a matter of time before his dear friend was likely to succumb from a second incident, this time when he might be at home and too far away to be saved by medical personnel and a defibrillator. His fears were realized when Heller died suddenly, two weeks after his initial episode, of ventricular tachycardia.

Of course, the idea of using electricity to regulate heart rhythms was nothing new. In fact, pacemakers were already in common usage, but no device existed that could detect ventricular fibrillation (a condition in which the heart's electrical activity becomes disordered and its lower chambers contract rapidly and ineffectively) and then shock the heart back into a normal rhythm. Fortunately, Mirowski asked the most important and obvious question: Why not?

"Michel made up his mind that he was going to make it his life's work to develop an implantable defibrillator," recalls Dr. Stephen Heilman.

Heilman, a former Army doctor who founded the medical device company Medrad, Inc., met Mirowski while attending the Fifth Asian Pacific Congress in Singapore. He was seeking dealers for his company's products when a mutual friend introduced them.

By this time, Mirowski had moved back to the U.S., where he was now working part time as coronary care director for Sinai Hospital in northwest Baltimore. While the position paid the bills, his true devotion was to his idea for a defibrillator that could be implanted directly into the body, using electrical impulses to convert an abnormal rhythm to a normal one.

Mirowski had been joined in his quest by another cardiologist named Morty Mower. They had fleshed out their idea enough to present it to Medtronic, a major medical device company, in 1967. For the next several years, the company worked with them, but in 1972, three significant events took place.

The first was that Mirowski found himself becoming increasingly unhappy with the slow pace at Medtronic. As he later told colleagues, the project manager seemed more interested in nice dinners than in moving the device along the development process.

Secondly, an editorial on Mirowski's device appeared in a major medical journal. The piece was authored by Bernand Lown, who was known throughout the profession as the leading expert on sudden cardiac death. It questioned the validity of the entire concept of an implantable device such as the one Mirowski had envisioned. In fact, the 1972 Circulation article offered numerous reasons why it was not only impossible to develop an ICD, but furthermore, was unethical to test its performance, since doing so would require having to induce ventricular fibrillation in a patient receiving such a device.

Lown's most damning contention was that, "If you found a patient dead with an implantable defibrillator, how would you know it wasn't the device that killed him?" recounts Heilman.

Lastly, and to make matters worse, results came in from a market survey Medtronic had just conducted suggesting that there simply wasn't a significant enough market for the device even if it should be offered to the profession. To put it bluntly, the company wasn't moving forward on the device, and in light of the evidence, probably wouldn't in the future.

Despite the criticism, when Heilman heard about the implantable defibrillator, he was intrigued by the concept and, like Mirowski, saw its potential. Heilman's original reason for founding the company Medrad was to create a means by which he could not only conduct research, but also produce the products that could help save patients' lives.

"When you're in research, even if you're in an academic setting, you have to fight for funds, and it frequently doesn't lead to a product," says Heilman. "So I made the calculation that maybe what I should do is to actually get into the business of developing medical devices, and hopefully if there was a company that could make some money, then that could be a source of discretionary income to use for development purposes."

The implantable defibrillator was just such a device – one that could make a significant clinical impact and save lives that, like Mirowski's esteemed colleague's, were otherwise being lost. The men struck a deal, and began working on developing the device using private funds held by Medrad.

Over the next eight years, the project faced tremendous technical hurdles. The first of these was transforming the large external defibrillators into much smaller devices that could actually be implanted inside the human body.

Fresh out of grad school, Langer was hired to develop the electronics and figure out how to regulate the electrical pulses the machine would produce. He quickly began working out the bugs for a system that had to work right the first time and every time.

The team began by experimenting with defibrillation thresholds. They performed numerous test defibrillations to study various waveforms and to learn how to reliably detect ventricular fibrillation.

"The work seemed to go really fast, because we weren't doing academic research or worrying about publishing papers; we were doing product development," says Langer. "A waveform not only had to defibrillate reliably, it had to be possible to generate it by practical miniaturized hardware. We were focused on developing the final version."

The goal from the very beginning was to produce a workable product that could be sold to the medical market. When problems arose, the team was able to overcome them through sheer determination and brain power.

"We originally used some catheter electrodes and were able to get them to work well, but only when they stayed firmly in position," says Langer. "So we switched to the implantable patch electrodes, which could be sutured in place and which, because of their large surface area, had a lower defibrillation threshold. That was a difficult transition, because the catheters have huge advantages in terms of easier implantation, but in our experience, they just didn't work as well as the patches, and we took the conservative approach."

In fact, much of the technology they required simply didn't exist in the form they needed. In one instance, they borrowed the technology developed for flash cameras to develop energy storage capacitors.

"A lot of people believed that you couldn't use that type of technology in an implantable device because it wasn't reliable enough, but it's still being used today," says Langer.

Several weeks after implanting their device into the first patient, the team conducted a test, in which they induced fibrillation and waited for the device to produce a shock. What seemed like an eternity passed, and as Dr. Mower was just about to manually defibrillate the patient, the implant came to life and did its job.

As time passed, other issues with the implant emerged. It soon became apparent, for example, that the device needed to perform an additional function. It also needed to shock lower-rate ventricular tachycardia. The detection system had to be modified to perform that function as well. As work on the next generation device began, the team was joined by another engineer and former medical student named Mir Imran.

After the initial human trial for the device in 1980, it was slowly adopted, but when it received FDA approval, it hit the general medical community like a storm. Finally, there was a way of dealing with one of the most stubborn problems facing cardiac patients. Still, the initial reaction from the leaders of the profession was anything but positive.

Langer recalled that when he attended defibrillation conferences and told others about the project, the reaction was invariably laughter. At that time, the preferred treatment for arrhythmia was drugs, and many cardiologists who supported that approach clearly felt threatened by this new device. In fact, the defibrillator was the first practical alternative to drugs and surgery.

"Somehow we drew the wrath of the 'pope' of the field of sudden cardiac death," says Mower.

This leading Boston cardiologist had been denouncing the new device from the bully pulpit of medical journals and professional meetings. When Mower and the others arranged a meeting with him to discuss his objections, everything went well until the subject of the device and its use came up.

"We had a very nice lunch at the Engineer's Club in Boston, and it was very interesting," Mower recalls. "He was very, very eloquent on every subject in the world, but as soon as we got around to the defibrillator, he almost became irrational. It was very difficult to determine what his objections were."

Yet despite these naysayers, the device was granted approval by the FDA and has subsequently become one of the most successful medical devices in history, with more than 300,000 implanted and helping damaged hearts beat normally. One model even monitors the heartbeat of Vice President Dick Cheney.

The developers of the device and the company that produced it enjoyed success beyond their wildest dreams.

"We made venture capitalists very happy at the time, but it would have been much better to have held on to that business," says Heilman. "But we ended up selling it for what was about a quarter billion dollars."

Heilman and Langer both went on to form new companies and are continuing to revolutionize the medical field with new devices. They, along with Mirowski and Mower, were inducted into the Inventors Hall of Fame for their work on the implantable defibrillator.

Mower himself has earned 26 patents, including one for a special ski boot designed to help skiers perform sharp turns in the snow. He has headed two other companies, one of which developed and sold an inexpensive computer that could perform complicated tasks far cheaper than powerful mainframe devices.

Mirowski died in 1990, but not before the device was brought to market and he realized the dream that had been born so long ago in Israel – an idea born out of the needless loss of his beloved friend and mentor, Harry Heller. Today, this lifesaving technology exists because of his genius and unrelenting determination.

Chapter 34

FRUITS OF THE VINE
WINEMAKING AND THE CREATIVE PROCESS

Winemaking and inventing. Grapes and the creative process. I'm sure you're already asking what these things have in common and what a chapter on winemaking is doing in a book about creativity and invention.

The process for creating great wines is very much like the process for inventing revolutionary new medical devices. The five step method for creating ideas that I outlined earlier has its parallel in winemaking.

Likewise, the process of stressing the vine allows the grape to grow deep roots that reach out for as many nutrients as it can. It becomes hungry and seeks out moisture. In the process, it becomes strong, innovative, and able to do things that a vine grown in more fertile soil simply could not.

When it comes to inventing, you need to be properly prepared to have an idea. While knowledge in your field is vital, it is seldom the progenitor of a new creation. If someone is overly fertile or comfortable, he won't be hungry enough to leave that comfort zone and create something new. Just as a problem must be observed, understood, and then solved in order for an idea to be created, so too must the vine of the grape be challenged so as to grow an extensive root system.

Aspiring Winemakers

Winemaking and inventing are so similar, that a number of great inventors have been driven to use the financial rewards of their creativity to purchase vineyards, where their creativity could be given yet another outlet.

I believe it's no coincidence that three of the inventors I've profiled in this book chose to buy California wineries after their inventions gave them the monetary resources to do so. But why?

After inventing the heart stent, Julio Palmaz turned his attention to resurrecting a winery in the fertile Napa Valley. Thomas Fogarty bought land high in the Portola Valley hills, where he planted vines and now operates one of the region's most successful vineyards. Robert Sinskey chose to develop vineyards in the Carneros region that would not just make good wine, but "the best wine."

Just as these inventors used the creative process to develop new medical devices, they have followed a similar process in producing great grapes and fine wines.

Palmaz's interest in wine developed when he was a young resident.

"I trained at UC Davis in the early '80s, and the wine school had just started offering evening courses on winemaking and wine appreciation," he recalls. "So I took wine appreciation courses. I visited the wine country. The whole thing was so glamorous. I thought it would be a great thing to retire to. So I began thinking about it and decided to make it a reality."

In those days, Palmaz had to contend with merely drinking wine, but as he acquired greater wealth thanks to the success of the stent, his thoughts soon turned to owning his own vineyard. He found one in the lush Napa Valley surrounded by steep hills and fertile pastures. The property had been abandoned for almost a century but retained a rambling main house and several outbuildings.

While much mystique surrounds the process, he saw it as a scientific method that could be mastered by anyone with a knowledge of chemistry.

"Many of these wine experts came in and tried to create this mystery surrounding the wine, but they got very nervous when I started asking them scientific questions," he recalls.

Palmaz and his wife, Amalia, set about building a winery that would produce only the finest of wine.

Some years earlier, Dr. Fogarty also made his own foray into winemaking. Where Palmaz saw elegance, Fogarty saw a health food that, consumed in moderation, would greatly reduce the risk of heart disease. He was first introduced to the industry in 1969, when he began teaching surgery at the Stanford University Medical Center. Intrigued by the creativity of winemaking, he would often help a Stanford colleague who operated a small winery with vineyard and cellar practices.

His interest blossomed, and he later purchased acreage in the Santa Cruz Mountains that eventually became part of what is now the Thomas Fogarty Winery and Vineyards. He built a small cellar on the property and at first, began making wine with grapes purchased from nearby growers. He planted his own vines in 1978, and established a commercial winery in 1981. The estate now consists of 325 acres, 25 of which are under vine.

Dr. Fogarty's interest in wine transcends its function as an enjoyable adult beverage. "Moderate wine consumption addresses the preventative aspects of good health," he says.

Medical experts have long realized that regular wine consumption could improve cardiovascular health. So it is perhaps only natural that this creative master's latest invention should be one of the ultimate health foods.

Palmaz, who Fogarty views as a friendly competitor in the wine business, agrees that wine can not only be a vital tool in promoting health, but can help in recovering from heart disease once it has struck. As a doctor whose practice and research centers around the heart, Palmaz is quick to cite studies that found that drinking two or more glasses of wine regularly after a heart attack reduced the risk of a second heart attack or other cardiovascular complications by 59 percent compared to nondrinkers.

Just as in developing an advanced medical device, experimentation and prototyping are vital to coming up with new varieties of wine. At the Robert Sinskey Vineyards, the ophthalmologist has placed great emphasis on cutting-edge research to develop the perfect Pinot Noir. In fact, when the original winemaker he hired refused to try new techniques and approaches to the process, Sinskey quickly replaced him with someone who was more inclined to think and innovate like an inventor.

"The guy we have now is running 20 to 30 experiments every year to make a better wine," he says. "It's not a magic process or an overnight process. It takes years to work out better wines."

Winemaking, much like creativity, is an art. There is science and a well-established process. However, the results aren't just determined by the science and the process, but by the art and imagination that is applied to it as well.

"The guys who are doing the best in the wine business use their imagination to stay ahead of the game, because they're always catching up with you," explains Sinskey.

In winemaking, the most important part begins with the harvesting of the grape. The transformation of grape juice into wine is a highly competitive art and a very precise science. To achieve the pinnacle of winemaking, it is necessary to apply science and quality control to an age-old profession.

It is quite possible to make poor wine from good grapes, but it is not possible to make good wine from lousy grapes. Similarly, a useless medical device can be created using what is a truly great idea, but it is not possible to make a great medical device out of a lousy idea.

Just as a great wine begins with great grapes, a landmark invention or medical device has its genesis in a great idea. In winemaking, you must recognize and harvest the best grapes, just as an inventor must "harvest" the best ideas from among many competing and often poorly developed ideas.

Similar to cultivating a great idea, the first step in producing great grapes is the preparation of the land to receive the vine. Extensive knowledge is required by the grower, who must be well versed in growing methods and in the particularities of the grapevine.

The perfect harvest begins with the landscape where the vineyard is situated and with the soil in which the vines are planted. In order to produce the best grapes, the ideal soil isn't rich and fertile. You need an extensive root system, and vines only put down deep roots when the soil has been drained of water. This produces the frustration that prompts the vine to put down deeper roots in search of moisture.

Out of this inhospitable soil springs a wonderful creation. In that same way, inventions are born out of stress, discomfort, and often the opposition of others.

Russian-born sculptor Louise Nevelson asserted, "I think all great innovations are built on rejections." Many an inventor has felt the sting of being told you can't and shouldn't do something. For instance, when Thomas Fogarty invented the balloon catheter to remove clots from blood vessels, much of the medical community initially rejected his idea. Worse still, every company he approached about manufacturing it told him they weren't interested. But those rejections just made him more determined to press forward, and today, his invention is the standard of care in vascular surgery.

Fogarty was faced with a difficult and often uncomfortable life as a boy. Born to a lower middle class family in Cincinnati, he was forced to begin working at 12 years old when his father died. From this challenging situation, he found within himself a creative nature that was manifested first in tinkering with mechanical devices like motor scooters. His frustration with their gears led him to build and sell a centrifugal clutch that is still in use today.

Economic struggle wasn't the only adversity Fogarty faced growing up. He took up boxing after being beaten up by toughs from a nearby neighborhood. Applying the same determination that drove him in everything else, he became so good that he won every match. The only exception was in a contest with a hard-hitting professional named Rafferty. The fight ended in a draw, but Fogarty was so hammered by the other man – who would later take on the great Sugar Ray Robinson – that he decided he didn't want to suffer the beating that a loss would produce.

"If this was a draw, there was no way I wanted to suffer the beating that a loss might produce," recalls Fogarty.

Virtually every inventor has a similar story of initial hardship or rejection followed by perseverance and ultimate victory. It is no coincidence that this pattern is so familiar as to be almost cliché.

When we are unstressed, we tend to drift along and creativity becomes difficult, if not impossible. When times are good and we're moving along in comfort, we just don't have the incentive to reach down and find the nutrients needed to grow innovative ideas. We readily accept the status quo, and innovations are never considered, much less developed.

In the life cycles of many companies, you can see this same process. An entrepreneur founds a start-up firm with a great market-disrupting product and an energetic team. They achieve success and the company grows. Soon, the flexible organization that could shift and change while reacting to new situations and new opportunities becomes a rigid bureaucracy. Innovation is replaced with turf wars and it's not long before the company's sales begin to falter as new, more nimble competitors enter the market.

The strength of an organization can only be maintained by continuing to challenge the people who make up that organization. Out of their discomfort will arise new creativity and ways of doing things that will enhance the overall health of the company.

The Discomfort of Inventing

Mir Imran, an inventor and entrepreneur with more than 200 patents and 18 companies to his credit, notes that there are many brilliant researchers in colleges and universities, but few of them are willing to leave the comfort of academia to put their ideas into practice in the rough-and-tumble world of commercial products.

"How many times have you met a person who says, 'I thought of this thing so many years ago, but now somebody else has made it a reality'?" he says. "Well, the reason they weren't able to make it a reality is either they didn't have a strong enough belief in their own abilities or they didn't want to take the initiative because they're afraid of failure."

You can find comfort and lack of innovation in any area of endeavor, including those that, on the surface, appear to be quite competitive. Many practicing clinicians have dealt with problems for so long that they've incorporated them into their daily routines, so that for them, they are no longer problems.

Prior to the 1960s, vascular surgeons accepted a nearly 50 percent mortality rate. As an outsider looking in, Thomas Fogarty, then a young scrub tech, saw that the situation was producing poor patient outcome and simply didn't work.

A quadriplegic with Duchenne muscular dystrophy, David Muir was faced with the loss of the ability to speak following a tracheotomy. The doctors told him to get used to it, because it was just the way things are. In their eyes, the surgery had been a success and his lack of speech wasn't a problem.

Yet faced with this trying situation, Muir was driven to invent the Passy-Muir speaking value that gave him, and thousands of others, a voice.

Imran, Fogarty, Muir, and countless others were hungry to find something new, just like the vine that produces the grape.

Similarly, there is a point when the grape comes to a peak. Just as the inventor first states the problem and then deliberates over it, the grapevines put down their roots into the soil until they are ready to bring forth the perfect fruit.

At this point, the grape must be harvested. It takes just the right amount of sunshine and warmth, as well as an astute and experienced grower to determine the right moment to harvest the grape. You also need to account for chemical and bio-chemical changes that must occur in the grape before it can be transformed into fine wine.

Similar factors are vital to you as an inventor. While you may not choose to own your own winery as Fogarty and Palmaz have done, you will profit by under-standing the path to creating the true fruit of the grapes of invention.

Chapter 35

THOMAS FOGARTY
RECOGNIZING AND FIXING PROBLEMS

When it comes to developing a new process or device, sometimes the most critical element is simply recognizing and analyzing the problem.

You can find no better example of this critical element than in the life and work of Dr. Thomas Fogarty. An inventor and entrepreneur since childhood, he has built a career out of recognizing and solving problems. He is a model of the successful inventor who realizes that action is the prime ingredient to any invention.

"Thinking and ideas do not equate to implementation," he says. "An idea is of no value unless it's implemented."

That commitment to action has been the hallmark of a career that began with the groundbreaking development of the Fogarty balloon catheter, and which has continued through more than 120 additional patents.

A scholar and founder of numerous companies, Fogarty is recognized and celebrated as one of the great inventors of medical devices, although there was a time when his ideas were the subject of ridicule.

Fogarty realized early on the connection between invention and financial reward. Precocious and enterprising as a child, he designed and built soapbox derby racers and model airplanes that he sold to kids in the neighborhood. His inventiveness was also on display when he developed an innovative centrifugal clutch for use in a motor scooter.

Fogarty's interest in medicine came early in life as well. In the 1940s, when he was just 12 years old, he began working at Cincinnati's Good Samaritan Hospital in order to help his mother make ends meet after the death of his railroad engineer father.

The only place where an underage boy could get a job was in a not-for-profit facility like the hospital. His first job was cleaning medical equipment, including the three-bottle stomach pumps in use at that time.

By the time he was 16, he had graduated to being a scrub technician in the operating room, where he got to watch operations close-up as he handed surgeons their instruments. He was distressed to see so many patients suffer needless amputations, or even die after surgery to remove blood clots from their arteries.

An obsessive problem solver, Fogarty knew there had to be a way of performing the surgery that could reduce the 50 percent mortality rate that was then the norm. Around this time he also became close friends with Dr. Jack Cranley, one of the leading surgeons in Cincinnati, with whom he worked during the summers.

"He challenged me to come up with a better way," recalls Fogarty.

The older doctor also encouraged him to think about medical school. Up until that time, between tinkering and working as much as possible, Fogarty had never been much of a student. In fact, he had trouble finding anyone who would even recommend him for admission to college. He was finally admitted to Cincinnati's Xavier College on the recommendation of the family priest.

With the help of Dr. Cranley and three part-time jobs, Fogarty was able to make his way through college. In spite of his workload, he also devoted time to figuring out a better way to remove the arterial blockages that were proving fatal to so many patients.

"The idea then was 'the bigger the incision, the bigger the surgeon,'" says Fogarty. "You could be disciplined, or even sued for malpractice, for not making the incision large enough to see all the pathology."

This standard of care called for the surgeon to make long incisions that opened up the entire artery in order to remove the blockage. The procedure clearly didn't work, because at least 50 percent of the patients were dying, and others were returning to the operating room two or three times.

The young Fogarty considered various ways to improve on the procedure. The key, it seemed, was to avoid the large incision and thus avoid major trauma to the patient. Working at home in the attic between sessions at the University of Cincinnati medical school, he labored to perfect the device.

He hit upon the idea of using a catheter that could be inserted through a small incision and then threaded past the clot. His first prototype was a urethral catheter to which he attached a balloon made from the tip of a No. 5 surgical glove. The makeshift balloon could then be inflated with saline to the size of the artery once it moved past the clot and then pulled back, taking the clot with it.

The idea was "pathetically simple" Fogarty recalls, but there was one immediate problem. The catheter was made of vinyl and the balloon was latex, and no glue would hold the two together.

Fortunately, the young inventor was also an avid fly fisherman, so he used his fly-fishing skills to tie the glove tip to the catheter. He experimented first by inserting the device into the tapered tube that was used to cross-match blood. At first, the balloon would rupture when he overinflated it or pulled it through the simulated artery. But he eventually figured out the type and thickness of rubber that was stiff enough to remove the clot but flexible enough to move through a narrow tube without breaking. Then he and Dr. Cranley made a trip to the morgue to test the device on cadavers.

Although Fogarty invented the device while in medical school, it would be ten years before he was finally able to try it out on a real, live patient. As Fogarty watched, Dr. Cranley made a small incision and threaded the balloon embolectomy catheter – named for the clot removal procedure – up the patient's blocked artery. When inflated and pulled back out, it worked just as he predicted, and brought the clot with it. On that day, minimally invasive surgery was born.

Even though the device worked perfectly, the greatest challenge still lay ahead. Every company Fogarty approached about making the device turned him down. He was eager to make the catheter more widely available to other surgeons. At that point, Fogarty and his colleagues were using models that Fogarty had manufactured by hand.

In addition to finding a company to build it commercially, Cranley had told him he should license the device so that his name would be on it.

"He said, 'Of course, physicians don't often get paid for inventing,' Fogarty recalls, "And I asked, 'Why not?'" As a struggling medical student, he was intrigued by the idea that he might be able to realize financial gain from his work, but it certainly wasn't his primary motivation.

"You know, money's not a bad motivator," says Fogarty, "but it was pretty clear that the way things were being done just didn't work."

So Fogarty continued to make the catheter by hand for himself and other surgeons even as the medical profession and its attendant device companies continued to reject his invention. An article about the device, authored by Fogarty and Cranley, was turned down by the four major medical journals because it defied the conventional wisdom of the day about how surgery should be done.

"They wouldn't make the balloon catheter for a number of years, and the reason was pretty clear," Fogarty recalls. "I had no stature, and everybody said, 'This is a crazy medical student,' and, in fact, I may have been crazy."
Nevertheless, he maintained complete faith in his device, based upon the evidence of his own experience and his ability to see the harsh reality of the surgery of that day.

He moved on to a surgical residency at the University of Oregon but never gave up on the idea of winning commercial approval for the catheter. While there, he was introduced to Lowell Edwards, an electrical engineer who was president of his own company. After watching the procedure, he agreed to begin manufacturing the device.

In 1969, a decade after he made the first prototype, Fogarty finally won a patent on the device. Edwards' Lifesciences licensed the patent from him and gave him a consulting role and royalties.

The logic of Fogarty's device slowly but surely became accepted throughout the medical community. He vividly recalls the moment when he realized that his device had truly become the industry standard: when a physician was sued for malpractice for not using it during surgery.

Today, the Fogarty balloon embolectomy catheter is used in more than 300,000 procedures each year and has saved both the lives and limbs of an estimated 15 million patients.

In the years since his original creation, Fogarty has followed a familiar pattern for inventors. He has continued to invent new devices, including variations of his highly successful catheter, and to obtain new patents. He has also founded more than 20 companies to market both his own inventions and those of others.

That first balloon angioplasty, performed with a Fogarty catheter in 1965, has led to more than 650,000 of these procedures each year.

In addition, his companies produce balloon devices used in laparoscopic hernia repair and other laparoscopy-assisted cardiovascular procedures. He has also developed a minimally invasive device for breast cancer diagnosis and therapy. One of the most successful of his inventions is the Fogarty stent graft, which repairs abdominal aortic aneurysms, a dangerous weakening of the large blood vessel in the abdomen. Fogarty's idea was that instead of removing the weakened section, he should strengthen it with an implant: a thin polyester tube called a stent that grabs on to the blood vessel with metal "rings." An inflatable catheter transports the stent to the blood vessel. When the balloon is inflated, the stent expands to the size of the artery and blood flows normally.

Now in his 70s, Fogarty is as active and as inquisitive as ever. In addition to presiding over a number of companies, he also serves as professor of surgery at Stanford University, where he performs both cardiac and peripheral vascular surgery.

Fogarty's success is also a godsend to other inventors, who benefit from his investments in new and groundbreaking devices. One of his companies provides venture capital to fund new devices and helps to bring them to commercial success.

"It's delusional to think that you have all the ideas," he asserts.

Rather, he prefers to talk directly to inventors who are pursuing new ideas to find out how they're doing and whether their devices may be the next success story.

Fogarty knew very little about the business side of medical devices and how to patent them when he made his first foray into the field. He realizes that most physicians aren't entrepreneurs, and may be easy victims for those who seek to steal their ideas or cheat them out of their fair share of the profits.

Although he has been deeply involved in the commercial side of inventing for the past 30 years, he knows his limits. When it comes to starting companies, he quickly gets them going and then turns them over to professional managers to run the operation.

In fact, one of his primary occupations is creating and nurturing new ideas. Virtually every moment of the day, he seems to be looking for new problems to solve and seeking solutions for them in the most unlikely places. He even draws inspiration from trips to toy stores, where he buys and examines products that are manufactured to be both cheap and safe. "Just the way medical devices should be," he says.

He also makes trips to the hardware store, where he not only buys his own light bulbs, but examines products for use in his own inventions.

One of Fogarty's secrets for finding a solution to a problem is in finding the commonalities among seemingly disparate objects. Certain ideas, on the surface, might appear unrelated, but the secret to progress lay in finding the similarities that might not be so apparent.

That ability served him well when he spent time working with engineers to create a new prototype of an invention.

"The key is to prototype, prototype, and prototype again," he says.

It's not surprising, particularly given his upbringing, that Fogarty is more impressed by the ability to get things done rather than education and advanced degrees. He holds in highest regard an elderly man who works at a winery he owns. Now in his 70s, the man never went beyond high school, yet he possesses an innate ability to understand how machines work and figure out virtually any project.

This obsession with practicality and accomplishment also helps to explain Fogarty's dedication to serving patients. He has little patience with procedures that might seem to work from the surgeon's point of view but that leave the patient in great pain.

"The outcome in the journal [article] is always about eight ankle brachial indexes and not whether the patient was truly satisfied," he insists. "What good does it do to replace one ABI with another ABI if you're left with causalgia?"

In addition to his medical inventions, Fogarty's varied interests have led him into other avenues of creativity. He first became interested in winemaking while teaching surgery at Stanford University Medical Center. The ancient art of viticulture appealed to his sensibilities as both a physician and a scientist, and he was intrigued by the creative process that produced a drink that not only appealed to the taste buds but to the mind and soul, and that could – consumed in moderation – provide health benefits as well.

On land purchased in the Santa Cruz Mountains of California, he built a small cellar and embarked on the process of making wine from grapes purchased from local vineyards. He eventually began planting his own vines, and by 1981, he had established the commercial winery that is now famous throughout the industry.

Today, Thomas Fogarty is just as creative and innovative as the young man who was troubled by the high mortality rate in vascular surgery and set out to find a better way. It's that curiosity and drive to recognize problems and then find solutions that still motivates him.

In fact, one of his current projects is to come up with the solution to a mundane problem with which people everywhere can relate. He's dedicated himself to finding a new and innovative way to clean toilets.

Based on his track record of a lifetime spent inventing, Fogarty will likely succeed.

Chapter 36

PALMAZ AND SCHATZ
THE STENT REVOLUTION

Drs. Julio Palmaz and Richard Schatz made medical history when they successfully developed the coronary stent and set off a new era in the treatment of heart disease. Today, the device is implanted in more than a million heart patients each year, saving countless lives, and these doctors are recognized as two of America's leading inventors of medical devices.

In addition to international notoriety, both have gained wealth far beyond their dreams, thanks to a device that generates more than $4.5 billion in sales each year.

With their financial futures assured, they have been able to pursue research and private practice just the way they always wanted. In addition, they've been able to pursue wide-ranging interests, like winemaking, that wouldn't have been possible without their combination of genius and good fortune. In the minds of many would-be inventors, their lives and careers epitomize the ideal to which they aspire.

However, the ease of their lives today is in stark contrast to the long, torturous, and often disillusioning process that turned an innovative idea into the patented invention that now dominates the market. They dealt with a multitude of problems and technical hurdles, as well as often fickle support from their financial backers. Even after their device had proven itself, they were attacked and scorned by colleagues who said that placing the stents in human hearts was something that couldn't – or perhaps shouldn't – be done.

The pair's story is one of the best examples of the need for perseverance and belief in your idea, even in the face of great odds and opposition.

"I didn't set out to invent anything," admits Palmaz.

In 1978, he was a young resident who had only recently moved to the U.S. from Argentina. At a medical conference in New Orleans, he attended a lecture by Dr. Andreas Gruentzig, the inventor of balloon angioplasty. He listened to Gruentzig describe this new and amazing technique for opening vessels through the use of a catheter. The doctor also told of the limitations of the procedure, showing the audience X-rays and microscopic images of how vessels would still collapse after the procedure was performed. Sitting there in the darkened auditorium, Palmaz began to think that these problems might be solved if one could somehow insert a tiny "scaffold" into the vessel to support it.

After the conference had ended, he shared a cab to the airport with Dr. Stewart R. Reuter, the faculty chairman at the University of California at Davis,

where Palmaz was doing a residency in radiology. Filled with passion and excitement, he described the concept to his superior, who asked that he put it down on
paper for consideration. This document would later prove to be of great importance in establishing the date of conception for the device when others claimed
that they had come up with the idea first.

"That's something I always recommend to inventors, that they write up their
idea first so that they have something that proves they originated a particular concept," says Palmaz . "Always extend your initial thoughts in terms of making a bib-
liographic search and then make detailed drawings, which sometimes are not intuitive. Yet the idea evolves as you put it down on paper."

His passion for the idea of creating a support for the vessel also began to grow
as he was faced with the same frustrations that Gruentzig had first described at the
conference. He assisted on his first angioplasty procedure just a few short weeks
after returning to the university and saw firsthand the shortcomings of the operation. One patient had to undergo emergency surgery following a procedure.

Faced with this bitter experience, Palmaz was determined to find a solution.
The most obvious answer lay in his evolving idea for a stent.

He started developing a prototype, working first with different types of woven
mesh. The structure was extremely important in ensuring that the device could
retain the shape of the balloon that inserted it.

When Dr. Reuter and other faculty members read the report, they encouraged
him to continue.

"I read about implantable metals and delved more into the subject," Palmaz
recalls. "I played at home with wires and pliers and solder material, making prototypes in the garage. We started buying balloons and doing angioplasty, but I was
washing the balloons afterwards and taking them home. I was making my own
nets there, playing with them, expanding them inside rubber tubes. I started having a feel for the mechanical problems that making a stent would impose."

Several years passed as he continued to work on the stent's design. He first
tried weaving cylindrical nets using pencils and pins, weaving copper wiring in and
out. He soon found that the net lacked plasticity, so the cross points of the weave
needed to be fixed. He tried welding the spots, using an iron solder, around the
circumference.

"I was also reading about implants and got the notion that implants needed to
be made of one material, otherwise there would be electrochemical corrosion,"
explains Palmaz. "The stumbling block was how to make the device in one piece if
the cross points needed to be welded."

Like so many other determined inventors, Palmaz discovered the answer by
taking an idea long used in an unrelated field and adapting it to the particular

challenge he faced. On the floor of his garage, he came across a small piece of metal lathe, the kind masons use to apply plaster. He scrutinized the tool's staggered openings and immediately recognized that this was the pattern that he needed to create for the stent. He cut out a small piece and then closed it by pushing the edges together with a hammer. He noticed that the staggered openings created staggered slots when closed.

"I thought, 'Well, if I make this pattern in a tube, then, when a balloon expands, it will become a mesh,'" says Palmaz. "And it's made of a single material. This was the inspiration for the slotted stent."

Palmaz made models out of cardboard, but soon realized that he needed more advanced techniques if he was going to build a successful working model.

For inventors like Palmaz, this dedication to an idea, combined with ceaseless effort, often spells the difference between just another good idea and a marketable commercial product.

Palmaz was convinced that the device had commercial potential. He approached several companies, but all of them said no to his idea. Most thought it was, at best, unproven, and at the worst, just a crazy idea. But even after these rejections, Palmaz was unwilling to give up. He knew the idea was right; he just needed to develop it further.

One company suggested he contact an expert who could help him in making a better prototype. The retired biotechnologist that Palmaz consulted offered him a number of suggestions, including going to a machine shop that could make the stent out of a better material than cardboard.

In 1980, Palmaz followed his mentor, Dr. Reuter, to the University of Texas Health Science Center in San Antonio. He was guaranteed lab space and research time to pursue his work on the stent. He talked to the university about the device and asked whether the institution would be interested in pursuing his work. Although the university politely declined the offer, they did allow him the opportunity to continue working on it on his own.

About that time, he also met Dr. Richard Schatz, who would become his collaborator and his link to the funding he needed to make his idea into a reality. Schatz, an ex-Army doctor, had been traveling down several "blind alleys" in his own research using lasers to combat the effects of atherosclerosis.

The two struck up a conversation about their work. Palmaz told him that he had been concentrating on improving the well-established concept of using a balloon to expand the arteries in the heart. Surgeons knew that once the procedure opened the vessels, they might collapse without some kind of support. He proposed to Schatz that by putting a piece of wire mesh on the balloon and then leaving it behind as a permanent implant, the vessel could be kept open. Schatz was intrigued, immediately recognizing the possibilities of the device – a vision few others shared.

"He worked very quietly on this for many years, and eventually moved on to a more sophisticated design, which later became the slotted tube design," recalls Schatz. "That was just a piece of metal tubing, the walls of which were etched out. So he removed 90 percent of the metal, but the pattern that he created became the basis of all the patents thereafter."

What the project needed was money, something that was sorely lacking. Palmaz had already borrowed more than $35,000 from another fund to keep his work going, and he was becoming concerned about how he could repay the funds with no other grants on the horizon.

His budding partnership with Schatz would prove to be extremely helpful. For Schatz was not only an accomplished physician; he possessed a well-developed talent for fundraising and making contacts in the business community. At conferences, when other doctors were in lecture halls listening to explanations of new procedures, he could be found networking in the exhibit hall or in hospitality suites.

In fact, Schatz discovered the angel they needed for their project during a swank dinner party at a local country club. Phil Romano, a restaurateur who owned eating establishments around the country, was looking for a place to invest the millions he had gotten from the sale of his Fuddruckers hamburger chain.

Schatz sketched out the idea on a linen napkin in between courses. He told Romano that Palmaz had invented the device but that the university wasn't interested in funding it.

Ironically, after years spent selling a product that some suspected might be a leading cause of heart disease, Romano was now presented with a way to help those same people.

Schatz invited him to the university to talk to Palmaz. When the colorful entrepreneur showed up sporting his trademark ponytail and wearing an expensive suit with no socks, Palmaz, ever the serious academic researcher, was concerned.

"I didn't know if I was going to get into trouble because of this guy," he says. Nonetheless, Palmaz made a clear and convincing case that appealed to the businessman.

"What I liked about it was the idea was good," recalls Romano. "They were able to explain it in layman's terms, so I was able to understand it. They thought if it could be brought to market, it would be very valuable."

In addition, Romano liked the two doctors. He ignored his attorneys and accountants when they advised him against investing in the project. At worst, Romano thought, he would be able to write off the research and development costs. He believed the potential was much greater than the risk.

So the entrepreneur invested $250,000 for a 30 percent share in the three-way venture. That funding gave the two doctors the ability to continue animal testing on their device.

At the time, Schatz was one of the country's leading experts on coronary angioplasty and he keenly understood the problems that such a device faced. But his collaboration with Palmaz helped produce the synergy needed to bring the project to completion. Palmaz was instrumental in makings changes to the design of the tiny expandable steel scaffold in order to quickly move the device through all the necessary animal trials.

What became known as the Palmaz-Schatz balloon expandable stent proved to be a technological breakthrough of immense proportions.

With money in hand and a flamboyant partner who understood the way to do business, the group, then called Expandable Graft Partnership, was able to attract the big companies who had originally ignored Palmaz's seemingly crazy idea.

It wasn't long before $42-billion-a-year healthcare giant Johnson & Johnson saw the possibilities of the stent and approached the three, checkbook in hand. They walked away from the New Brunswick, New Jersey, offices of the company with $10 million and the promise of future royalties. By the time Johnson & Johnson bought all the rights to the device in 1998, they had paid Romano and the inventors more than $500 million.

In May of 1987, Schatz and Palmaz performed the first peripheral stent placement on a patient at Freiburg University in West Germany. Later that same year, Palmaz and his colleagues did the first coronary stent placement in Sao Paolo, Brazil. Both procedures were highly successful.

Prior to their collaboration, neither Palmaz nor Schatz had ever thought of themselves as being particularly creative or inventive. Yet this device has been responsible for changing the way medicine is practiced when it comes to healing hearts.

It also drastically changed the lives of both doctors. Neither had been financially well-off before, but in the years that followed, they were rewarded for their work with wealth beyond their imagination.

"I never thought there was going to be any financial gain until [Romano] came along," Palmaz admits. "Up until then, I thought it was just an interesting research project."

Palmaz has continued to be involved in research and has extended his efforts into activities most university faculty members can only dream about. He has done other deals, acting as a venture capitalist on his own.

"It also allowed me to do two things that were fascinating to me," he says.

In addition to collecting vintage Porsche racing cars, he also purchased a

California winery that had been inactive for more than 100 years and "resurrected it." He flies to the vineyard for a few weeks each month aboard a jet he recently purchased.

"I did it because I thought wine was beautiful, and I appreciated the serene atmosphere of the vineyard," says Palmaz.

The winery also appeals to the inventor in him. When faced with the problem of determining the proper amount of moisture in the soil, he rejected the common practice of taking measurements in three or four spots. Instead, he devised a grid system that measures multiple small areas and provides a much more comprehensive average for the entire property.

He has also invested heavily in developing a truly state-of-the-art winery. Carved out of a California hillside, the operation extends down almost 12 stories underground. Multiple small fermenting tanks, rather than a few large ones, are arranged on a circular, movable platform that can place each tank under the grape crushing station. The wine flows by gravity from fermentation to blending, to first and then second-year barrel storage, and finally to bottling, all without the use of pumps, which disrupt the delicate molecules that give wine its fine characteristics.

Palmaz believes this unique process will produce a better wine, and that each barrel represents a prototype and a means for additional feedback on his quest for the perfect wine.

The success of the stent also changed the life and career of his partner, Richard Schatz, who has continued to focus his problem-solving ability on other fields of medicine, including infertility. He has formed several companies and invested in new medical devices. His wealth has allowed him to create a boutique medical practice that handles only the most interesting cases, with less regard for cost or insurance issues.

The pair's perseverance and dedication to the inventing process has enhanced not only their lives, but the lives of millions of heart patients as well.

Chapter 37

ROBERT SINSKEY
PERFECTING INNOVATION

When is comes to the creative process, there are basically two types of inventors. One produces something that is unique – perhaps even groundbreaking. It doesn't matter whether the device is simple or extremely complex; it is truly something new. The process for the second type is incremental in nature and often involves improving on something that already exists. While it may not be the birth of something never seen before, it often results in a device far more useful than it could ever have been otherwise.

Dr. Robert Sinskey is the perfect example of the second kind of inventor, and he brought his genius for improvement to the field of ophthalmology when he first conceived, and later perfected, the modified J-Loop Intraocular Lens.

Introduced in 1977, the original J-Loop was the first flexible loop, posterior-chamber lens available for implantation in human eyes. It represented a giant leap forward in the art of ophthalmology, and doctors were quick to adopt it for use in cataract surgery.

"The flexibility made it much easier to put in the eye and was much safer once it was in the eye than the previous type of lens, which went in front of the iris or was supported by the iris," says Sinskey, who helped introduce the new device and implanted many of them in his own patients.

Although a great innovation at the time, the lens was not without its shortcomings. Due to the immense variation in the shape of the eyes, and thus the ability of a surgeon to view the pathology, some found it difficult to insert the stiff upper loop into the eye and behind the iris. This sometimes resulted in complications affecting the visual outcome of the surgery.

As Sinskey traveled around the country teaching the procedure to as many as 10 groups of doctors each month, he began to question the design of the lens. Perhaps it could be redesigned and made even more flexible, and thus easier for a surgeon to place in the eye.

It was during one of these demonstrations, in fact, that Sinskey received the inspiration to modify his design. As he finished the procedure, he realized that if the angle of the loops coming out of the lens was changed, it would make the loop more flexible, and would go into the eye more easily.

After consulting with the president of the company who manufactured the lens, and with whom he had worked on previous modifications of iris-supported lenses, Sinskey was quickly able to come up with a new design. In fact, the entire redesign was accomplished in one prototype. The only variation to his original concept was to make the overall diameter of the lens plus the loops larger.

The modified J-Loop lens is but one of the many inventions resulting from the combination of Sinskey's fertile imagination and talented hands. He is responsible for the development of several new surgical instruments, including the Sinskey suture forceps and the Sinskey hook, which has become the world's most widely used ophthalmic instrument. He also developed new operative procedures, including one that corrects bulging eyes in hyperthyroid patients and another that stops the constant movement of the eyes in patients with nystagmus.

After developing his new lens and implanting it in scores of patients, Sinskey was able to obtain special permission from the FDA to implant it in the eye of a six-year-old child with cataracts – a procedure that was considered fraught with complications.

"I thought my new lens was safe enough and trouble-free enough to last a lifetime in the eye," says Sinskey. "When I presented the child's postoperative results to a cataract congress in Houston, the first question I was asked after I was finished was, 'What's the matter? Don't you like children?'"

Today, despite the predictable initial opposition, performing this procedure in children is widely accepted.

Yet a lifetime of practice in diverse and sometimes difficult situations had given the surgeon a confidence that was lacking in many of his colleagues. He was ready to push forward and take calculated risks, while others were content to keep doing things the way they had always been done – even if there was a better way and one that would be of greater benefit to the patient.

"Some doctors finish their residency, and 20 years later, they're still doing procedures the same way," he says. "I had difficulty convincing my own fellows, 15 to 20 years later, to change their techniques to accommodate the new innovations in cataract surgery."

Sinskey has never been content to settle for the routine, especially when life on the medical frontier offered the promise of better, more efficient results. Late in his own career, he made the switch from his one-handed surgical technique for cataract removal to a new two-handed procedure, even though it meant relearning the operation and abandoning the one in which he had grown skilled over the previous 20 years.

"I sweated bullets learning this technique at age 70," he explains. "Yet I felt that if I was going to keep doing surgery, I'd have to go through this relearning process, because it really would make cataract surgery easier and safer."

Throughout his career, Sinskey sought out new experiences that might offer different insights and opportunities for learning. After an ophthalmology residency at Duke University, his postdoctoral fellowship was with the Atomic Energy Commission, which led to a special assignment with the Atomic Bomb Casualty Commission in Japan. There, he studied the effects of the explosions on the eyes of victims in Hiroshima and Nagasaki. In 1955, he became the first full-time instructor in ophthalmology at the University of California at Los Angeles and opened its eye clinic, and later his own eye institute.

He has continued to teach, both throughout the U.S. and around the world, performing surgical demonstrations in 42 countries. A frequent contributor to medical journals, Sinskey also contributed to a number of ophthalmology textbooks. His skill and expertise also helped build a large and highly successful private practice.

Yet even as he generously shared his knowledge with a host of fledgling doctors, he found the process even more beneficial to himself.

"I've learned more from teaching than I gave to patients or to students," he says. "When you're teaching and operating, you have to think about everything that you're saying and doing to be able to defend your position. Students ask you questions while you're operating. They want to know why you did a procedure a particular way, and I would think, 'I did it this way because I was taught this when I was in my residency, and I've always done it this way.'"

Those questions prompted him to consider that always doing things the way you were taught might not always be the best approach.

It takes courage to learn new ways of doing things, and when it comes to inventing, it also takes a lot of confidence in yourself and belief in your ideas. When Sinskey invented his J-Loop lens, corporate giant Johnson & Johnson offered him a six-figure consultation fee. He turned it down in favor of royalties.

"At the time, I thought if the lens flies, that's fine," says Sinskey. "If it doesn't, that's the way it is. But I had total confidence that the lens was going to make it."

When this new lens became one of the most popular of its kind for use in cataract surgery, Sinskey was rewarded with millions of dollars, and his bold rejection of guaranteed income from the consultation fee was justified.

Like many other successful inventors, his proclivity for inventing opened up a new world to him. For one, he decided to enter the wine business. But his goal wasn't just to make wine. Rather it was to make a "superior" wine. "We fired the first winemaker because I felt he was too rigid. Every time I asked him, "Why don't we try this?" he'd say, 'Because that's never been done before and it's not going to work.' I nicknamed him Dr. No!"

Just like in his approach to medicine, the vineyard owner believes that the traditional approach is not always the best one. In fact, the vineyards are now certified organic, and Sinskey's current winemaker is now running 20 to 30 experiments a year in the hopes of constantly creating better wines.

Says Sinskey: "It's not a magic process or an overnight process. It takes years to work out better wines."
His career in winemaking came about when he realized he could no longer tolerate his usual scotch and bourbon, particularly after an unhappy divorce led to a flare-up of his ulcer.

"I found that I could tolerate wine, and it also made dinner and conversation more enjoyable," he laughs. "In addition, studies now say that drinking red wine in moderation is healthier than not drinking at all."

As a physician he found the appeal of wine irresistible. As an inventor he found the process equally so. In many ways it was a natural extension of his talents and interests.

The inventing process is never easy – it involves the courage to take risks and to survive the disappointment when a new idea doesn't work out – whether it involves making wine or practicing medicine. But it's a necessary one if you're going to grow and continue to be of service to your patients, and perhaps to the larger profession as well.

A Final Word

We've come to the end of Innovative Doctoring, but not, I hope, the end of your interest in developing your talents when it comes to creativity and invention.

And that, after all, is the whole point. Down through the ages, individuals have thought of ideas that could make a substantial impact on their own lives, the economy, and perhaps even history. Yet, time and again, they put the idea aside and went about their everyday lives until one day someone else "discovered" their idea and made it a tangible and often profitable reality.

In the stories of inventors such as Mir Imran, Thomas Fogarty, Paul Yock, David Muir, and countless others can be found the seeds of inspiration and dedication to ideas. Each of them faced obstacles in their path to inventing. All of them would have found it easier in some sense to attend to their daily struggles rather than seeking solutions to problems that others simply accepted.

Yet they each chose the more difficult, but ultimately immensely more satisfying, path of creativity and invention. While many of them realized wealth and fame, it's obvious that those were not their primary goals. Money and recognition are simply the outward manifestations of dedication to a life of problem solving.

It's important too that you understand that I'm not presenting an activity that you just engage in on the weekends or in your spare time. Creativity and invention are very much a lifestyle of passion and dedication. They are a way of living in which you devote yourself to making the best use of your time in the pursuit of your highest and greatest goals.

The Five Steps to Creativity – preparation, frustration, problem definition, deliberation, and illumination and documentation – are activities that you engage in every day. Through this process, you will make your life better and richer as you remove obstacles and create greater efficiency and achievement for yourself and others. As the ideas flow from your consciousness, some will no doubt produce improved techniques and devices that you can develop, commercialize, and sell. Yet these achievements are merely the byproducts of your life, imagination, and dedication to creativity. They are simply stops along the journey.

The most important part is that you simply begin.

Appendix

CONFIDENTIALITY AND NONDISCLOSURE AGREEMENT

This AGREEMENT is made and entered into by <u>COMPANY/ INDIVIDUAL</u> (hereinafter "DISCLOSEE") and <u>INVENTOR'S NAME</u> (hereinafter referred to as "DISCLOSER"). DISCLOSER and DISCLOSEE sometimes will be referred to collectively hereinafter as the "PARTIES."

RECITALS

A.   DISCLOSER, THROUGH THE EXPENDITURE OF SUBSTANTIAL TIME, EFFORT, AND MONEY, HAS INVENTED, DEVELOPED, OWNS, AND/OR HAS RIGHTS TO CERTAIN VALUABLE TRADE SECRETS, KNOW-HOW, AND CONFIDENTIAL AND PROPRIETARY INFORMATION (HEREINAFTER REFERRED TO COLLECTIVELY AS THE "CONFIDENTIAL INFORMATION") RELATING TO THE TECHNOLOGY PROJECT, AS HEREINAFTER DEFINED, AND DESIRES TO MAINTAIN THE CONFIDENTIAL INFORMATION IN SECRET.

b.   DISCLOSEE desires to discuss with DISCLOSER certain aspects of the CONFIDENTIAL INFORMATION in order to evaluate the TECHNOLOGY PROJECT, and DISCLOSEE may, during the course of such discussions, acquire knowledge of the CONFIDENTIAL INFORMATION.

c.   DISCLOSEE understands that all information disclosed by DISCLOSER to DISCLOSEE, whether oral, in writing, or any other media, in regard to the TECHNOLOGY PROJECT may be or include CONFIDENTIAL INFORMATION, and DISCLOSEE is willing to maintain the secrecy of all such information.

AGREEMENT

In consideration of the disclosure by DISCLOSER to DISCLOSEE of CONFIDENTIAL INFORMATION, and other good and valuable consideration, the receipt and sufficiency of which are hereby acknowledged by the PARTIES, the PARTIES agree as follows:

1. This AGREEMENT itself, verbal and written descriptions, and any associated technical information regarding the TECHNOLOGY PROJECT or inventions listed below are CONFIDENTIAL INFORMATION and TRADE SECRETS, and are being provided in confidence to DISCLOSEE solely for the purpose of evaluating a business relationship. The CONFIDENTIAL INFORMATION contains technical information and possible business applications for the TECHNOLOGY PROJECT, which is defined as:

   A method and apparatus relating generally to an orientation device for injections.

2. DISCLOSEE agrees that it will maintain in confidence and as secret all CONFIDENTIAL INFORMATION, and that it will not, without the express written consent of an authorized officer of DISCLOSER, for any reason or at any time use, sell, publish, copy, disseminate, or otherwise dis close to any person, except on a need-to-know basis as necessary to carry out the purposes of this AGREEMENT, including without limitation any director, officer, agent, or employee of DISCLOSEE who has not read and agreed to be bound by this AGREEMENT, any portion of the CONFIDENTIAL INFORMATION or any fact or information relating to the CONFIDENTIAL INFORMATION, and shall at all times treat such CONFIDENTIAL INFORMATION as the property of DISCLOSER. DISCLOSEE will not permit others to analyze or subject the TECHNOLOGY PROJECT or any CONFIDENTIAL INFORMATION to any tests that would disclose the identity or makeup of the TECHNOLOGY PROJECT or any CONFIDENTIAL INFORMATION. DISCLOSEE shall not disclose the CONFIDENTIAL INFORMATION to any third party without first obtaining written permission from DISCLOSER.

3. Where used in this AGREEMENT, CONFIDENTIAL INFORMATION shall include all information relating to the TECHNOLOGY PROJECT,

whether oral or in writing or any other media, including without limitation trade secrets, descriptions, drawings, process equipment specifications and layouts, equipment and utility costs, manuals, customer lists, purchase and sales records, marketing information, computer programs, concepts, techniques, methods, formulas, and research, whether developed by DISCLOSER or furnished to DISCLOSER by others, and all information that relates to the DISCLOSEE's use of the CONFIDENTIAL INFORMATION.

4. CONFIDENTIAL INFORMATION shall not include:
    a. Information which at the time of disclosure is in the public domain. However, no disclosure of CONFIDENTIAL INFORMATION shall be construed to be a public disclosure for any purpose whatsoever.
    b. Information which after the time of disclosure becomes part of the public domain through no fault of the DISCLOSEE, but only after and to the extent that such information is published.
    c. Any information that is disclosed to DISCLOSEE by a third party having legitimate possession thereof and the unrestricted right to make such disclosure.

5. CONFIDENTIAL INFORMATION that is specific as to techniques, methods, or the like shall not be deemed to be in the public domain merely because such information is embraced by more general disclosures in the public domain, and any combination of features shall not be deemed within the foregoing exceptions merely because individual features are in the public domain if the combination itself and its principles of operation are not in the public domain.

6. The restrictions set forth in this AGREEMENT shall apply to DISCLOSEE and its officers, directors, agents, employees, and any parent or subsidiary companies to which the CONFIDENTIAL INFORMATION may be disclosed as permitted by this AGREEMENT. DISCLOSEE shall exercise efforts that are reasonable under the circumstances to maintain the secrecy and/or confidentiality of the CONFIDENTIAL INFORMATION. DISCLOSER may enforce the provisions set forth in this AGREEMENT without proof that any violation thereof causes monetary damage to DISCLOSER. DISCLOSER is disclosing the CONFIDENTIAL INFORMATION for informational purposes only, and at this time the information may not be complete or completely accurate and therefore is not warranted as to completeness or accuracy.

7. Neither discontinuation of the discussions between DISCLOSER and DISCLOSEE regarding the TECHNOLOGY PROJECT, nor any other fact except modification in writing of the obligations stated herein, shall relieve DISCLOSEE of any of its obligations hereunder.

8. DISCLOSEE agrees to return all documents and things, including reproductions and copies thereof, delivered to DISCLOSEE hereunder as soon as DISCLOSEE has evaluated the documents and things if no further agreement is reached between the PARTIES and in any event prior to the termination of this AGREEMENT as set forth below, unless the PARTIES agree otherwise in writing.

9. Nothing in this AGREEMENT shall be construed to constitute the grant of a license to DISCLOSEE of any of the DISCLOSER's trade secrets or other intellectual property rights, or in any other way limit the rights of DISCLOSER under the patent, trademark, copyright, trade secret, other intellectual property, or unfair competition laws of the United States, any individual states, or any other country.

10. Neither this AGREEMENT nor any rights granted hereunder may be assigned, transferred, conveyed, or encumbered by the DISCLOSEE without prior written consent of DISCLOSER.

11. This AGREEMENT shall inure to the benefit of DISCLOSER and its successors and assigns, and shall be binding on DISCLOSEE, its subsidiaries and their successors, administrators, and representatives.

12. This AGREEMENT shall extend for a period of three (3) years from the date of execution hereof with respect to the CONFIDENTIAL INFORMATION, not including trade secrets, and indefinitely from the date of execution hereof with respect to the trade secrets, but shall terminate immediately in regard to individual aspects of the CONFIDENTIAL INFORMATION in the event that those individual aspects of the CONFIDENTIAL INFORMATION are revealed to the public in writing by DISCLOSER, or a patent shall issue thereon, but only to the extent revealed.

The PARTIES have caused this AGREEMENT to be executed by their duly authorized representatives as of this __ day of _____, ____.

_____

COMPANY/INDIVIDUAL

Date: _____

By: Print Name: _____

    Title: _____

_____

INVENTOR'S NAME

Date: _____

Investor's Checklist

When you prepare to present your idea to an angel investor or venture capital firm, there are certain questions they will want you to answer upfront. Devote some time to how you will answer these questions and you will greatly increase the likelihood that they will provide you with the funds you need to carry your idea to fruition.

The answers to these questions should be included in the Executive Summary of your presentation or business plan.

1. What is the problem you are trying to solve and what is the market size (number of treatable patients)?

2. How is your idea different from other technologies and what protection, such as patent filings, does it have?

3. What is the business model for your technology? Is it a disposable product or a piece of capital equipment? Who makes up the market your salesmen will be trying to reach? Does the buyer (such as a clinician) have a history of adopting new technologies?

4. Who will make up the management team and what relevant experience will they bring to the job?

5. What is the most likely regulatory path to market for your idea? Will your idea require a pre-market approval (PMA) that includes clinical trials, or will it follow a more direct path, such as through a 510(k)?

About the Author

Dr. Jeffrey S. Grossman is a full-time non-surgical spine and pain specialist and part-time inventor. He developed a laser-guided alignment device, called the Percutaneous Needle Alignment System, which is designed to improve the accuracy of interventional pain procedures. Along with successfully selling his invention to a major medical device company, he also obtained U.S. and international patents for the device. Active in the medical device community, he serves on the Advisory Board for the Southeast Medical Device Association.

Board certified by the American Board of Pain Medicine and the American Academy of Physical Medicine and Rehabilitation, he is also a certified Independent Medical Examiner by the American Board of Independent Medical Examiners.

A graduate with high honors from the University of Michigan, he was conferred the Doctor of Medicine degree by Emory University School of Medicine. He completed an internship at Atlanta Medical Center and a residency in Physical Medicine and Rehabilitation at Emory University School of Medicine.

Dr. Grossman is an active board member of the Medical Association of Atlanta and the co-chair of the Membership Committee for this organization. He also serves as a delegate to the Medical Association of Georgia. He is a member of the International Spinal Injection Society, North American Spine Society, American Academy of Physical Medicine and Rehabilitation, and the American Society of Interventional Pain Physicians. He was president of his medical school class and currently serves as a mentor to Emory medical students and residents.

Index